INTERNETWORKING

A Guide to Network Communications

LAN to LAN; LAN to WAN

INTERNETWORKING

A Guide to Network Communications

LAN to LAN; LAN to WAN

MARK A. MILLER, P.E.

M&T Books
A Division of M&T Publishing, Inc.
411 Borel Ave., Suite 100
San Mateo, CA 94402-3522

Library of Congress Cataloging-in-Publication Data

Miller, Mark, 1955-
     Internetworking: a Guide to Network Communications / by Mark A. Miller
     p.   cm.
     Includes bibliographical references and index.
     ISBN 1-55851-143-1: $34.95
     1. Computer networks   2. Local area networks (Computer networks)
     3. Computer network protocols   I. Title.
     TK5105.5.M55   1991
     004.6--dc20   90-25705
                                                                CIP

Trademarks: All products, names and services are trademarks or registered trademarks of their respective companies. See "Trademarks" section beginning on page 413.

Cover Design: Lauren Smith Design

94   93   92   5   4   3

To Holly

Contents

Table of Illustrations

Preface

From about 1985 to 1989, the January issues of most popular computing magazines proclaimed each new year as the "Year of the LAN." By January 1989, the business community finally believed that LANs were installable, configurable, and maintainable by network managers. I wrote the *LAN Troubleshooting Handbook* (M&T Books, 1989) and the *LAN Protocol Handbook* (M&T Books, 1990) in support of that belief.

1990 brought a new challenge: How do you connect dissimilar LANs — running under different network operating systems, and physically located at several sites — into a single cohesive network? Alas, the era of internetworking had dawned. With that era came more challenges: Should the individual LANs be connected with an analog or digital leased line, or should we consider TCP/IP as the internetworking software platform? For those just beginning to feel confident with a single LAN, the challenges of internetworking could seem daunting.

To head those potential problems off at the pass, I have assembled this handbook of hardware and software solutions to the internetworking challenge. This volume is structured like the others, with chapters that stand relatively independently. The chapters are ordered according to the OSI model, beginning with the Physical Layer (Chapter 1) and ending with the Application Layer (Chapter 9).

Here is a brief overview of the text. Chapter 1 addresses various internetworking standards, including contributions from ANSI, IEEE, and ISO. Chapter 2 focuses on LAN-to-LAN connections, assuming a local (not wide-area) internetwork. Chapter 3 discusses the various wide-area transmission facilities, ranging from dial-up analog to wideband digital. Chapter 4 discusses products that utilize these transmission facilities to connect LANs in different locations — either across the country or in different parts of the world.

Chapters 5, 6, and 7 address the OSI Network and Transport Layers, and the three protocol suites used extensively for internetwork connections. These are the X.25, TCP/IP, and XNS protocols, respectively.

Chapters 8 and 9 address higher-layer protocol (Session, Presentation, and Application) issues. Chapter 8 is devoted to the internetworking and interoperability functions included in today's popular networking software (including Apple Computer's AppleTalk, Sitka Corporation's TOPS, and Novell's NetWare), and several implementations of Microsoft Corporation's OS/2 LAN Manager (including products from 3Com, IBM, and AT&T). Chapter 9 is devoted to reviews of a dozen gateway products that connect LANs to other LANs, and LANs to minicomputers. Chapter 10 concludes with a checklist for internetwork implementation.

Appendixes A through E provide Addresses of Standards Organizations, Selected Manufacturers of Internetworking Products, North American Private Line Carriers, North American Public Data Networks, and Acronyms, respectively.

Given the breadth of this industry, no single person can be an expert at everything. As a result, I depended upon many other experts for their knowledge in selected areas. Kirk Preiss contributed to the discussion on bridging methodology and standards. Dan Callahan added his vast experience to the implementation chapter. Carl Shinn, Jr. provided many insights into applications and interoperability, in addition to reading the entire manuscript for clarity.

My editors at M&T Books, Brenda McLaughlin and Tom Woolf, kept the project on schedule and moving in the right direction. Carol Cheh tackled a myriad of details and made sure that everything happened on time.

A number of manufacturers contributed as well. Those individuals (with titles ranging from engineer and product manager to president) reviewed product-specific sections of the manuscript to ensure accuracy in product descriptions and applications. In alphabetical order, they are: Holt Adams, Karen Andresen, Don Bailey, Karen Barton, Doug Beard, Abhay Bhushan, Bill Bliss, Richard Borden, Dave Brooks, Linda Brukardt, Marilyn Callahan, Bruce Campbell, Linda Collins-Hedegard,

Teddi Converse, Dick de Wit, Jack Douglas, Bill Fanslow, Joe Furgerson, Robert Fields, Phillip Galli, Peter Galvin, Manoj Goel, Michael Grimshaw, Nancy Hamilton, Dana Harrison, Guy Hoffman, Rex Jackson, Bill Jeppesen, Geoff Karlin, Lori Hultin, Dave Kishler, Dennis Klein, Gregory Koss, Gary Krall, Kurt Kruger, Ed Lakin, Pierre Leclercq, Beth Logan, Donna Loughlin, Bruce MacAloney, Catie Martin, John McCarthy, Ed McCauley, Kathryn Merriam, Chris Miranda, David Nagy, Mike Neirby, Harold Noborikawa, Tucam Truoc Nguyen, Joe Ozorkiewicz, Krista Passarelli, Lisa Ping, Diane Rahe, Bob Shea, Paul Shreve, Anastasia Shilling, Marie Smith, John Stidd, Ronald Stone, Jean Taber, Paul Ticknor, Rene Trezise, Christine Washburn, Wayne Wilkinson, Lauren Wright, Bob Yori, and Mary Ann Yule.

Krystal Valdez again did a superb job of word processing and research. Junior Valdez made some much-appreciated technical contributions that made the deadlines achievable. Thanks to both of you for all the hard work.

Finally, Holly, Nathan, and Nicholas contributed their encouragement and support when the hours got long or the FAX machine jammed. Thanks again for your love.

Mark A. Miller
December 1990

Why This Book is for You

This, the third volume in the LAN Handbook series, is written for network designers, managers, and administrators who need to connect their LANs to any other type of network. Examples would be links to another, dissimilar LAN (such as a Token Ring connecting to an Ethernet) or to a remote minicomputer across the country. Individual sections of this handbook discuss:

- Internetworking standards—detailing the differences between Transparent Routing, Source Routing, and Source Routing Transparent bridging methods.

- Selecting hardware—when to use a repeater, bridge, brouter, router, or gateway in the internetwork.

- Selecting the optimum LAN-to-WAN transmission facility, such as an analog or digital leased line, T-1 circuit, or Public Data Network connection.

- Implementing internetworking protocols, including X.25, TCP/IP, and XNS.

- Designing the internetwork, with over 40 examples of internetworking hardware and software solutions.

- Interoperability between popular LAN operating systems.

- Providing gateways to connect your LAN and minicomputers or main-frames.

If your LAN requires local or remote connectivity to any other system, this handbook belongs in your technical library.

CHAPTER 1

Internetworking Principles and Standards

The term "internetworking" has many different meanings for many different people. The *IBM Dictionary of Computing* defines internetworking as "communication between two or more networks." The term network has several definitions, one of which is "a configuration of data processing devices and software connected for information interchange". A new definition for internetworking might be "communication between data processing devices on one network and other, possibly dissimilar, devices on another network".

A simple definition of the term internetworking doesn't describe the dissimilar problems that network designers and administrators experience, however. One network manager may need to have a DEC minicomputer communicate with an IBM mainframe. Another may wish to set up an Ethernet Local Area Network (LAN) that has remote access capabilities. Maybe an administrator is dealing with dissimilar hardware or software platforms, and needs to integrate Macintosh, PC, or UNIX workstations. Perhaps an internetwork is outgrowing its analog leased lines, and the system designer is considering an upgrade to a digital transmission facility such as Fractional T-1 (FT-1). All of these are specific, and very different, examples of internetworking possibilities.

This book focuses on the internetworking of LANs, minicomputers, and mainframes. Our discussions will be about linking dissimilar systems—such as Ethernet and Token Ring networks—together. We'll explore the many techniques, employing either hardware and/or software products, for making the necessary connections.

The book is organized according to the OSI Reference Model, starting with the Physical Layer issues and ending with Application Layer challenges. This first chapter lays the foundation by discussing internetworking standards. Chapter 2 discusses LAN-to-LAN connections, and the integration of repeaters, bridges, brouters and routers into the LAN. Chapter 3 discusses Wide Area Network (WAN) transmission facilities, so that the LAN-to-WAN design and devices can be explored in Chapter 4. Chapters 5, 6, and 7 deal primarily with the OSI Network and Transport Layers, discussing X.25, TCP/IP, and XNS protocols, respectively, in detail. Chapter 8 explores how popular networking software architectures, such as those of Novell and 3Com, handle internetworking. In Chapter 9, we'll look at the OSI Application Layer, considering gateways to link dissimilar applications. Chapter 10 concludes with a plan to facilitate the implementation of these previously discussed ideas. Let's begin our study by looking at a brief history of the concept of computer internetworking.

1.1   Internetworking History

In the late 1960s and early 1970s, computer networks were defined by the mainframe used. After careful consideration, a company would select the minicomputer or mainframe environment of a proprietary vendor such as IBM, Honeywell, DEC, or Sperry (now Unisys). The customer was committed to their architecture of choice until obsolescence necessitated a complete redesign. If the system required minor additions or alterations, the company called the manufacturer's rep, who supplied the required upgrade. The company rarely considered adding on third-party equipment because of the proprietary nature of the network architectures in use.

The mid-1970s brought a change to the concept of proprietary computer architecture. The idea of an "open" system—an architecture adhering to published standards with defined interfaces—became popular. A crack appeared in the foundation of proprietary architectures. The possibility of a DEC minicomputer accessing an IBM mainframe became more than a wild idea. (DEC, in its DECnet Phase IV [released in 1982] did in fact implement connections into IBM's System Network Architecture [SNA].) Two groups became the driving forces behind the

4

movement to develop open-system standards: users, who wanted vendor-independent solutions; and vendors, who wished to develop marketable products. The collaboration of these two groups resulted in jointly-developed standards. A number of standards organizations emerged, including the International Telegraph and Telephone Consultative Committee (CCITT); the International Organization for Standardization (ISO); and the American National Standards Institute (ANSI). (Appendix A lists addresses of these and other standards organizations.)

The growing need for network-to-network communication (or internetworking) inspired the research that led to what we now know as the Open Systems Interconnection (OSI) Reference Model. First published in 1978 by the ISO, the familiar OSI model defined the computer communication function in terms of seven distinct layers. In the next section, we'll briefly examine the functions of the seven layers, then see how they are used to solve internetworking requirements.

Excellent texts on the subject of the OSI reference model include references [1-1] through [1-5]. References [1-6] and [1-7] offer interesting perspectives on the interoperability issue. Two projections on the networking industry's growth are given in references [1-8] and [1-9]. We'll reference specifics of these works throughout this chapter.

1.2   Open Systems Interconnection Principles

The Open Systems Interconnection (OSI) Reference Model is designed as a standard to allow various "open" systems to communicate. A system that complies with standards (specifically OSI standards)—also referred to as protocols—for communication with other systems is defined as being "open." An open system is standards-based instead of proprietary-based; my system can thus communicate and cooperate with your system using interfaces and protocols that both systems understand.

In creating the OSI model, the International Organization for Standardization (ISO) divided the network communication functions into seven layers (see Figure 1-1). We'll summarize the seven functions here; for a more in-depth discussion, refer

5

to the complete standard (reference [1-10]), Tanenbaum (reference [1-1]), or Black (reference [1-3]).

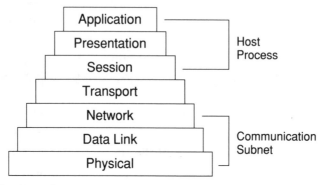

Figure 1-1. The Open System Interconnection (OSI) Reference Model

The Physical Layer handles bit-transmission between one node (e.g., host, workstation) and the next. The Physical Layer functions include interfacing with the transmission media; encoding the data signal; defining the range of the voltage or current magnitudes; defining the connector sizes, shapes and pinouts; and anything generally associated with the physical transmission of the bit stream.

The Data Link Layer maintains a reliable communication link between adjacent nodes. As such, it assumes that the Physical Layer is noisy or prone to errors. Data Link provides a reliable delivery mechanism to transmit a frame (or package) of data bits to the next node. The Data Link Layer inserts addresses in the data frame (including source and destination) and provides error control for the data—usually implemented with a Cyclic Redundancy Check (CRC).

The Network Layer establishes a path for the traveling data packet along the communication subnet from the source node to the destination node. The Network Layer switches, routes, and controls the congestion of these information packets within the subnet.

The Transport Layer provides reliable delivery of host messages originating at Layer 7, the Application Layer, in the same way that the Data Link Layer assures reliable delivery of frames between adjacent nodes. The major difference between the Data Link and Transport Layers is that the Data Link domain lies between adjacent nodes, whereas the Transport Layer's domain extends from the source to the destination (or end-to-end) within the communication subnet. Issues concerning source-to-destination messages are important in the Transport Layer. For example, the Transport Layer segments a long message into smaller units (packets) prior to transmission, and assures the reassembly of those packets into the original message at the receiver's end.

The Session Layer establishes and terminates process-to-process communication sessions between hosts. Translation between name and address databases, as well as synchronization between the two hosts, may be required to manage the sessions.

The Presentation Layer establishes the syntax (or form) in which data is exchanged between the two hosts. As such, the Presentation Layer provides a data manipulation function, not a communication function. Data compression and data encryption are two examples of Presentation Layer services.

The Application Layer provides end-user services, such as Application Layer file transfers, electronic messages, virtual terminal emulation, and remote database access. The end user interacts with the Application Layer.

The seven layers divide into two important subsets. The first is comprised of the lower three layers (the Physical, Data Link, and Network layers) and termed the communications subnetwork, subnet, or the carrier portion of the system. The upper three layers (the Session, Presentation, and Application layers) are collectively known as the host process, sometimes called the customer portion of the system. The middle layer (Transport) is the first end-to-end layer, and acts as a buffer between the two subsets. As such, the Transport Layer is often grouped with the upper layers as part of the host process.

A specific internetwork architecture results when two open systems are linked directly—with a single cable, for example (see Figure 1-2). In this configuration, protocols operate on a peer-to-peer basis between each of the layers and are shown as dashed lines to indicate their logical (or virtual) communication paths. The *interface* between the layers within the same system is a vertical relationship, whereas the *protocol* is a horizontal relationship between peer layers of the adjacent system. The actual communication path originates in Open System A as an input to its Application Layer. The message then proceeds down through the seven layers (7 through 1) of System A, across the physical media (cable), and up the seven layers (1 through 7) of System B. Details of this process are shown in Figure 1-3, taken from reference [1-11]. Data from Application process X is passed to the Application Layer protocol, which adds its Application Header (AH). The header contains protocol control information (PCI) necessary for the peer process (Y) to interpret the data. The AH plus Application Data (AD) is then passed down to the Presentation Layer. The Presentation Layer treats the AH and AD as its own data, appends the Presentation Header (PH) and passes the data unit down to the Session, Transport, and Network Layers in turn.

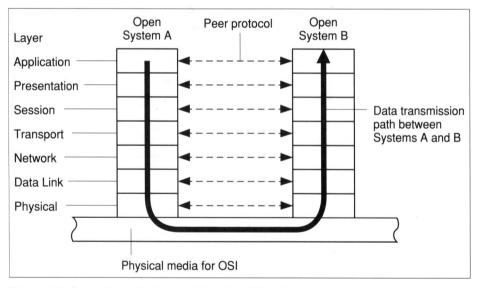

Figure 1-2. Seven Layer Reference Model and Peer Protocols

When the encapsulated message reaches the Data Link Layer, Framing (F), Address (A), and Control (C) information is added as the Data Link Layer header. The Frame Check Sequence (FCS) and possibly additional Framing (F) characters are appended as the Data Link Layer trailer. The assembled frame is then passed to the Physical Layer. The Physical Layer encodes the data for transmission, accesses the transmission medium, and monitors the serial bit transmission. At the destination node, the reverse of this process occurs. The Physical Layer hands its bits to the Data Link Layer, which decodes and then strips off the Data Link Layer header and trailer. The Data Link Layer data unit is then passed to the Network, Transport, Session, and higher layers in turn. The process is completed when the electronic message (shown again as Application data) is delivered to Application Y.

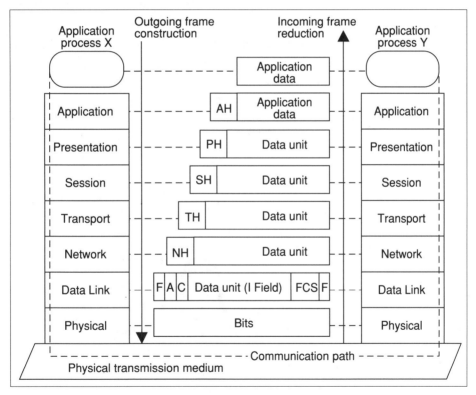

Figure 1-3. Building a Frame for Transmission
© 1987 IEEE

When the systems are not connected by the same physical cable, a relay open system (see Figure 1-4) must be used. The relay is also known as a switching node, and implements the lower three (communication subnet) layers of the OSI model. More than one relay may (and most likely will) exist. A good example of the relay open system is the Public Switched Telephone Network (PSTN) which is used to connect dial-up voice and data calls. The various switching centers (known as Central Offices, or C.O.s) route and switch the telephone call. You, as an end user, do not know (nor do you really care) how many of these offices your call traverses, or which connection paths they take. As long as the telephone call to the distant end goes through, you deem the process satisfactory. The same is true with internetworks using relay open systems. A number of these switching nodes could exist between source and destination hosts (e.g. Open Systems A and B). The data from the originating system (A) passes through the communication subnet on its way to the destination system (B). No alteration of the application data occurs within the subnet; it acts as a transparent pipe for that data. An excellent description of this process from a LAN perspective is found in references [1-12] and [1-13].

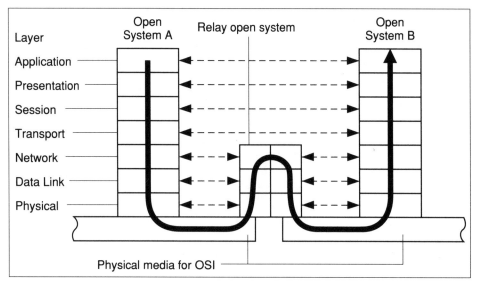

Figure 1-4. Communication Involving Relay Open Systems

What does all of this have to do with internetworking? Let's reserve that question for section 1.4, and look next at specific protocols defined by the ISO.

1.3 OSI Protocols for Internetworking

The ISO's development of the OSI Reference Model has resulted in the ongoing development of associated protocols (see Figure 1-5). These protocols describe internetworking utopia—if all vendors used identical protocols at all layers, our internetworking problems would be solved. Unfortunately, the predominance of SNA, DECnet and other proprietary networking architectures has slowed industry evolution towards a fully OSI-compliant architecture. Let's see what each layer of an ideal internetworking environment would represent.

OSI Layer	Example ISO Protocols			
Application	ISO 9040/9041 VT	ISO 8831/8832 JTM	ISO 8571/8572 FTAM	ISO 9595/9596 CMIP
Presentation	ISO 8823/CCITT X.226 Connection-Oriented Presentation Protocol			
Session	ISO 8327/CCITT X.225 Connection-Oriented Session Protocol			
Transport	ISO 8073/CCITT X.224 Connection-Oriented Transport Protocol			
Network	ISO 8473 Connectionless Network Service		ISO 8208/CCITT X.25 Packet Level Protocol	
Data Link	ISO 8802-2 ISO 9314-2 FDDI / ISO 8802-3 CSMA/CD BUS / ISO 8802-4 TOKEN BUS / ISO 8802-5 TOKEN RING		ISO7776 CCITT X.25 LAP/LAPB	ISO 7809 HDLC
Physical	Options from EIA, CCITT, IEEE, etc.			

Figure 1-5. ISO Protocol Examples

The Physical and Data Link Layer protocols offer a multitude of options for accessing LAN, WAN, and mini/mainframe systems. Many existing standards, such as IEEE 802 have ISO counterparts: ISO 8802-2, 8802-3, 8802-4 or 8802-5. Other ISO standards define connectors (e.g. the ISO 8877, the familiar 8 pin modular plug sometimes known as an RJ-45) or frame formats (e.g. ISO 7809—HDLC [High Level Data Link Control]) similar to IBM's SDLC (Synchronous Data Link Control). Other standards associations such as the Electronic Industries Association (EIA), American National Standards Institute (ANSI) or International Telegraph and Telephone Consultative Committee (CCITT) have also developed Physical and Data Link Layer standards that are widely accepted. An example of a Data Link Layer protocol is ISO 7776 which is also CCITT X.25 LAP/LAPB. This standard defines the Link Access Procedure/Link Access Procedure Balanced protocol used within the X.25 protocol suite.

Network Layer standards can define either a connection-oriented (virtual circuit) or connectionless (datagram) service. ISO has defined a connectionless service with ISO 8473, "Protocol for Providing the Connectionless-Mode Network Service." The ISO Internet protocol (ISO IP) is similar to the U.S. Department of Defense (DoD) Internet protocol from the TCP/IP suite that we will study in Chapter 6. There are several interesting differences, however. First, ISO IP allows variable address lengths where most protocols usually define a fixed address length; a preliminary field in the ISO IP header defines the length of the field which contains the addresses themselves. Secondly, an options field is also included within the ISO IP header for specifying optional parameters, such as the quality of service or routing information. (Weissberger & Israel [1-14] present a good tutorial on connection-oriented and connectionless service.) Another Network Layer standard is ISO 8208/CCITT X.25 which specifies the Packet Layer Protocol—the subject of chapter 5.

At the ISO Transport Layer, a number of protocol options are available depending upon the type of underlying network (i.e., the communications subnet) being used. Three different classes of networks—Types A, B, and C—are defined. Type A represents an optimum service, error-free, no-Network-Layer-reset (N-RESETS) network. Type B networks assure perfect packet delivery, but have

N-RESETS due to network congestion or hardware/software failures. Type C networks provide unreliable service, possibly losing packets, and also have N-RESETS. Tanenbaum [1-1] cites LANs, Public Data Networks (PDNs), and packet radio networks as respective examples of Type A, Type B, and Type C networks.

Within the three network types, there are five Transport Layer protocol classes:

- Class 0: Simple class, used for network type A. No sequence or flow control.

- Class 1: Basic error recovery class, used for network type B. Has sequencing to handle N-RESETS.

- Class 2: Multiplexing class, used for network type A. Enhances class 0 to permit multiplexing.

- Class 3: Error recovery and multiplexing class, used for network type B.

- Class 4: Error detection and recovery class, used for network type C. Assumes the worst case (unreliable) network type, and necessarily the most complex protocol treatment.

Of the above protocols (designated TP0-TP4), TP4 bears the greatest resemblance to our familiar U.S. Department of Defense (DoD) Transmission Control Protocol (TCP), and is the most frequently discussed. Two standards detail the Transport Layer protocols: ISO 8072 (Connection-Oriented Transport Service) and ISO 8073 (Connection-Oriented Transport Protocol); the CCITT equivalent of ISO 8073 is CCITT X.224. Further details on the three network types and five Transport classes are found in Black [1-3] and Stallings [1- 15].

The Session Layer provides four services. The first is to establish the connection, exchange data and then terminate the connection. The second is to use tokens to manage the exchange of that data, synchronize the connection, and determine if half- or full-duplex transmission is required. The third service is to establish synchronization points within the data stream so that communication can be resumed from that point if interruptions occur. The fourth service interrupts the data transfer continuing from a pre-determined synchronization point. (An excellent tutorial on these services is given in reference [1-16].) At the Session Layer, standards ISO 8326 (Connection-Oriented Session Service) and ISO 8327 (Connection-Oriented Session Protocol) are employed. The CCITT equivalent of ISO 8327 is CCITT X.225.

Rather than serving a communication function, the Presentation Layer deals in the realm of data representation. This layer preserves the semantics (or meaning) of the data being transmitted, regardless of the syntax (or form) that is used. The standards used at the Presentation Layer are ISO 8822 (Connection-Oriented Presentation Service) and ISO 8823 (Connection-Oriented Presentation Protocol). The data structure entitled Abstract Syntax Notation 1 (ASN.1) is also defined as ISO 8824. These standards relate to functions such as data encryption and compression.

The Application layer of the Reference Model has standards for several specific functions. ISO 9040/9041 defines the Virtual Terminal Service/Protocol. ISO 8831/8832 defines Job Transfer and Management Service/Protocol for remote program execution. ISO 8571/8572 is the File Transfer Access and Manipulation Service/Protocol which defines remote file manipulation services. ISO 9595/9596 define the Common Management Information Service/Protocol used for network management. References [1-17] and [1-18] are good articles that explain the Application Layer functions.

Organizations such as the Corporation for Open Systems in McLean, Virginia, are interested in testing vendor compliance with the OSI protocols. An interesting review of this compliance-testing process is given in reference [1-19].

With this background in the OSI protocols, let's next explore how connectivity devices stack up.

1.4   Applying Connectivity Devices to the OSI Model

Let's explore how connectivity devices work with regard to OSI protocols. We'll return to the peer protocol model (Figure 1-2) and assume that the two open systems are connected with a physical transmission medium such as a twisted pair or fiber optic cable. What happens if the cable length is so long that the signal loses power? We can solve this by adding a repeater (see Figure 1-6) that will amplify (or regenerate) the physical signal. Repeaters function at the Physical Layer and operate between like networks, such as Token Ring to Token Ring, or Ethernet to Ethernet. A repeater can be added to the internetwork to extend the range of the network; connected segments behave physically (and logically) as a single network.

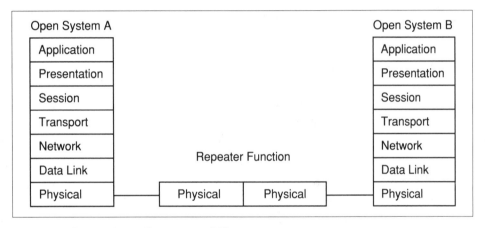

Figure 1-6. Comparing a Repeater to OSI

When repeating a signal is insufficient for the existing network, a bridge adds the functionality of the Data Link Layer (Figure 1-7). The bridge logically separates two network segments by operating upon the address within the Data Link Layer (or IEEE Medium Access Control [MAC]) frame. Information that is either stored at the bridge or provided within the transmitted frame assists the bridge in making a rather simple decision: pass the frame to the next segment (known as forwarding) or do not pass the frame to the next segment (known as filtering). Bridges operate on networks having compatible Data Link Layer addressing schemes (such as IEEE 802.3 to

802.3, or 802.3 to 802.5), but are transparent to the protocols of the Network and higher layers.

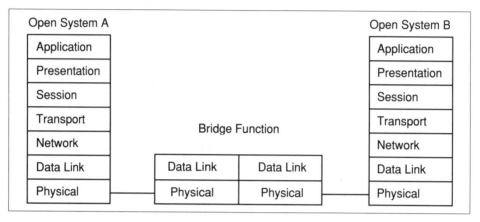

Figure 1-7. Comparing a Bridge to OSI

Routers operate at the Network Layer (see Figure 1-8), and may interpret either one or more protocols at that layer. Recall that the Network Layer makes a choice between available paths within the communication subnet, eventually connecting the source and destination hosts. A router performs similarly, reading information about the destination network address, and forwarding that packet to the appropriate destination network. (Bridges, as discussed above, make a simple binary decision to forward or not forward a frame after examining the Data Link Layer address). The router thus serves a network-wide connectivity function. Routers may operate on one Network Layer protocol, such as the DoD Internet Protocol (IP), or multiple protocols such as IP, DECnet, and Novell's IPX (Internetwork Packet Exchange).

Finally, gateways may operate at all seven OSI layers (see Figure 1-9). Gateways are application-oriented, and may be responsible for connecting incompatible electronic mail systems, converting and transferring files from one system to another, or enabling interoperability between dissimilar operating systems. Chapter 9 will be devoted to various application-specific gateways.

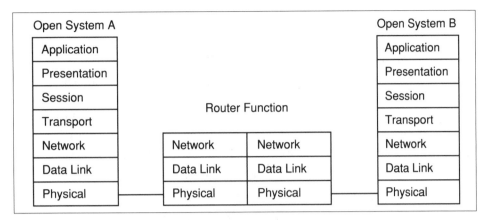

Figure 1-8. Comparing a Router to OSI

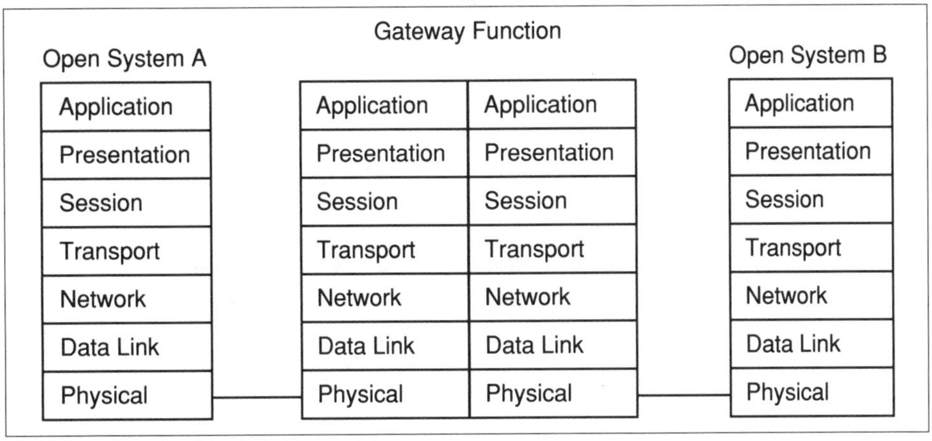

Figure 1-9. Comparing a Gateway to OSI

A great deal of literature is available on the subject of LAN connectivity devices. Reference [1-20] is a good overview of the technologies, and discusses device operation in depth. Reference [1-21] looks at the connectivity design issues from an OSI perspective. Bridges and their applications are discussed in reference [1-22]; router architecture is explored in references [1-23] and [1-24]; gateways are profiled in [1-25].

1.5 IEEE Project 802

No reference on internetworking would be complete without information on LAN standards and associated frame formats. The companion volumes, references [1-26] and [1-27], discuss these issues in detail; a summary is provided here.

Recognizing a need for standards in the LAN market, the Institute of Electrical and Electronics Engineers (IEEE) undertook Project 802. Named for the month (February) and year (1980) of its inception, Project 802 addresses LAN standards at the Physical and Data Link layers of the OSI model (see Figure 1-10).

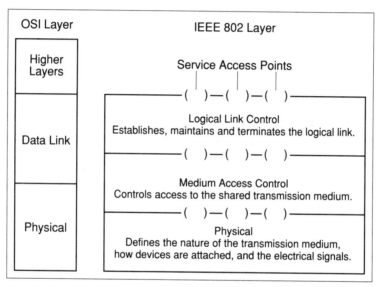

Figure 1-10. Comparing IEEE Project 802 with OSI
© *IEEE*

The Physical Layer of the IEEE LAN model is similar to its OSI counterpart. Its responsibilities include signal encoding and decoding, serial bit transmission and reception, and providing the physical connection to the transmission medium via twisted-pair, coaxial, or fiber-optic cable.

The IEEE Medium Access Control (or MAC) Layer extends below to the Physical, and above to the Data Link layers. This layer, as its name implies, controls access to the transmission medium, and is further subdivided into other standards:

802.3: Carrier Sense Multiple Access Bus with Collision Detection (CSMA/CD)

802.4: Token Passing Bus

802.5: Token Passing Ring

Each of these MAC standards defines a unique frame format, discussed in section 1.6 and detailed in references [1-28], [1-29], and [1-30], respectively.

The highest layer of the IEEE LAN Model is the Logical Link Control (LLC) Layer, defined by the IEEE 802.2 standard. While the LLC bears a close resemblance to the OSI Data Link Layer, there are also some important differences. Both Data Link and LLC must reliably transmit frames of information between adjacent stations. In the LAN model, however, there is no need for the network layer functions of routing and switching. Since there is only one available "route" (the cable), the addressing defined in the MAC Layer frame is sufficient for delivery of the frame. Other functions such as flow control (which assures that a fast sender does not overwhelm a slow receiver) and error control are also handled by the Data Link Layer.

The major difference between the OSI Data Link Layer and the IEEE 802.2 LLC Layer is that multiple endpoints to the data link can exist in the IEEE model. With a LAN, communicating between one source and multiple SAPs (or Service Access Points) is often required. SAPs function in a manner somewhat analogous to ports. Thus, a workstation that has one MAC Layer address (provided by the hardware or Network Interface Card [NIC]) can communicate with several higher layer processes. Each of these processes would have a unique SAP address. Both Source (SSAP) and Destination (DSAP) addresses are specified in the 802.2 LLC Protocol Data Unit (Figure 1-11).

DSAP address	SSAP address	Control	Information
8 bits	8 bits	8 or 16 bits	M*8 bits

DSAP Address = destination service access point address field

SSAP Address = source service access point address field

Control = control field (16 bits for formats that include sequence numbering, and 8 bits for formats that do not)

Information = information field

* = multiplication

M = an integer value equal to or greater than 0. (Upper bound of M is a function of the medium access control methodology used.)

Figure 1-11. The Logical Link Control (LLC) Protocol Data Unit
© *IEEE*

Three types of LLC operations are defined:

Type 1 (unacknowledged, connectionless services): the sending and receiving of frames in a datagram fashion. Point-to-point, multipoint, and broadcast transmissions are supported by Type 1.

Type 2 (connection-oriented services): a logical connection between SAPs providing sequence control, flow control, error control, and acknowledgments.

Type 3 (acknowledged connectionless services): a datagram, point-to-point service with acknowledgments.

For further information, see reference [1-31].

1.6   LAN Frame Formats

The four major LAN architectures—Ethernet, Token Ring, ARCNET, and FDDI (Fiber Data Distributed Interface)—have different transmission formats for their Data Link Layer frames. We'll look at these individually.

1.6.1   Ethernet

The Ethernet frame format (reference [1-32]) was developed by DEC, Intel Corporation, and Xerox Corporation and is slightly different from the IEEE 802.3 format. The specific fields are shown in Figure 1-12. The Ethernet frame begins with a Preamble (eight octets) that is an alternating 1010 pattern that ends in 10101011. The Preamble provides synchronization. The Destination Address is a six-octet field that can either define a Physical Layer address or a multicast address, which is determined by the LSB (least significant bit) of the first byte of that field. A Physical Layer address (usually burned into a ROM chip) sets LSB to 0, and is unique across all Ethernet networks. A multicast address can go to a group or be broadcast to all stations, and has LSB=1. In the case of a broadcast address, the destination field is set entirely to 1's—that is, FFFFFFFFFFFFH. (Throughout this text we will use a capital "H" to designate hexadecimal notation.)

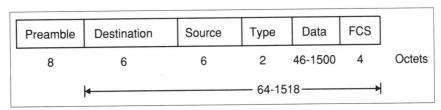

Figure 1-12. The Ethernet Frame Format

The address fields are further subdivided: the first three octets are assigned to a manufacturer in blocks (formerly by Xerox, but now assigned by the IEEE), and the last three octets are assigned by the manufacturer. Should the NIC become defective but the node address need to remain consistent (such as a well-known address for a gateway), the ROM chip containing the original address can be removed from the old board and inserted on the new board, or the address can be set in a register using the

NIC diagnostic disk. Regardless of the technique used, care should be taken when human intervention is needed to replace the automated address administration safeguards.

The Source Address—the address of the station originating the frame—is the next field specified.

The Type field, sometimes referred to as the Ethertype, is a two-octet field that specifies the higher layer protocol used in the Data field. Some familiar Ethertypes would be 0800H (TCP/IP) and 0600H (XNS).

The Data field is the only variable-length field, and can range from a minimum of 46 to a maximum of 1500 octets. The contents of this field are completely arbitrary, and are as determined by the higher-layer protocol in use.

The last field is an FCS that is a 32-bit CRC based upon the contents of the Address, Type, and Data fields.

The allowable frame length, not including the Preamble, ranges from 64 to 1518 octets. Frames outside that range are considered invalid.

1.6.2   IEEE 802.3

The IEEE 802.3 frame format is shown in Figure 1-13. This frame begins with a Preamble (seven octets) that is an alternating pattern 1010. The Start Frame Delimiter (SFD) is next, defined as 10101011. Note that if the 802.3 Preamble and Start Frame Delimiter fields are combined, a pattern identical to the Ethernet Preamble will result.

The SFD is followed by the Destination Address field which can be either two or six octets in length, although a six-octet length is most common. The Individual/Group (I/G) field corresponds to the Physical/Multicast designation of Ethernet; the Universal/Local (U/L) field indicates whether the address is administered universally (by the IEEE) or locally (by the network administrator). The Source Address comes next, and must match the Destination Address field in length (either two octets for Destination and two for Source, or six octets for Destination and six for Source, but not two and six).

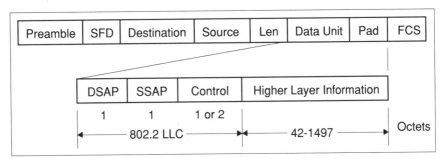

Figure 1-13. The IEEE 802.3 MAC Frame Format
© *IEEE*

The Length field is two octets long and indicates the number of LLC octets in the Data field. A minimum of 46 octets of data is required; when the LLC data is less than 46, the Pad field is used. Maximum length of the Data and Pad fields combined is 1500 octets. Note that the 802.2 LLC PDU would be completely encapsulated within the Data Unit of the 802.3 MAC frame.

Finally, the FCS, which is based upon a 32-bit CRC, is computed according to the contents of the Destination Address, Source Address, Length, Data, and Pad fields (see reference [1-28] for further details).

Again referring to Figures 1-12 and 1-13, note the differences between the Ethernet and IEEE 802.3 frames. To start with, 802.3 replaces the Type field with a Length field. This difference has two implications. First, the frames are the same length at the Data Link Layer, but are incompatible at the Network and higher layers. Second, if the length of the data must be specified within an Ethernet frame, some parameter defined by the Network Layer (and contained within the Data Link Layer Information field) must convey that quantity. In addition, Ethernet has no provision to pad the data to its required 46-octet minimum, but 802.3 does. Thus, in Ethernet, the Network Layer will consider this parameter and pad the length.

1.6.3 IEEE 802.5

Because of the nature of Token Ring network operation, three different frame formats are required. The three-octet Token, shown in Figure 1-14a, circulates around the ring, passing network access control to the various workstations. The multi-octet Frame, shown in Figure 1-14b, contains either user data or ring-management data. The two-octet Abort Sequence in Figure 1-14c is used for correcting error conditions, such as errors internal to the workstation. We'll next review each transmission type.

The 24 bits of the token (Figure 1-14a) are divided into three octets: the Starting Delimiter, which contains violations to the Differential Manchester Code (thus indicating a unique data sequence) plus binary 0's; the Access Control field, which grants network access; and the Ending Delimiter, which contains Differential Manchester Code violations, binary 1's, and two additional bits—Intermediate and Error Detect—described below.

Starting Delimiter	Access Control	Ending Delimiter	
1	1	1	octets
VV0VV000	PPPTMRRR	VV1VV1IE	

V	= Differential Manchester Violations	P	= Priority Mode	V	= Differential Manchester Violations	
		T	= Token Bit			
		M	= Monitor Count			
0	= Binary ZERO	R	= Priority Reservation	1	= Binary ONE	
				I	= Intermediate	
				E	= Error Detect	

Figure 1-14a. The IEEE 802.5 Token Format
© IEEE

The Access Control field starts with three Priority (P) bits that set the priority of that Token. The Token (T) bit delineates either a Token (T=0) or a Frame (T=1). Each workstation is assigned a priority for its transmissions, 000 being the lowest and 111 being the highest. The Reservation (R) bits can be used by a workstation to request the reservation of the next Token as a transmission passes by. In order for a workstation to transmit, its priority must be greater than or equal to the priority of that Token.

The Monitor Count (M) bit is used to prevent high-priority tokens or any frames from continuously circulating around the ring. It is set to M=0 by the transmitting station, and set to M=1 by the Active Monitor. If the monitor sees an incoming priority token or frame with M=1, it assumes that the transmitting station did not remove the token or frame after one round trip, and removes that token or frame, purges the ring, and issues a new token.

The Ending Delimiter includes Differential Manchester Code violations and binary 1's; an Intermediate frame (I) bit which, when set, indicates that this frame is part of a multi-frame transmission; and an Error detect (E) bit that is set when a frame contains an FCS error, a non-integral number of octets, or a Differential Manchester code violation between Starting and Ending delimiters.

The variable-length frame shown in Figure 1-14b is transmitted by the workstation following the successful capture of the token. The first two octets of the frame, the Starting Delimiter and Access Control, are taken from the token format described above. The Frame Control field defines two types of frames—either LLC frames that carry user data, or MAC frames that carry ring-management data. The Destination and Source Address fields, either two or six octets in length, follow the same format as the 802.3 address fields.

An optional Routing Information (RI) field precedes the variable-length Information field. The RI field is used when the transmitting frame must go between multiple rings via bridges. A source-routing protocol, which we will discuss in section 1.7.2, defines route control information as well as ring and bridge designators, and is used for these multiple ring topologies.

For LLC frames, the Information field contains the LLC Protocol Data Unit (PDU). The PDU includes the DSAP and SSAP addresses and Control information, plus the data from the higher layers (Network and above). For MAC frames, the Information field contains Commands and Parameters for ring management.

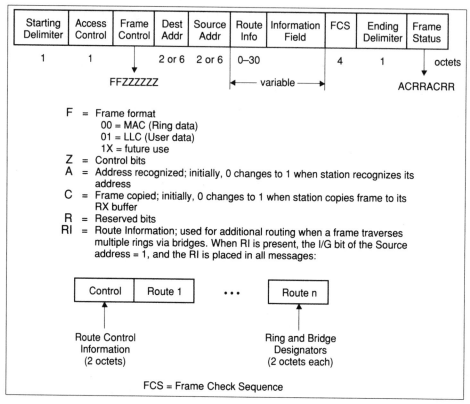

Figure 1-14b. The IEEE 802.5 MAC Frame Format
© *IEEE*

A Frame Check Sequence (FCS) follows the Information field. The Ending Delimiter field is taken from the Token frame. The Frame Status field ends the 802.5 frame. It includes the Address Recognized (A) and Frame Copied (C) bits that verify that the receiving station has properly processed MAC frames. These bits do not have meaning for LLC frames in multiple ring topologies.

The Abort Sequence format shown in Figure 1-14c is used when certain error conditions occur. The Starting and Ending Delimiter fields are identical to the corresponding fields in the token.

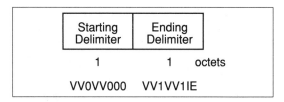

Starting Delimiter	Ending Delimiter	
1	1	octets
VV0VV000	VV1VV1IE	

Figure 1-14c. The IEEE 802.5 Abort Sequence Format
© *IEEE*

1.6.4   Sub-Network Access Protocol

An extension to the IEEE 802.2 LLC header, known as the Sub-Network Access Protocol or SNAP (reference [1-33]), has been defined by the Internet community. This extension was made in order to encapsulate Internet Protocol (IP) datagrams and Address Resolution Protocol (ARP) requests and replies within an 802.X (802.3, 802.4, or 802.5) frame.

The SNAP header immediately follows the 802.2 header, and is encapsulated within the 802.X frame (see Figure 1-15). For the 802.2 header, both DSAP and SSAP fields are set to AAH, and the Control field is set to 03H (for Unnumbered Information). The Protocol ID or Organization Code is three octets, and is specified in RFC 1042 (reference [1-33]) as all ZEROs. The Ethertype (two-octets) completes the SNAP header. By using 802.2 and SNAP within the same 802.X MAC frame, both SAP addresses and Ethertypes can be specified.

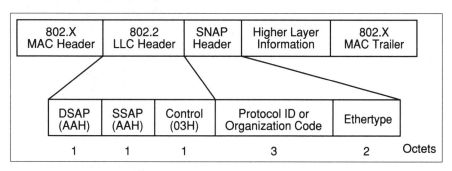

Figure 1-15. Sub-Network Access Protocol (SNAP) Header Encapsulated Within an IEEE 802.X Frame

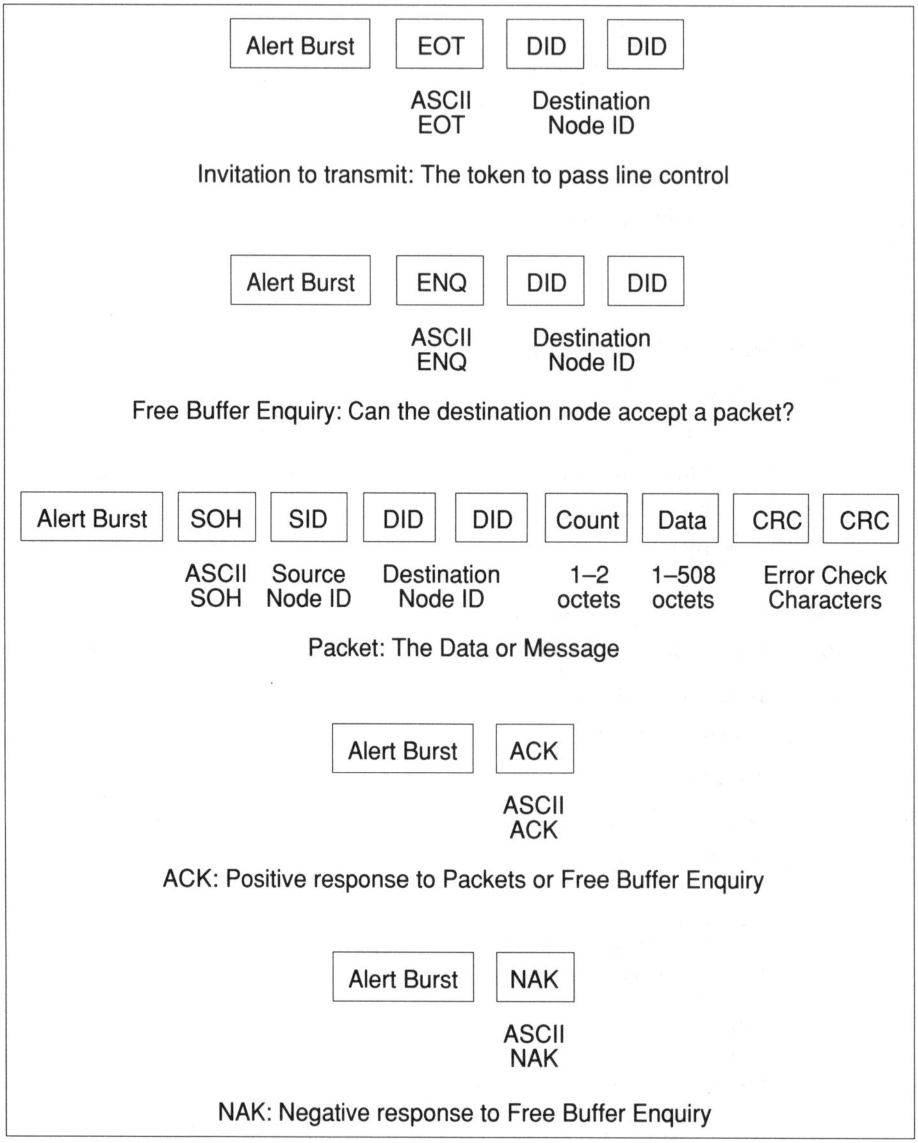

Alert Burst	EOT	DID	DID

ASCII   Destination
EOT   Node ID

Invitation to transmit: The token to pass line control

Alert Burst	ENQ	DID	DID

ASCII   Destination
ENQ   Node ID

Free Buffer Enquiry: Can the destination node accept a packet?

Alert Burst	SOH	SID	DID	DID	Count	Data	CRC	CRC

ASCII   Source   Destination   1–2   1–508   Error Check
SOH   Node ID   Node ID   octets octets   Characters

Packet: The Data or Message

Alert Burst	ACK

ASCII
ACK

ACK: Positive response to Packets or Free Buffer Enquiry

Alert Burst	NAK

ASCII
NAK

NAK: Negative response to Free Buffer Enquiry

Figure 1-16. The ARCNET Frame Formats

1.6.5 ARCNET

ARCNET, originally developed by Datapoint Corporation, is not part of the IEEE Project 802 standards. It bears some resemblance to the IEEE 802.4 Token Passing Bus architecture, but a comparison of specifics such as node addressing reveals incompatibilities. For example, the original 2.5 megabits per second (Mbps) ARCNET uses eight-bit addresses, where the IEEE standard uses 48-bit addresses. Nevertheless, the ARCNET architecture has received wide acceptance in the industry and continues to experience growth.

ARCNET has five frame formats, as depicted in Figure 1-16. The Invitation to Transmit (ITT) is the token that passes control of the network from one workstation to another. The Free Buffer Enquiry (FBE) is a query from a station desiring to transmit to determine if the intended receiver has sufficient buffer space available to hold the incoming frame. The Packet (PAC) is the frame itself, and can contain up to 508 octets of data. An Acknowledgment (ACK) confirms the receipt of a packet or offers a positive response to an FBE. The Negative Acknowledgment (NAK) indicates a refusal to accept a packet or a negative response to an FBE. For further information on the ARCNET protocols, see reference [1-34].

1.6.6 FDDI

The Fiber Data Distributed Interface (FDDI) is a 100-Mbps network developed by the American National Standards Institute (ANSI). It has a number of standards (reference [1-35]) and is designed for both LAN and MAN (Metropolitan Area Network) configurations. A popular LAN application using FDDI as a high-speed backbone will be explored in Section 2.3.3. As its name implies, its physical topology is a fiber optic token passing ring, somewhat similar to IEEE 802.5. The FDDI frame formats also resemble those defined in IEEE 802.5. The encoding scheme used with FDDI defines a "symbol" which is equal to four bits.

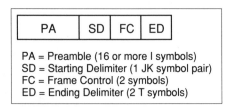

Figure 1-17a. FDDI Token Format

The first FDDI format, the Token (see Figure 1-17a), consists of four fields. The Preamble (16 symbols) is used for synchronization. The Starting Delimiter, SD (2 symbols), indicates the start of the frame. The Frame Control, FC (2 symbols), defines the frame type and function. The subfields are:

C: Frame class (asynchronous or synchronous)

L: Frame address length (16 or 48 bits)

F: Frame format (defines LLC or MAC data)

Z: MAC control bits (indicating the MAC control frame type)

The Ending Delimiter, ED (2 symbols), indicates the end of the frame. The second FDDI format, the Frame (see Figure 1-17b), adds four fields between the FC and ED:

DA: Destination Address (4 or 12 symbols, same format as IEEE 802)

SA: Source Address (must match DA in length)

INFO: Information (variable)

FCS: Frame Check Sequence, a 32-bit Cyclic Redundancy Check (8 symbols)

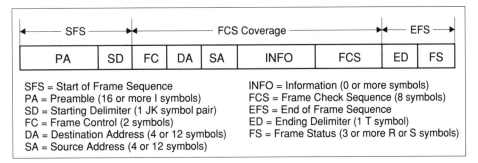

Figure 1-17b. FDDI Frame Format

The Ending Delimiter (1 symbol) indicates the end of the frame. The Frame Status, FS (at least 3 symbols), includes Error Detected (E), Address Recognized (A), and Frame Copied (C), as in IEEE 802.5.

The vendor community is very interested in the use of FDDI networks as backbones. Two excellent articles on the subject are references [1-36] and [1-37].

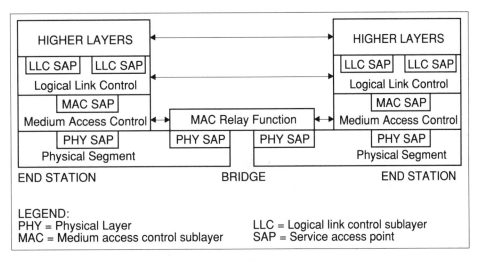

Figure 1-18. Protocol Flows for Bridged Local Network
© 1988 IEEE

1.7 IEEE Bridging Standards

As we studied in section 1.4, a bridge is an internetworking device that relays frames of data from one network segment to another, making the multiple segments appear as one contiguous LAN. Figure 1-18 shows an architectural model of a bridge, with the protocol relationships between the various peer processes indicated by horizontal lines. Several design issues are worth noting (reference [1-38]). First, each segment (left or right) may have its own Physical (PHY) and Medium Access Control (MAC) layers. No requirement exists for consistency on each side. Second, Logical Link Control (LLC) and higher-layer protocols pass transparently through the bridge; the bridge is independent of higher-layer protocol. Third, bridges do not provide data flow control; therefore, congestion within them is possible. When this occurs, any frames that were discarded or lost must be recovered by a higher layer protocol process.

Since some frames will be forwarded (or passed across the bridge relay) and others will be filtered (not passed across the bridge), another question arises: How does the bridge make its relaying decision? The two predominant methods of bridging have been Transparent Bridging (TB) and Source Routing (SR). The IEEE 802 committee is currently in the process of adopting a Source Routing Transparent (SRT) method that provides both Transparent Bridging and Source Routing. We'll look at these three methods individually.

1.7.1   Transparent Bridging Method

The Transparent Bridging Method is so-named because the intelligence necessary to make the relaying decision exists in the bridge itself, and is thus "transparent" to the communicating workstations. Backes [1-39] describes three distinct functions of the Transparent Bridge:

1.   Frame forwarding

2.   Learning workstation addresses

3.   Assuring that no topological loops exist

The first function, frame forwarding, is best described with a diagram (Figure 1-19). Traffic on LAN 1 (e.g. workstation A to B) remains on LAN 1 and is not relayed to LAN 2. Traffic from LAN 1 to LAN 2 (e.g. workstation B to C) is relayed by Bridge 1, but ignored by Bridge 2. Traffic from LAN 1 to LAN 3 (e.g. workstation A to E) is relayed by both Bridge 1 and Bridge 2.

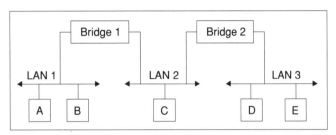

Figure 1-19. Bridge Forwarding
© 1988 IEEE

The second function of the TB, learning workstation addresses, is done by monitoring both incoming and outgoing ports (see Figure 1-20). A database of workstations (on either side of the bridge) is developed by listening to all transmissions—a process known as learning. The bridge keeps a list of which stations transmit to each port, thereby allowing the forwarding or filtering decision to be made based upon the MAC-Layer address read.

The TB bridge's third function is to provide overall control of the relaying operation—described in Figure 1-20 as the Bridge Protocol Entity. The topological assumption required by the TB bridge is that the network has formed a spanning tree. Backes describes the spanning tree as a network in which "there is only one path of bridges and LANs between any two LANs in the entire bridged LAN." In other words, there is only one (not two or more) path from LAN 1 to LAN 2 so that the possibility of a loop (Figure 1-21) does not exist. If workstation A were to broadcast a frame having an unknown destination address, both Bridge 1 and Bridge 2 would forward that frame. A loop could cause frames to pass from LAN 1 to LAN 2 ad infinitum, giving new meaning to the phrase "you can't get there from here!" To eliminate the loop, one of the bridges must be (logically) disconnected, thereby making only a single path from LAN 1 to LAN 2 available.

33

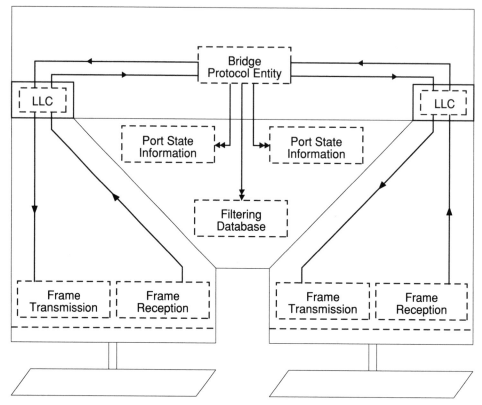

Figure 1-20. Operation of Inter-Bridge Protocol
© *IEEE*

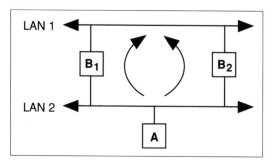

Figure 1-21. Loop of Bridges
© *1988 IEEE*

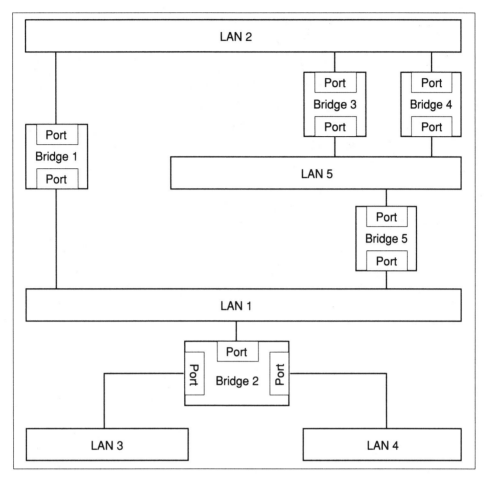

Figure 1-22. Bridged Local Area Network
© *IEEE*

The algorithm that takes the physical network topology and creates a logical Spanning Tree is known as the Spanning Tree algorithm. Bridges communicate with each other through messages known as Hello Bridge Protocol Data Units (BPDUs). One bridge becomes the "root" and all bridges transmit frames in the least-cost direction of that root. The root port is the port of each bridge which is communicating to or from the root. The root is selected depending upon transmission of Hello BPDUs, and the minimum-cost path decision. An example from IEEE 802.1d

35

(reference [1-40]) shows a physical topology (see Figure 1-22) that becomes a logical topology (see Figure 1-23) after the Spanning Tree algorithm is used. The resulting Spanning Tree is shown in Figure 1-24. Note that Bridge 1 has been selected as the root, and Bridges 3 and 5 have been logically disconnected. The Spanning Tree algorithm defines the logical topology: Bridge 1 connects LAN 1 and LAN 2; Bridge 2 connects LAN 1 and LAN 3, as well as LAN 1 and LAN 4; and finally, Bridge 4 connects LAN 2 and LAN 5. Details of the algorithm are found in the standard (reference [1-40]).

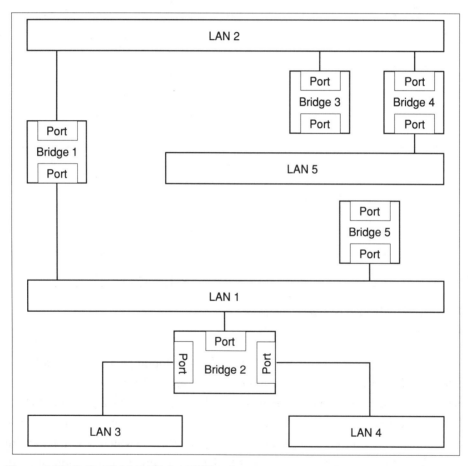

Figure 1-23. Active Bridged Network Topology
© *IEEE*

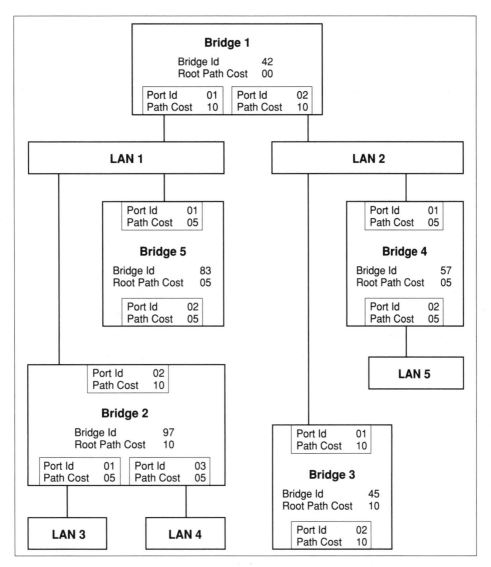

Figure 1-24. Spanning Tree
© *IEEE*

The Spanning Tree algorithm has been widely used in IEEE 802.3 networks, and supported by vendors such as Digital Equipment Corporation (DEC) and Vitalink Communications Corporation.

1.7.2 Source Routing Method

While the TB Bridging Method depends on bridge intelligence, the Source Routing Method (SR) requires that the workstation (a source) determine the frame route. Interestingly enough, the SR algorithm was developed by IBM. The SR-compliant bridge requires less processing power, since much of its work is done for it by the originating workstation.

The key to the SR Method is the optional Routing Information field (RI) shown in Figure 1-14b, and the I/G bit of the Source Address field, known as the Routing Information Indicator (RII). When RII=1, RI is present, indicating that this frame can be source routed through source routing bridges. Frames with RII=0 will not be forwarded by source routing bridges; i.e., they will remain on the local ring.

The format of the RI field is shown in Figure 1-25, and consists of a Routing Control field (two octets) followed by up to 14 two-octet Route-Designator pairs. The Route-Designator pair consists of a ring number (12 bits) and a bridge number (4 bits). A total of 14 route segments are possible, making the largest internetwork span 13 bridges (or hops). (The IBM implementation uses a maximum of 8 Route-Designator pairs or 7 hops.) The RI field is determined by a discovery process originating at the workstation. A "discovery" frame is circulated to the various rings via the bridges until the intended destination station is located using a Spanning Tree. On its way back to the originator, each bridge adds its designator (ring ID and bridge number) until the reply finally reaches the transmitting station. The route from source to destination is thus selected from the RI fields shown on the returning frames.

An example of this process, taken from reference [1-41] (also described in reference [1-42]) is shown in Figure 1-26. Workstation A wishes to communicate with Workstation B which is not on its ring. The discovery process yields the RI Field 0830 AA03 AA14 AA20H. As shown in Figure 1-26a, workstation A is attached to ring number AA0, then to ring AA1 via bridge 3. Ring AA1 attaches to ring AA2 via bridge 4. The complete RI field is shown in Figure 1-26b.

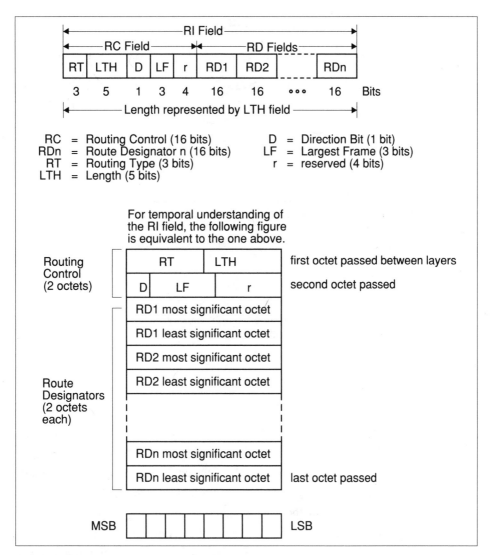

Figure 1-25. Routing Information Field
© *IEEE*

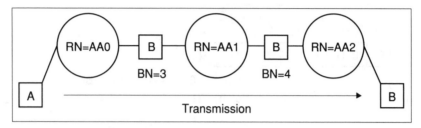

Figure 1-26a. Source Routing Example
© 1988 IEEE

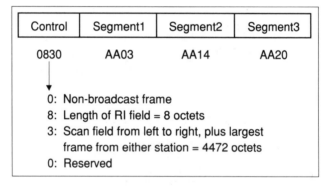

Figure 1-26b. Routing Information Field Example
© 1988 IEEE

In order to communicate with B, Workstation A thus inserts 0830 AA03 AA14 AA20H in the RI field, and sets the I/G bit of the Source Address (RII) equal to 1. The completed frame (including data) is then placed on the network. As the frame passes bridge 3, the bridge first sees RII=1, and looks for the RI field. The bridge recognizes its address (3) in the concatenated segment list, since it knows it is connected to both ring AA0 and AA1. Bridge 3 then copies the frame, and places it on ring AA1 which is copied by bridge 4. Bridge 4 in turn places the frame on ring AA2 where workstation B is located. The response from B to A might follow the same (reverse) route, or take some other route on a more complex network topology.

Because the discovery process and the insertion of the RI field is done by the source workstation, the term "source routing" is used. While this technique places more processing responsibility on the workstation, the bridge's job is simpler—look for RII, decode the RI field, copy the appropriate frames, and forward to the next ring.

1.7.3   Source Routing Transparent Method

As we have studied, the TB Method has been widely used in IEEE 802.3 networks, and SR was designed for IEEE 802.5. What happens if you need to connect a TB-based network to an SR-based network? You have two choices. The first is to combine the TB and SR Methods in one box. IBM's 8209 LAN Bridge (which we will study in section 2.3.2) is an example of this type of configuration which connects to an Ethernet/IEEE 802.3 network on one side, and an IEEE 802.5 network on the other. Unfortunately, this approach requires the network to be segmented into two domains (TB and SR), with the bridge translating the frames in between (reference [1-43]).

The second choice, currently being reviewed by the IEEE 802.1 committee (reference [1-44]), is known as the Source Routing Transparent (SRT) method. As the name implies, the SRT algorithm combines both methods:

Source Routing (SR) is performed when a frame is received with the RII=1 (indicating the presence of the RI field).

Transparent Bridging (TB) is performed when a frame is received with the RII=0 (indicating the absence of the RI field).

The draft SRT standard (reference [1-44]) defines operation on two network types, both having an RI field defined:

IEEE 802.5/ISO 8802-5 Token Ring

ANSI X3.139/ISO 9514 FDDI

Operation of the SRT algorithm is illustrated in Figure 1-27. Two sections of logic exist within the bridge's MAC Relay Entity: SR and TB. Frames entering the

MAC entity with RII=0 (non-source routed) are either forwarded or discarded according to the TB Method we discussed in section 1.7.1. If the received frame has RII=1 (source routed), then the SR logic is used. The SR logic depends on the type of frame received.

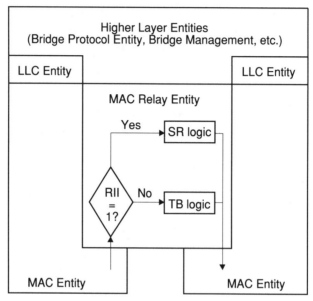

Figure 1-27. SRT Bridge Operation Logic
© *IEEE*

The SRT algorithm has several distinct advantages (reference [1-45]). The ability to mix SR and TB on the same LAN eliminates the previous interoperability between the two techniques. As a result, SR stations and TB stations can now communicate, and connectivity is assured. Finally, since SRT applies to both the ANSI FDDI and IEEE 802 standards, an upward migration path to the faster FDDI backbone is guaranteed. Two other good references for comparisons between the SR and TB methods are [1-46] and [1- 47]. Reference [1-48] discusses source routing in more detail. To simplify the internetwork design, look for SRT support in products when shopping for your next Ethernet/IEEE 802.3 to IEEE 802.5 bridge.

Those of you who have successfully made it through all of this theory are about to be rewarded. In the next nine chapters, we will take off our "standards" hat and replace it with our "implementation" hat. We'll begin in Chapter 2 by looking at devices that solve the LAN-to-LAN connectivity issue.

1.8   References

[1-1] Tanenbaum, Andrew S. *Computer Networks*. 2d ed. Prentice-Hall, 1988.

[1-2] Stallings, William. *Data and Computer Communications*. 2d ed. New York: Macmillan, 1988.

[1-3] Black , Uyless. OSI, *A Model for Computer Communications Standards*. Prentice-Hall, 1991.

[1-4] McConnell, John. *Internetworking Computer Systems*. Prentice-Hall, 1988.

[1-5] Rose, Marshall T. *The Open Book*. Prentice-Hall, 1990.

[1-6] Ungermann-Bass, Inc. (Allan H. Stacy and Mike Work.) *Interconnectivity— Open Enterprise Networking*. 1988. Santa Clara, CA.

[1-7] Buerger, David J. "Major Network Vendors Advocate Interoperability." *Infoworld* (June 11, 1990): 8.

[1-8] Gantz, John. "Does the World Need MANs?" *Networking Management* (June 1990): 70–72.

[1-9] Greenstein, Irwin. "Internetworking Industry Sees Rapid Growth Despite User Confusion." *Networking Management* (May 1990): 68–75.

[1-10] International Organization for Standardization, Information Processing Systems—Open Systems Interconnection—Basic Reference Model, ISO 7498-1984.

[1-11] Voelcker, John. "Helping Computers Communicate." *IEEE Spectrum* Vol. 23, No. 3 (March 1986); 61-70 (also published in Computer Communications: Architectures, Protocols and Standards. 2d ed., IEEE Computer Society Press, 1987: 9–18).

[1-12] Stallings, William. "Interfacing to a LAN: Where's the Protocol?" *Data Communications* (April 1987): 121– 133.

[1-13] Stallings, William. "When One LAN Is Not Enough." *Byte* (January 1989): 293–298.

[1-14] Weissberger, Alan J. and Jay E. Israel. "What the New Internetworking Standards Provide." *Data Communications* (February 1987): 141 –156.

[1-15] Stallings, William. "Can We Talk? " *Datamation* October 15, 1985, pp. 101–106.

[1-16] Stallings, William. "Is There an OSI Session Protocol in Your Future? " *Data Communications* (November 1987): 147–159.

[1-17] Roux, Evelyne. "OSI's Final Frontier: The Application Layer." *Data Communications* (January 1988); 137–145.

[1-18] Mantleman, Lee. "Upper Layers: From Bizarre to Bazaar." *Data Communications* (January 1988): 110–128.

[1-19] Cashin, Jerry. "Test Suites Rolling Out Ensure 'Open' Systems." *Software Magazine* (August 1990): 75–79.

[1-20] Witkowicz, Tad. "Connecting LANs." *LAN Magazine* (February 1988): 34–36.

[1-21] Perlman, Radia, et al. "Choosing the Appropriate ISO Layer for LAN Interconnection." *IEEE Network* (January 1988): 81–86.

[1-22] Koshy, George T. "Understanding Multiple LANs: The Why and How of Linking Up." *Data Communications* (May 1986): 221–227.

[1-23] Boulé , Richard and John Moy. "Inside Routers: A Technology Guide for Network Builders." *Data Communications* (September 21, 1989): 53–66.

[1-24] McQuillan, John M. "Routers as Building Blocks for Robust Internetworks." *Data Communications* (September 21, 1989): 28–33.

[1-25] Mier, Edwin E. "LAN Gateways: Paths to Corporate Connectivity." *Data Communications* (August 1989): 72–84.

[1-26] Miller, Mark A. *LAN Troubleshooting Handbook*. Redwood City, CA : M&T Books, 1989.

[1-27] Miller, Mark A. *LAN Protocol Handbook*. Redwood City, CA: M&T Books, 1990.

[1-28] Institute of Electrical and Electronics Engineers. *Carrier Sense Multiple Access with Collision Detection (CSMA/CD) Access Method and Physical Layer Specifications. ISO 8802-3, ANSI/IEEE Std 802.3.* 1988.

[1-29] Institute of Electrical and Electronics Engineers. *Token Passing Bus Access Method. ISO/IEC 8802-4, ANSI/IEEE Std 802.4.* 1990.

[1-30] Institute of Electrical and Electronics Engineers. *Token Ring Access Method. IEEE Standard 802.5.* 1989.

[1-31] Institute of Electrical and Electronics Engineers. *Logical Link Control. ISO 8802-2, IEEE Std 802.2.* 1989.

[1-32] Digital Equipment Corp. *Ethernet Data Link Layer and Physical Layer Specifications.* Document no. AA-K759B-TK, November 1982.

[1-33] DDN Network Information Center. *A Standard for the Transmission of IP Datagrams Over IEEE 802 Networks.* RFC 1042, February 1988.

[1-34] Datapoint Corp. *ARCNET Designer's Handbook.* Document 61610, 1988.

[1-35] American National Standards Institute, X3.166: 1989, X3.148: 1988, X3.139: 1987.

[1-36] Kessler, Gary C. "FDDI." *LAN Magazine* (August 1989): 84–96.

[1-37] Wolter, Mark S. "Fiber Data Distributed Interface (FDDI)—A Tutorial." *Connexions the Interoperability Report* (October 1990): 16–26.

[1-38] Dixon, Roy C. and Daniel A. Pitt. "Addressing Bridging and Source Routing." *IEEE Network* (January 1988): 25–32.

[1-39] Backes, Floyd. "Transparent Bridges for Interconnection of IEEE 802 LANs." *IEEE Network* (January 1988): 5–9.

[1-40] Institute of Electrical and Electronics Engineers. *MAC Bridges.* P802.1d/ D9, July 14, 1989.

[1-41] Texas Instruments. *TMS380 Adapter Chipset User's Guide Supplement.* document SPWU003, 1987.

[1-42] Hamner , M. Claire and Gerald R. Samsen. "Source Routing Bridge Implementation." *IEEE Network* (January 1988): 33–36.

[1-43] Greenfield, David M. "An End to a Bridging Feud." *Data Communications* (May 1990): 49–50.

[1-44] Institute of Electrical and Electronics Engineers. *MAC Bridges Source Routing Supplement.* P802.1X draft standard, July 21, 1990.

[1-45] Pitt, Daniel and Kirk Preiss. "SRT Bridging." *IBM* (July 10, 1990)

[1-46] Soha, Michael and Radia Perlman. "Comparison of Two LAN Bridge Approaches." *IEEE Network* (January 1988): 37–43.

[1-47] Zhang, Lixia. "Comparison of Two Bridge Routing Approaches." *IEEE Network* (January 1988): 44–48.

[1-48] *Institute of Electrical and Electronics Engineers Source Routing Tutorial for End System Operation IEEE 802.5D/D16—Source Routing.* "Changes to 802.5 Text."

CHAPTER 2

LAN to LAN Internetworking

Now that we've discussed the various standards for both LANs and internetworking devices, it's time to examine some of the products that enable those connections. Before we dive in, allow me to present a road map for this and other related chapters. In this chapter, we will focus on LAN to LAN internetworking devices, and will discuss, in order, repeaters, bridges, brouters and routers. In Chapter 4, we will discuss LAN to WAN hardware, including asynchronous communication servers; analog and digital leased line-compatible bridges and routers; and hardware to access Public Data Networks (PDNs) and T-1 facilities. In Chapter 8 we'll look at the internetworking and interoperability of networking software. In Chapter 9, we will complete the product reviews by looking at application-specific gateways. Appendix B lists selected manufacturers of internetworking products.

Admittedly, many products would fit equally well in either of these four chapters; however, an attempt has been made to place them in the category that seems most appropriate from an internetwork-design point of view. Let's begin our review of products by discussing the design of the internetwork itself.

2.1 Designing the LAN-to-LAN Connection

Many interesting events that have had an impact on the job of the network manager and/or designer have occurred in American business in the last few years. First, the proliferation of personal computers has fostered a tremendous growth in the number of workstations connected to a single LAN. An annual growth of

100–200 percent per year of workstations per network is not uncommon. Second, a number of business mergers and acquisitions have forced system growth, and forced it on an instantaneous basis. Third, in a development that relates to the first two, there is a need to connect networks in different geographical areas. This requirement adds another variable—the Wide Area Network (WAN) transmission facility—to the design.

Hopefully, your reason for needing a LAN-to-LAN connection falls into one of the above three categories: growth, major addition/merger or WAN requirements. Several internetworking devices are available for these applications. You must decide which one is most appropriate.

2.1.1 Repeating, Bridging, Brouting or Routing?

Let's establish some general guidelines for the selection of the internetwork hardware and software. We'll assume that the need for internetworking is driven by the need to address one (or more) of the following situations: multiple transmission media types, dissimilar LAN architectures, several protocols, or incompatibility between different application programs. We'll also assume that the LAN started out relatively small (i.e. less than 100 nodes) and that growth has doubled or tripled the network's size. We could use four types of devices to handle this growth: repeaters, bridges, brouters, and routers.

Repeaters are used to extend the physical cable length, or the number of workstations allowed per segment. For example, a thin Ethernet/IEEE 802.3 network can support 30 attachments per 185 meter segment. If either the number of attachments or length is exceeded, a repeater can be installed between the two segments. Token Ring and ARCNET networks have similar constraints on cable length and number of attachments used. (We will explore repeater usage in section 2.2.)

Bridges are used to segment networks based upon network traffic. Segmentation divides the network into logical subsets, keeping traffic from workstations that frequently communicate on a common LAN. (We'll look at bridge examples in section 2.3.) Brouters are also traffic-sensitive devices—however, they include the capacity to logically segment the network based upon the routing algorithm, higher layer protocol, or WAN facility in use. (Section 2.4 is devoted to brouters.)Routers segment network traffic based upon the Destination Network address (not the Workstation hardware address) of interest. As such, routers are heavily dependent upon the Network Layer Protocol (e.g. IP, XNS) in use. We'll study router examples in section 2.5. Gateways are application specific devices that connect different network architectures. We'll look at gateways in chapter 9.

Figure 2-1 summarizes the functions of these five devices. Reference [2-1] is an excellent tutorial on the subject of internetwork device selection and applications.

Repeater
    Operates at OSI Physical Layer
    Regenerates or repeats physical signals
    Used to extend LAN range
Bridge
    Operates at OSI Data Link Layer
    Logically separates network segments
    Independent of higher layer protocols
    Used for LAN traffic management
Brouter
    Operates at OSI Data Link and Network Layers
    Combines the protocol transparency of a bridge with the ability to route
       certain protocols
    Used for networks with mixed-protocol traffic
Router
    Operates at OSI Network Layer
    Logically separates subnetworks
    Dependent upon Network Layer protocol
    Must obtain knowledge of network topology
    Used for internetwork communication
Gateway
    Operates at OSI Higher Layers (Session through Application)
    Dependent upon user application
    Used for application-to-application communication

Figure 2-1. Comparing Internetworking Devices

2.1.2 Analyzing the Network

As an example, let's assume that cable distance is not the issue, and that a WAN facility is not required. Traffic on the network, however, has increased over time, and with that, users are now complaining of longer delays or higher response times. Without becoming mathematicians, let's describe pictorially what is occurring, aided by research done on CSMA/CD networks by bridge manufacturer Retix (reference [2-2]).

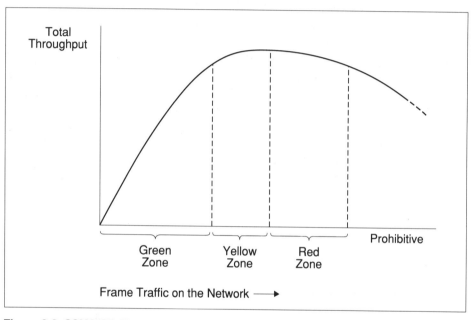

Figure 2-2. CSMA/CD Throughput as a Function of Network Traffic
(Courtesy Retix)

CSMA/CD networks operate quite efficiently under light to medium traffic loads. As more workstations attempt to access the network, however, network throughput declines, as shown in Figure 2-2. As additional workstations are added, their traffic increases the aggregate network traffic accordingly. At a certain point (shown as the red zone in Figure 2-2), the total throughput actually declines. This is caused by frame collisions. When two stations collide, the CSMA/CD algorithm requires that both back off and attempt the transmission later. More traffic creates more collisions, which creates more stations that have data to send and are waiting to transmit on a clear channel. Since more stations are waiting to send, more collisions occur and the actual throughput declines. The collisions thus waste network time that could otherwise be used to transmit data.

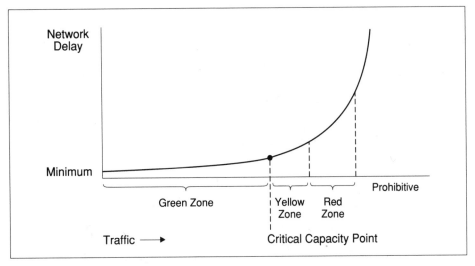

Figure 2-3. CSMA/CD Network Delay as a Function of Network Traffic
(Courtesy Retix)

A second approach to analyzing the network is to measure network delay—the time required to access the network and complete a transmission to a distant node. Retix's research (see Figure 2-3) indicates that this delay is rather stable at less than 20 percent of CSMA/CD network capacity.

This should not be confused with two other benchmarks: network capacity and network utilization. Network capacity is the maximum bandwidth (in Mbps) of the network. For example, an Ethernet has a maximum capacity of 9,922,048 bps when the 9.6 microsecond interframe gap is considered, not 10,000,000 bps as one might immediately expect (reference [2-3]). Network utilization is an instantaneous measurement, a ratio between the number of bits transmitted in a given period, such as one second divided by the network capacity. A typical network utilization would be 20-30 percent.

53

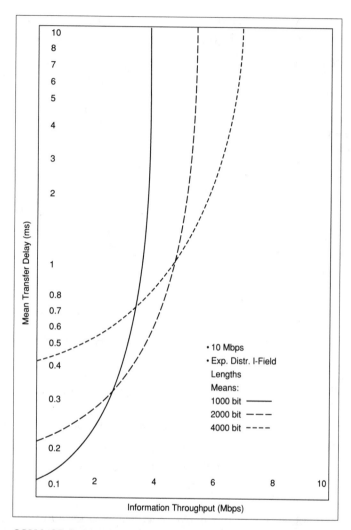

Figure 2-4a. CSMA/CD Delay-Throughput Characteristics: 10 Mbps Transmission Rate
(Reprinted by permission. International Business Machines Corporation.)

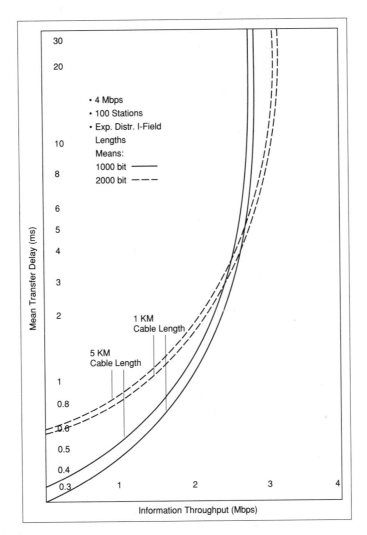

Figure 2-4b. Token Ring Delay-Throughput Characteristics: 4 Mbps Transmission Rate
(Reprinted by permission. International Business Machines Corporation.)

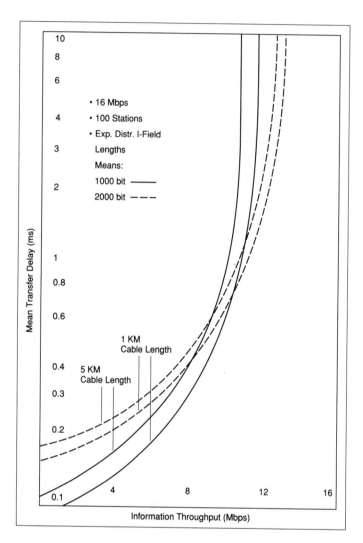

Figure 2-4c. Token Ring Delay-Throughput Characteristics: 16Mbps Transmission Rate
(Reprinted by permission. International Business Machines Corporation.)

For CSMA/CD networks, the network performance is also related to the type of device generating that traffic (see Figure 2-5). The higher the traffic per device, the fewer devices of that type that can be allowed on the network.

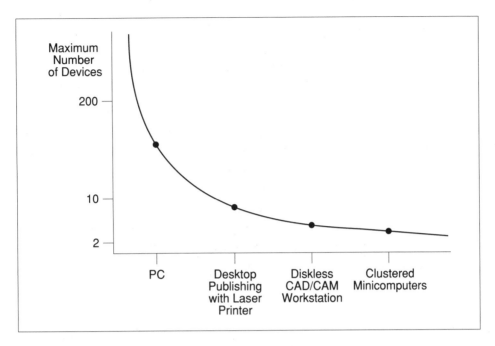

Figure 2-5. Maximum Number of Devices Supported on a CSMA/CD Network
(Courtesy Retix)

IBM's research has compared CSMA/CD and Token Ring networks (references [2-4] and [2-5]) with similar results. CSMA/CD networks show some variance in the instability point (Figure 2-4a) based upon the mean length of the Information field. In all cases, however, this instability occurs between 2-4 Mbps (or 20-40 percent of maximum) throughput for a 10 Mbps network. Token Ring networks demonstrate similar characteristics for either 4 Mbps (see Figure 2-4b) or 16 Mbps (see Figure 2-4c) transmission rates. Note that the instability point has shifted to approximately 80 percent of maximum throughput.

We can conclude that neither a throughput nor a network utilization of 100 percent is attainable. When traffic increases on a network, internetworking devices such as bridges must be added to keep the network's performance stable.

Let's now assume that you, the network administrator, have used a network management tool such as a monitor or protocol analyzer to measure the network traffic or utilization. You have determined that your network is in the "yellow zone" and heading for the "red zone". A simple solution will avoid sleepless nights: divide the network into two distinct segments, and install a bridge in between. The result should be similar to the configuration shown in Figure 2-6. The bridge isolates the traffic of the two segments, thus allowing each segment to operate at a higher throughput. From Figure 2-6, the bridge effectively multiplies the throughput so that the aggregate peak utilization occurs at a higher traffic load. The peak throughput has thus moved from traffic level A (without the bridge) to traffic level B (with the bridge). The bridge has thus reduced the collision probability, by providing some isolation between segments. With fewer workstations on the network (or segment), the likelihood of collision decreases and network throughput correspondingly increases.

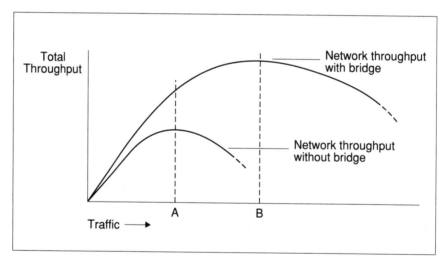

Figure 2-6. CSMA/CD Network Throughput With and Without a Bridge
(Courtesy Retix)

Where do we place the bridges for greatest efficiency? How do we decide which stations (e.g. workstations, hosts, and servers) are to be placed on either side of the bridge? A network management tool for recording the traffic between pairs of stations (often called pair counts) is invaluable here. Stations that communicate with each other on a frequent basis should be placed on the same side of the bridge. A rule of thumb (also from reference [2-2]) suggests that the 80/20 rule be followed: 80 percent of the traffic remain on the local segment, and 20 percent cross the bridge(s) to other segment(s).

Note that an important assumption has been made here: the bridge has somehow acquired the intelligence to know which of the frames that it examines should be forwarded across the bridge. This decision is based either upon a table lookup within the bridge (for Transparent Bridges, discussed in section 1.7.1) or information sent along within the frame (for Source Routed Bridges, discussed in section 1.7.2). It is also important to note that the addresses referred to here are Data Link Layer addresses, which have a flat (i.e. non-hierarchical) nature. In other words, each address is a unique entity, unrelated to the other addresses. (We'll look at hierarchical addressing in section 2.5.) Thus far, we have only discussed solving the internetworking problem for like-topology systems such as Ethernet to Ethernet. Let's look now at internetworking dissimilar architectures.

2.1.3   Connecting Dissimilar LANs

Let's throw another variable into the network design formula, and now assume that we have LANs of two (or more) different architectures, such as Ethernet and Token Ring. How can we connect these? Three approaches are commonly used: a LAN-to-LAN bridge; internal bridging (or routing) at a server; or using a common-denominator protocol such as TCP/IP.

The LAN-to-LAN bridge for dissimilar networks is probably the most limiting solution, since so few products are available; the most common configuration is the recently available Ethernet-to-Token Ring bridge, manufactured by IBM, Ungermann-Bass, Inc., and CrossComm Corporation. A second drawback to using the LAN-to-LAN bridge to connect dissimilar networks is that additional hardware—costing in the neighborhood of $7,000-10,000—is required for the bridge. We'll study the technical challenges of this alternative in detail in section 2.3.2.

In contrast to the hardware solution, internetworking at the server offers a software solution to the problem of connectivity. Network Operating Systems (NOSs)—such as Novell's NetWare and Banyan Systems' VINES—have an architecture that facilitates an internetworking solution. The NOS can be divided into three general components: a driver for the Network Interface Card (NIC) hardware (operating on the OSI Physical and Data Link Layers); internetworking protocols (operating on the Network and Transport Layers); plus application program support (operating on the Session, Presentation and Application layers).

Suppose that at the server, you install two (or more) dissimilar NICs. Each NIC has a unique hardware address, and receives its higher layer information from a NOS driver. In other words, an Ethernet driver talks to the Ethernet NIC with hardware address A, and a Token Ring driver talks to a Token Ring NIC having hardware address B. If all the higher layer (Network through Application) protocols are the same, internetworking between these dissimilar architectures is thus automatic. (We'll study this concept more fully in Chapter 8, which is devoted to the internetworking capabilities of such popular network software as those by Novell, 3Com, IBM, Banyan, and Apple.)

Our third option for connecting dissimilar networks is to find a common-denominator protocol to facilitate internetworking. One obvious example is the TCP/IP (Transmission Control Protocol/Internet Protocol) suite, which was developed specifically for this purpose. If both dissimilar systems can access the common denominator (TCP/IP), then communication between the two becomes possible. A requirement for application program (e.g. electronic mail) compatibility may still exist, and must be addressed. (We will study the TCP/IP and related protocols in Chapter 6, and application-dependent gateways in Chapter 9.)

2.2　Repeaters

A repeater, as the name implies, performs the function of signal amplification (i.e., repeating). This permits the originally-transmitted signal to go further than the attenuation limits of the transmission media (e.g., twisted pair, coaxial) will allow.

Repeaters used thus depend on two variables: the network architecture (Token Ring, Ethernet or ARCNET) and the media type being used. In this section, we'll look at examples of repeater products available for each of the three predominant LAN architectures. Let's start with Token Ring.

2.2.1   Andrew TRR 8218 and TRR 8219

Andrew Corporation of Torrance, California is one of the major vendors of Token Ring/IEEE 802.5 networking hardware. Andrew manufactures two repeaters with advantageous design features. The TRR 8218 is a copper media repeater operating at 4 Mbps. It supports IBM Types 1 and 2 (shielded twisted pair) plus Type 3 (unshielded twisted pair). While the typical hermaphroditic (or data) connectors are used for Types 1 and 2, Andrew substitutes modular RJ-45 connectors on the unshielded cable, making installation somewhat easier. A second advantage is that a fewer number of repeaters is required. Most Token Ring networks are wired with a primary and a backup transmission path. With other vendors (such as IBM) a total of four repeaters would be required: two at each end for both primary and backup paths. Andrew Corporation combines the primary and backup circuits into a single repeater, thus saving hardware expense. The third advantage of Andrew's products is the built-in diagnostics LEDs which indicate a normal signal, unusable (noisy) signal, or signal loss, as well as active stations.

The Andrew Corporation TRR 8219 Fiber Optic Repeater also operates at 4 Mbps, and is used to connect geographically-separated multi-station access units (MSAUs) via fiber optic cables. Four different cable types are supported: 62.5/125 micron, 50/125 micron, 85/125 micron, and 100/140 micron. Bayonet-type ST connectors are used for attachment to the fiber optic cable.

Sample applications of the Token Ring repeaters are shown in Figure 2-7a for both copper and fiber optic cable designs. A second application (Figure 2-7b) shows the repeaters being used to extend the maximum lobe distance to a single workstation. This configuration would eliminate the need for an MSAU and a second repeater at the remote location.

To summarize, Andrew's Token Ring repeaters are extremely user-friendly, adding a choice of media types, connectors and diagnostics to an otherwise fundamental device.

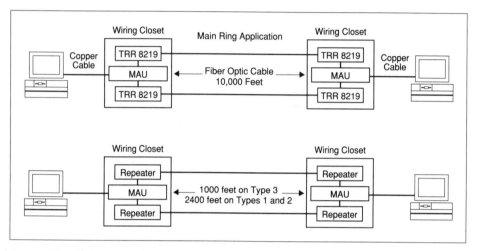

Figure 2-7a. Token Ring Repeater Application
(Courtesy Andrew Corporation)

2.2.2 Cabletron MMAC

Cabletron Systems, Inc. of East Hartford, New Hampshire is one of the oldest suppliers of Ethernet/IEEE 802.3 internetworking hardware and software. They manufacture a variety of transceivers, repeaters, bridges, and network interface cards. What is unique to the Cabletron hardware is the number of media choices available, including unshielded and shielded twisted pair, fiber optic, and thin or thick Ethernet cables.

The heart of Cabletron's System is a Multi Media Access Center (MMAC), which is a modular chassis allowing a number of Ethernet/IEEE 802.3 interfaces. Every port, regardless of the media type, is a repeated port. Several different module types are available: twisted pair, fiber optic, coaxial AUI, and intelligent repeaters. A Token Ring and FDDI bus is also available on the MMAC, allowing integration of Ethernet, Token Ring, and FDDI architectures into one MMAC chassis. The twisted pair module supports IEEE 802.3 10BASE-T connections for workstations located up to 100 meters from the MMAC. IBM data grade cable (Type 1) can be used at distances of up to 150 meters. The fiber optic module is used to connect fiber optic transceivers (and workstations), fiber optic repeaters, or a remote MMAC. A distance of up to 3 kilometers is permitted over 50, 62.5 or 100 micron cable. The coaxial media interface provides up to twelve Ethernet/IEEE 802.3 connections for either thin or thick segments. The Intelligent Repeater Module (IRM) provides the repeater functions for all other ports, such as twisted pair, fiber optic or coaxial. It is an IEEE 802.3-compliant repeater, which supports the Auto Partitioning/ Reconnection algorithm specified in 802.3c and 802.3d. In a nutshell, the repeater algorithm senses colliding ports, and isolates them from the remainder of the network until the problem has been solved.

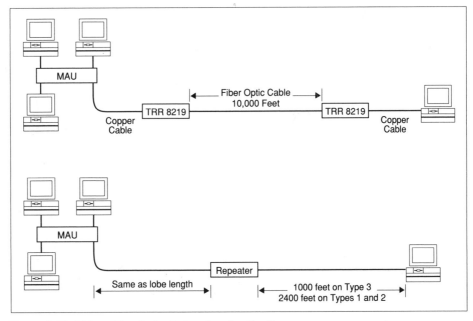

Figure 2-7b. Token Ring Lobe Extension Application
(Courtesy Andrew Corporation)

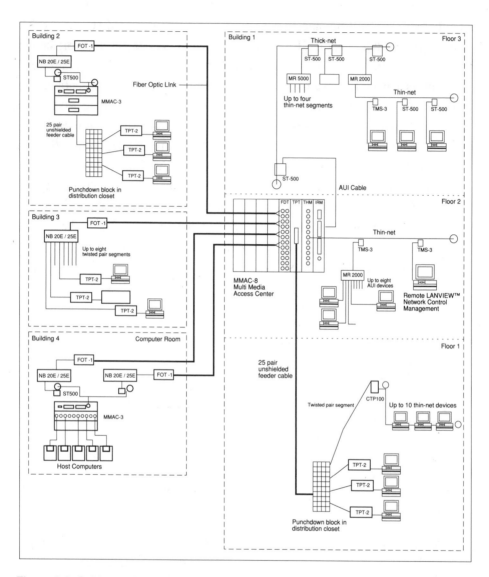

Figure 2-8. Cabletron Multi Media Access Center
(Courtesy Cabletron Systems Inc.)

The IRM also contains Cabletron's Remote LANVIEW network management system, which manages the MMAC through three increasing levels of control and monitoring: the MMAC as a whole, the board level, and the port level. These three tiers allow the network manager to compile performance statistics, set alarm limits, and log events that are critical to the operation of the network. Figure 2-8 shows the MMAC and representative media configurations.

To summarize, Cabletron's MMAC provides the ultimate Ethernet/IEEE 802.3 multiport repeater, by concentrating connections for all possible media types into one modular chassis. The integration of Token Ring and FDDI into the MMAC further strengthens its internetworking capabilities.

2.2.3 SMC Active Hubs

SMC (Standard Microsystems Corporation) of Hauppauge, NY was the first manufacturer of ARCNET controller chips, and has long been known as a premier ARCNET hardware vendor. The topology of ARCNET, which can either be a bus, a star, or a combination, yields itself to a great deal of flexibility. SMC has capitalized on this by offering numerous media choices, including RG-62/U coax, shielded and unshielded twisted pair, and duplex fiber optic cables. Obviously, each type has advantages and disadvantages. Twisted pair is low in cost and easy to install, but limits the transmission distance. Coaxial cables have longer distance limits, but are more expensive and bulky. Fiber optic cables have the advantage of grounding and lightning protection, as well as security, but they are also more expensive.

Active Hubs (see Figure 2-9) are used in star-topology ARCNETs to connect individual workstations. SMC manufactures three types: coax, twisted pair, and fiber optic. All three types are cascadeable and may be interconnected. Active links (not shown) are used to extend one coax segment or to connect a coax segment to a twisted pair segment. Twisted pair repeaters are used to connect two daisy-chained twisted pair segments, thus extending the maximum point-to-point distance.

The beauty of the ARCNET architecture is its ability to interconnect different media types. If you want to run terminals in the computer room on RG-62/U coax,

PCs in the accounting department on twisted pair, and workstations in the factory on fiber optic, ARCNET active links do this with elegance. SMC has taken great advantage of this architectural strength in the design of their hub, link and repeater hardware products.

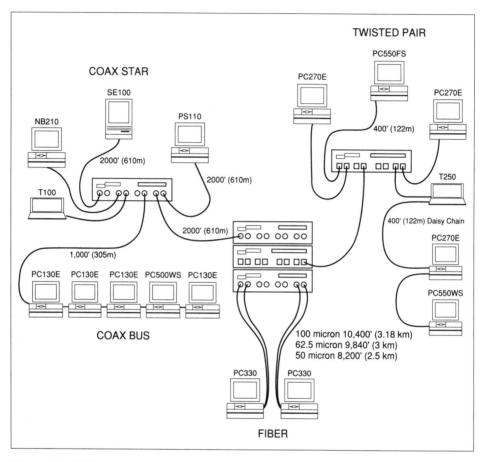

Figure 2-9. ARCNET Connectivity
(Courtesy Standard Microsystems Corporation)

2.3   Bridges

Bridges are devices which operate at the Data Link Layer and relay or forward frames between networks. Most bridges operate on networks of similar architecture, such as Token Ring to Token Ring, or Ethernet to Ethernet. This is not necessarily a hard and fast rule, however, since the IEEE 802.X standards contain a common denominator in the 802.2 LLC format and the use of either two or six-octet addressing. Given these assumptions, therefore, a bridge can be constructed between dissimilar 802.X LANs. In this section, we will look at three examples of bridges: the Retix local and remote Ethernet to Ethernet bridge; the IBM 8209 Token Ring to Ethernet bridge; and the Ungermann-Bass FDDI to Ethernet or Token Ring bridge. Because of their popularity, these bridge products and their operation have been profiled in a number of recent articles. References [2-6] through [2-9] are examples worth reading.

2.3.1   Retix Local and Remote LAN Bridges

As we discussed in Section 2.1, Retix of Santa Monica, California has made a number of contributions to Ethernet internetworking. This company manufactures both local and remote bridges—we'll look at the Retix 2200 series of local bridges first (see Figure 2-10a). All members of the 2200 series family are dual port, MAC-layer bridges. They have a maximum frame filtering rate of 12,000 frames per second, and a maximum forwarding rate of 8400 frames per second for frames between 64 and 1518 octets in length. The two ports can connect to thin or thick Ethernet/IEEE 802.3 backbones or to a StarLAN (IEEE 802.3 1BASE5) network via an optional adapter.

Four models are available. The Model 2244 is suggested for PC workgroups and has filtering/forwarding rates of 10,000 and 6000 frames per second, respectively. The Model 2244M includes network management software plus support for the IEEE 802.1d Spanning Tree algorithm. The Model 2265 is the high-performance bridge, designed for attaching DEC VAX clusters to Ethernet backbones. As before, the Model 2265M adds network management and 802.1d support to the standard

Model 2265. Retix recently introduced a local bridge that has performance figures even greater than the Model 2265. Called the Model 4660, this high-performance bridge filters at the maximum Ethernet rate of 14,880 frames per second on either port, or 29,000 on both. The Model 4660's forwarding rate is 13,650 frames per second, which is sufficient for even the most heavily-loaded Ethernet LANs. It is designed for high volume applications such as networks with diskless workstations handling high volumes of traffic from their servers.

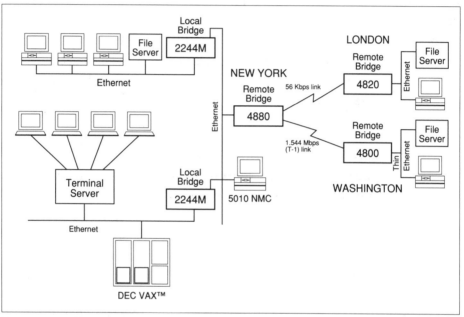

Figure 2-10a. Retix 2265M Bridge Configuration
(Courtesy Retix)

For internetworks requiring remote connections, Retix 4800 series bridges connect Ethernets via WAN facilities. The Model 4820 supports one or two links operating at 56, 64, or 128 Kbps, while the Model 4880 supports one or two links operating at 1.544 or 2.048 Mbps. Both bridges offer a single LAN port, and can connect to thin or thick Ethernet/IEEE 802.3 networks, or to StarLAN (see Figure 2-10b). The Model 4820 filters and forwards at 9000 and 870 frames per second, respectively. The Model 4880, designed for high throughput, filters at the maximum

Ethernet/IEEE 802.3 rate of 14,880 frames per second, and forwards at 8000 frames per second. Two high-speed LAN-WAN-LAN links can thus be fully utilized. Both models support the PC-based Retix Network Management Center (NMC) or a RISC workstation-based NMC. The NMC compiles statistics on network traffic, and remotely controls each bridge and its filter tables. Another recent addition is the Model 4942 remote bridge/router. It has the same interfaces and throughput as the 4880, but it also offers routing. Some networks require logical partitioning of TCP/IP, for example, and bridging of all other protocols. The Model 4942 was designed for these applications.

In summary, the Retix Ethernet/IEEE 802.3 bridges provide an excellent combination of simplicity for low-end applications with high throughput for LAN-WAN-LAN connections.

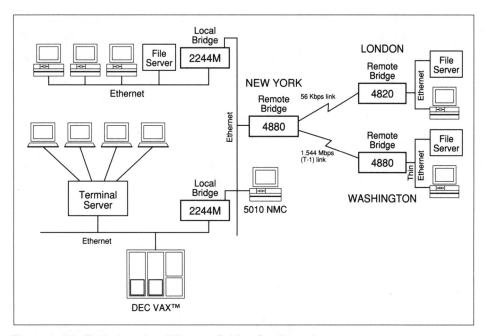

Figure 2-10b. Retix Local and Remote Bridge Configurations
(Courtesy Retix)

2.3.2　IBM 8209 LAN Bridge

IBM has gone out of its way to open up its Token Ring products for internetworking applications. One example is the Etherand driver within the OS/2 LAN Server Version 1.3 which supports both Ethernet Version 2.0 and IEEE 802.3 framing (see section 8.3). The second is the IBM 8209 LAN Bridge which allows communication between Ethernet/IEEE 802.3 LANs and Token Ring (IEEE 802.5) LANs.

Bridging these dissimilar networks is not an easy task. To begin with, the frame sizes of Ethernet/IEEE 802.3 are different, with Ethernet transmitting up to 1500 octets of data per frame, and Token Ring transmitting 4500 octets (at 4 Mbps) or 18,000 octets (at 16 Mbps) per frame. Data throughput, which is typically measured in frames per second, becomes more difficult to benchmark (reference [2-10]).

A second issue affecting bridge operation (not the end user) is the bit order of the network addresses. Ethernet/IEEE 802.3 and IEEE 802.5 represent the Medium Access Control (MAC) addresses in different manners. The LSB of each octet of an Ethernet/IEEE 802.3 address has the same meaning as the MSB of an IEEE 802.5 address. Thus, when identical Ethernet/IEEE 802.3 and IEEE 802.5 addresses are displayed in hexadecimal, they would appear different. When either type is transmitted, however, the Individual/Group (I/G) address bit is sent out first. Information within the Data Field is not a problem, since the same hardware (e.g. Token Ring and Token Ring) exists on both ends of that side of the bridge. The Address fields, however, require bit swapping before a frame can be forwarded from one side of the bridge to the other.

Third, the bridge must be prepared to handle the Source Routing (SR) method on the Token Ring port (developed by IBM and submitted to IEEE as part of IEEE 802.1d) or the Transparent Bridging (TB) method on the Ethernet/IEEE 802.3 port (developed by DEC—see reference [2-11]). As we studied in section 1.4, the SR method requires the originating station to specify the path to the destination via intermediate bridges. As a result, bridges require less processing to forward frames. The TB method, in contrast, places the processing responsibility on the bridge, and it makes the forwarding (i.e. send across the bridge) or filtering (i.e. do not send across the bridge) decision based upon tables that have either been manually loaded into, or dynamically discovered by, the bridge itself.

Thus, the Token Ring-to-Ethernet bridge problem is what engineering profes-
sors call a "non-trivial problem." IBM, however, has solved these problems in the
design of the 8209, which supports either a 4 or 16 Mbps Token Ring and another
connection to an Ethernet/IEEE 802.3 network (see Figure 2-11a). The 8209 can also
be used in networks with other Token Ring-to-Token Ring bridges (see Figure 2-11b).

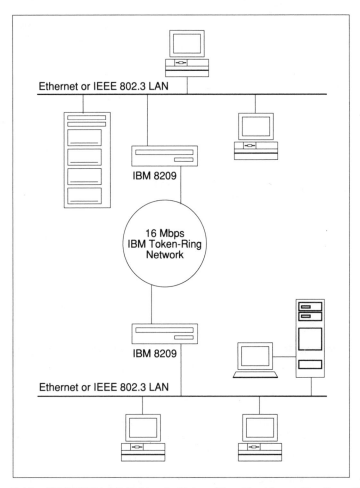

Figure 2-11a. IBM 8209 LAN Bridge in Token Ring Backbone Configuration
(Reprinted by permission. International Business Machines Corporation.)

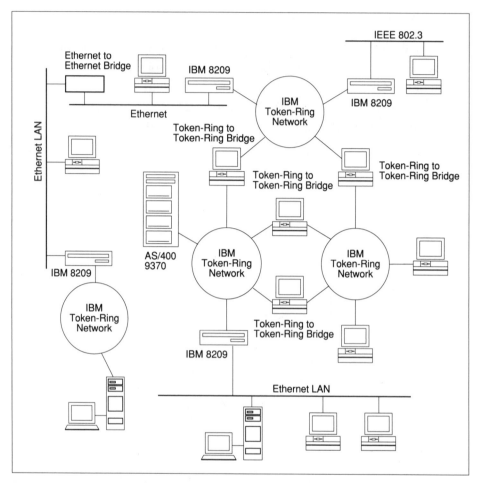

Figure 2-11b. Connecting Multiple LANs with the IBM 8209 LAN Bridge and Other Bridges *(Reprinted by permission. International Business Machines Corporation.)*

Two modes of 8209 operation support different protocols. Mode 1 is used for Ethernet version 2.0 LANs, and supports TCP/IP, SNA 802.2 LLC, and NetBIOS traffic. Mode 2 allows connection to IEEE 802.3 LANs, and supports 802.2 LLC, TCP/IP, NetBIOS and SNA traffic. An "auto-detect" selection is available that supports both Mode 1 and Mode 2 on a dynamic, switchable basis.

Parallel bridges are allowed between Token Ring and Ethernet. Only one of the bridges can be active at a time, however, to eliminate the possibility of a frame that loops between the LANs. Workstations on the Token Ring side treat the 8209 as a standard SR-compliant bridge. Workstations on the Ethernet side treat the 8209 as a transparent bridge, with all workstations on the Token Ring side appearing as if they were on the near side of the bridge. As a final detail, the 8209 is supported by IBM's LAN Manager, the network management program.

To summarize, the IBM 8209 LAN Bridge solves many network managers' worst nightmare: how to connect Token Ring and Ethernet architectures without a third party server (such as Novell's) or a major redesign of the internetwork.

2.3.3 Ungermann-Bass Access/One FDDI Bridges

Ungermann-Bass, Inc. of Santa Clara, California is well-known as an innovator in both networking hardware and software products. Two examples of Ungermann-Bass' strength are their excellent references, [1-6] and [6-21]. Most bridged networks connect LANs having similar architectures but with different transmission media types or speeds. One example of this would be multiple thin-Ethernets bridged to a single thick-Ethernet backbone. Many campus environments use this type of architecture. A second example would be a 16 Mbps Token Ring backbone, with multiple 4 Mbps rings connected via bridges. Ungermann-Bass' products demonstrate an improvement on this technique by using a backbone technology (FDDI) that is dissimilar to that of the connecting LANs (Ethernet or Token Ring). Before we examine Ungermann-Bass' product in detail, let's take a quick look at the FDDI architecture upon which their design is based (reference [2-12]).

Recall from our discussion in section 1.7.4 that FDDI (Fiber Data Distributed Interface) is a token passing ring network, operating at 100 Mbps over fiber optic cable and adhering to the ANSI X3T9.5 standard. The topology of a four-node FDDI network is shown in Figure 2-12a (note the dual-ring topology). The primary ring is the data path, while the secondary ring provides redundancy or additional bandwidth. Up to 500 stations can exist on the network, with up to 2 Km of cable between stations. The current standard uses 62.5/125 micron fiber optic cable, with a wavelength of 1300 nanometers (nm). The fiber optic cables are called duplex cables because there are actually two of them: one for the transmitting path, and one for the receiving path.

Since the ring architecture would become disabled if one of the stations lost power, an external optical bypass relay (OBR) is used (see Figure 2-12b). The OBR connects the inbound and outbound cables, thus assuring network integrity.

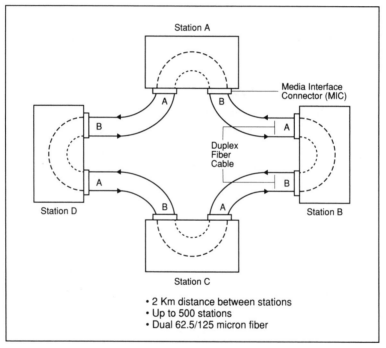

Figure 2-12a. FDDI Dual-Ring Topology
(Courtesy Ungermann-Bass)

The Access/One FDDI SuperLAN Bridges (see Figure 2-12c) product utilizes FDDI as a backbone. Two versions are available: one for Ethernet/IEEE 802.3 networks and the other for 4 Mbps IEEE 802.5 Token Ring. The two versions support the Transparent Bridging (TB) and Source Routing (SR) methods, respectively. As

Figure 2-12c illustrates, two of the SuperLAN bridges can exist on the same FDDI backbone, permitting communication between Ethernet and Token Ring networks via the FDDI backbone. A proprietary algorithm provides the TB to SR conversion. A Network Resource Monitor (NRM) provides network management functions from either the Ethernet or Token Ring side of the network. Statistics such as the amount of transmitted and received data, collisions, corrupted frames, etc., are measured.

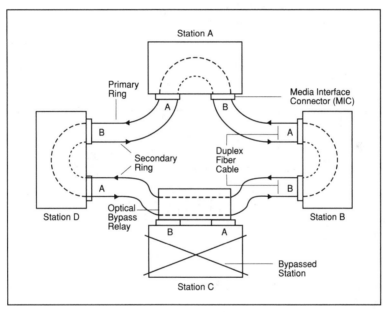

Figure 2-12b. FDDI Ring With Optical Bypass Relay
(Courtesy Ungermann-Bass)

To summarize, Ungermann-Bass has made several advances with its SuperLAN bridges. Utilization of FDDI technology for the backbone provides a guarantee against network obsolescence, and the coexistence of Ethernet and Token Ring networks eliminates many internetworking challenges. This is a unique product with what may be a long life.

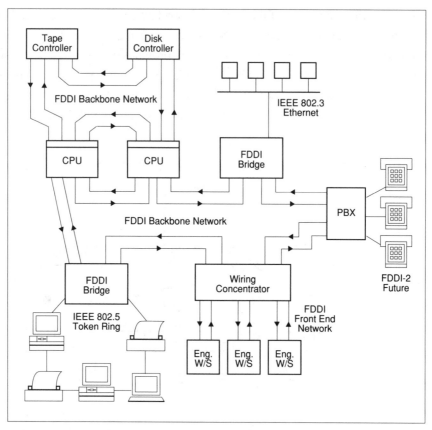

Figure 2-12c. FDDI as a Network Backbone
(Courtesy Ungermann-Bass)

2.4 Brouters

The brouter, sometimes known as a routing bridge, is designed to provide the processing speed of a bridge, but with the internetworking capabilities of a router. Bridges are protocol-independent devices which make a forwarding or filtering decision based upon the Data Link Layer address of the frame. Routers, on the other hand, choose the outgoing path based upon the Network Layer address. A router is therefore protocol dependent and must understand the particular Network Layer protocol in use, such as IP, IPX, DECnet or ISO. The brouter is a hybrid of the bridge and the router: it provides the protocol independence of a bridge while adding the ability to direct LAN traffic to one of a number of other networks, depending upon the Network Layer Protocol being used. In this section, we'll look at two brouters: Halley Systems' ConnectLAN and 3Com Corporation's NETBuilder family.

2.4.1 Halley Systems ConnectLAN 200

Halley Systems, Inc. of San Jose, California manufactures three families of ConnectLAN products. The ConnectLAN 100 Ethernet brouters connect either local or remote Ethernet/IEEE 802.3 networks. The ConnectLAN 200 Token Ring brouters are used for IEEE 802.5 networks and have seven models for local or remote connections. The ConnectLAN 300 family is a 16/4 Mbps Token Ring bridge. We'll look at the Model 202 local Token Ring brouter here.

For Token Ring networks, the major internetworking issue is the presence (or absence) of support for the Source Routing method developed by IBM. The Token Ring brouter, therefore, must be able to forward frames as a bridge does. It must also have the intelligence to participate in the route discovery process initiated by the workstation that wishes to communicate with a device not on its immediate ring.

Halley Systems' ConnectLAN 202 supports both SR and non-source-routing methods by means of a proprietary learning process. Source-routed frames are recognized by the RII (Routing Information Indicator) being set, indicating the presence of the routing information field. If the RII is not set, the brouter determines the route from its internal tables. The device is specified for a filtering rate of 40,000 frames per second and a forwarding rate of 3.2 Mbps.

Halley is to be commended for designing the ConnectLAN products with multi-vendor interoperability in mind. If all bridges (from any vendor) support source routing, then the Halley brouter can interoperate in any configuration, as shown in Figure 2-13a. If a combination of source and non-source routing bridges exist in the network, then the ConnectLAN devices must be the first and last bridges in the chain. The first-and-last requirement enables the original Frame Check Sequence (FCS) to be carried along with the original frame.

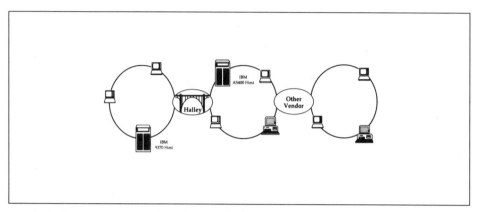

Figure 2-13a. Source Routed Bridge Configuration
(Courtesy Halley Systems)

Figure 2-13b shows this mixed environment, as well as Halley's support for IBM, Novell, 3Com, and Banyan operating systems. All higher-layer protocols, such as TCP/IP and IPX, are thus transparent to the brouter's operation.

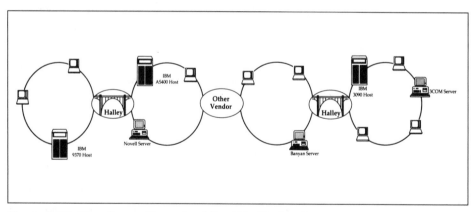

Figure 2-13b. Non-Source Routed or Mixed Traffic Configuration
(Courtesy Halley Systems)

In summary, Halley's brouter is a Token Ring internetworking device which provides the user with a guarantee against near-future obsolescence. With its ability to support either source or non-source routing, it offers a solution for users waiting for their Network Operating System to support the emerging SR standards.

2.4.2 3Com NETBuilder Family

3Com Corporation of Santa Clara, California is a company that most network managers would identify as a significant contributor to Ethernet technology. Its founder, Robert Metcalfe, is the inventor of Ethernet. 3Com has continued its tradition of designing innovative Ethernet solutions with two families of products that are designated the NETBuilder internetworking system. Each NETBuilder platform consists of a single board run by a Motorola 32-bit 68020 microprocessor and a floppy disk drive for loading the system's configuration. Enhancements can also be loaded with software, eliminating the expense of hardware upgrades.

Two families of products are built upon the NETBuilder platform. The IB family products are high-performance Ethernet bridges which also boast network management capabilities. The IB/2000 is a local bridge, supporting both thin and thick Ethernet/IEEE 802.3 connections. The IB/3000 is a remote bridge, with RS-232 or V.35 interfaces to serial lines operating at 9.6 Kbps to 2.048 Mbps. Each remote bridge can be configured to support two low-speed lines, two T-1 (1.544 or 2.048 Mbps) lines, or one of each. The BR family of products combine a bridge plus a multiprotocol router. The BR/2000 supports both thin and thick local Ethernet/IEEE 802.3 connections, and the BR/3000 adds capabilities for WAN links. Both products can be configured as bridges, multiprotocol routers, or as brouters. (3Com defines the brouter function as one of concurrent bridging and routing.) The flexibility that 3Com has designed into the NETBuilder family permits configurations that support very complex network and internetwork designs. Let's look at the bridging family (IB series) first.

From a systems engineering perspective, all members of the IB family have three common features: support for the Spanning Tree algorithm, custom filters, and source-explicit forwarding. Let's look at these three functions in some detail.

The IB bridge capabilities support the IEEE 802.1 Spanning Tree bridging method that was discussed in section 1.7.1. This method allows loops (multiple paths between two segments) to exist within a bridged network. Loops can be used effectively to optimize the transmission path or provide an alternative route if a failure occurs. The bridged network, however, must become aware of changes (such as failures) within the network topology and be prepared to adjust that topology accordingly. The Spanning Tree algorithm is designed to accomplish this. Figure 2-14a illustrates how the algorithm establishes the active and backup paths between two Ethernet segments A and B.

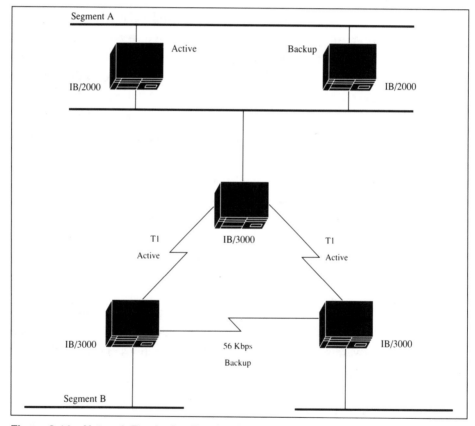

Figure 2-14a. Network Employing Routing Bridges
(Courtesy 3Com Corporation)

Custom filtering is the ability of the bridge to examine (i.e. filter) all frames received, passing (or forwarding) some and rejecting others, depending upon predefined conditions. The filtering/forwarding algorithm may operate on several parameters: the address type of the frame (multicast or broadcast); the protocol contained within the frame (e.g. XNS, IP, ARP, etc.); or the length of the frame. Filtering allows logical network segmentation by containing all traffic specific to that filter class (e.g. IP traffic) on one segment. The custom filtering thus allows greater management and control of the network.

Source Explicit Forwarding (SEF) is the third feature of 3Com's IB family. The SEF function is used in conjunction with a routing table to authorize the forwarding of specific frames. The local administrator can manually authorize the forwarding of address-specific frames on a per-port basis. Fault isolation and network security are two applications of this function. Figure 2-14b illustrates the SEF operation. Assume that SEF is turned on for Port 1 to Port 2 traffic, but off for traffic in the opposite direction. All frames travelling from P1 to P2 must match the address table to be forwarded. No SEF filtering is applied in the P2 to P1 direction; all traffic proceeds as normal. An application of SEF would be the segmentation of a large corporate network into multiple segments based upon departments. Financial traffic could thus be isolated from engineering traffic for security and load balancing.

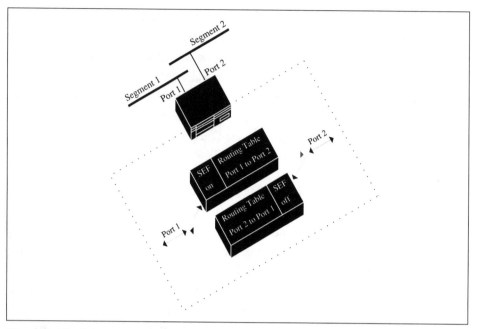

Figure 2-14b. Source Explicit Forwarding Example
(Courtesy 3Com Corporation)

The final feature of the IB bridge family is its network management capabilities (see Figure 2-14c). These management capabilities can be accessed from a local management console or from any other terminal or PC running TELNET (see Section 6.6) located within the internetwork, or from 3Com's Network Control Server. Password protection restricts unauthorized access. All members of the NETBuilder family collect statistics on a per-interface basis. These statistics include the amount of data transmitted and received, the number of frames that contain errors, and the percentage of utilization of that interface. Support for two standard network management protocols—SNMP (Simple Network Management Protocol) and CMOT (Common Management Information Protocol over TCP/IP)—is available. This allows any SNMP or CMOT-based network management product to administer a network containing NETBuilder components.

The NETBuilder brouters (BR/2000 and BR/3000) are local and remote devices that can be configured as bridges, routers, or brouters. As bridges, the products provide the same features as the IB family. As routers and brouters, the products support XNS, TCP/IP, and OSI protocols. The BR family can be included in the same SNMP and CMOT-based network management system as the IB family. With bridging and routing designed into a single platform, protocols that were not designed to be routed (such as NetBIOS, DEC LAT (Local Area Transport), or the IBM LU 6.2 protocols) can be bridged, while other protocols can be routed.

The BR family supports three routing protocols: XNS, TCP/IP, and OSI. For XNS environments, such as Novell's NetWare (see Chapter 7), the Internetwork Datagram Protocol (IDP) and Routing Information Protocol (RIP) are implemented. TCP/IP networks can utilize the Internet Protocol (IP) and the Exterior Gateway Protocol (EGP), plus the IP version of RIP (RIP-IP). Support for the Internet Control Message Protocol (ICMP) and the Address Resolution Protocol (ARP) is also included. For OSI environments, the Connectionless Network Protocol (CLNP, ISO 8473), End System to Intermediate System (ES to IS, ISO 9542), and Network Service Access Point Addressing (NSAP, ISO 8348) can be used. By combining the current (XNS and TCP/IP) and future (ISO) standards into one routing platform, network managers have a clear migration path as the ISO standards become more prevalent.

To summarize, 3Com offers some of the most sophisticated internetworking capabilities with the NETBuilder bridges, brouters or routers. The flexible hardware platform and support for standards-based network management are significant advantages of these products.

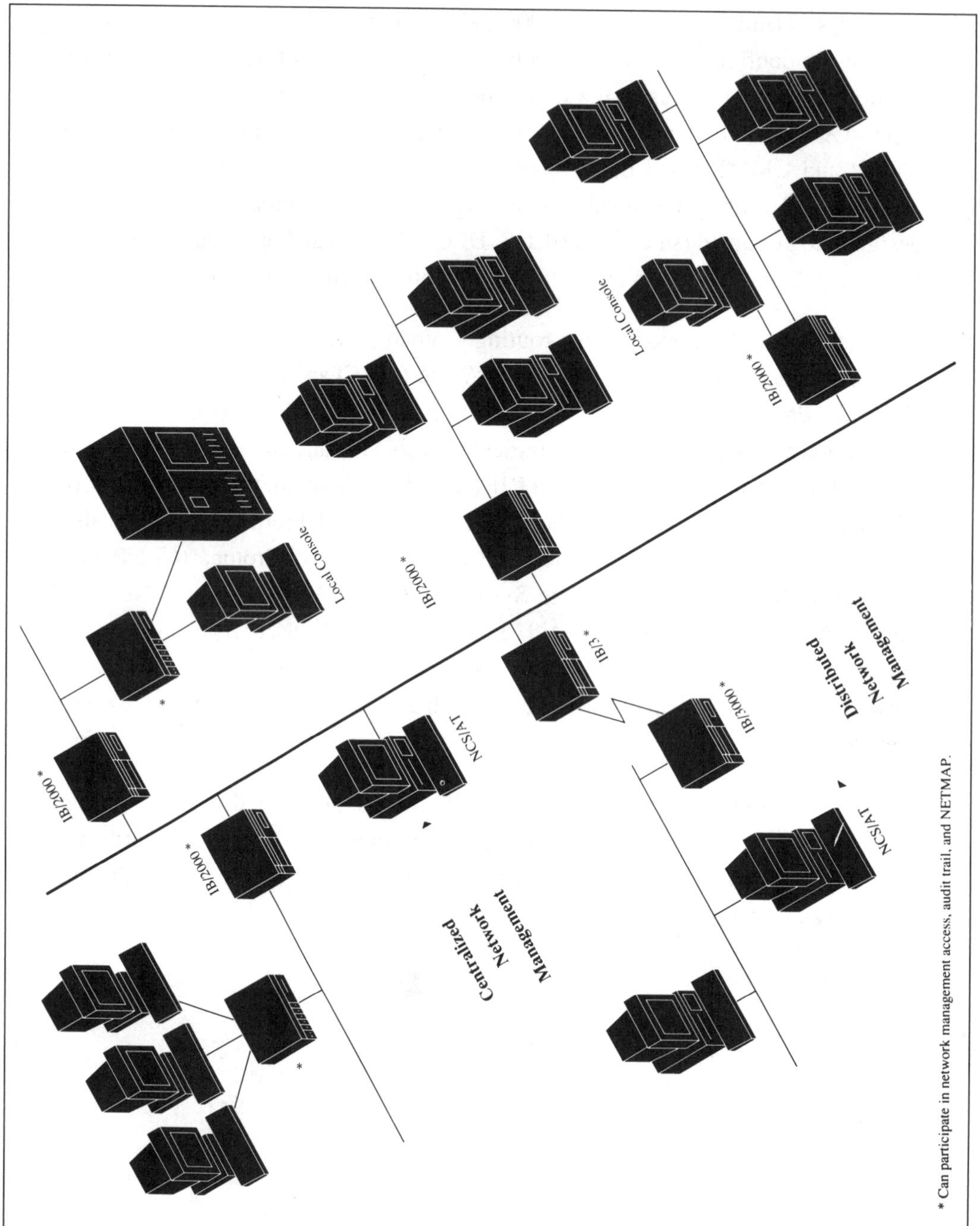

Figure 2-14c. 3Com Network Management
(Courtesy 3Com Corporation)

* Can participate in network management access, audit trail, and NETMAP.

2.5 Routers

Routers operate at the OSI Network Layer and determine the correct network address to which they forward the data packet. Because of a router's additional functionality, it is more complex. The router is a protocol-dependent device, and operates with a hierarchical address that is defined by that protocol. Recall that while bridges operate at the Data Link Layer and use flat addresses, routers operate at the Network Layer, and use hierarchical addresses. (A good example of a hierarchical addressing system is a telephone number, which is divided into four sections: country code, area code, central office code, and line number.) Thus, an IP (Internet Protocol) router would necessarily have difficulty understanding an address scheme that did not match its own format, such as one used by ISO protocols. We'll explore two protocols for router address recognition, the Routing Information Protocol (RIP), and Open Shortest Path First (OSPF), in section 6.3.

Figure 2-15 (taken from reference [2-13]) illustrates how router addresses are used. Consider three networks, designated 1, 2, and 3; three host computers, A, B, and C; and two gateways (actually IP routers), R and S.

The 32-bit IP addresses are expressed in a shorthand notation, known as dotted decimal (see section 6.4), with each number representing 8 bits. Each portion of the address can take on a value from 0-255. Networks 1, 2, and 3 have unique addresses, 128.6.4, 128.6.21, and 128.121, respectively. Hosts attached to those networks reflect a network ID, and a host ID in their address (e.g. host A is attached to network 128.6.4 and has address 128.6.4.2). Gateways (IP routers) have multiple addresses which represent the two networks which they connect. Thus Gateway R contains addresses 128.6.4.1 and 128.6.21.2, and connects network numbers 128.6.4 and 128.6.21. Communication between host A (on network 1) and host C (on network 3) must traverse two gateways, R and S.

Host A must contain a routing table based upon these hierarchical addresses:

Network	Gateway	Hops
128.6.4	none	0
128.6.21	128.6.4.1	1
128.121	128.6.4.1	2

The "hop count" indicates how many gateways must be traversed between Source and Destination Network Address. Destinations beginning with 128.6.4 require no further processing, the host suffix (128.6.4.3) is sufficient. Destinations beginning with 128.6.21 must be routed to gateway 128.6.4.1 (1hop), destinations beginning with 128.121 must go to gateway 128.6.4.1 and then access a similar table at Gateway R before reaching their final destination (2 hops).

A layered architectural model of a router (see Figure 2-16, from reference [2-14]) makes this process a little more clear. The router does not need consistent Physical or Data Link Layer protocols on an end-to-end basis, as long as each router-half communicates with its respective side. Protocol consistence in the Network Layer at both Source, Router, and Destination is required for addressing consistence. Higher-layer data (e.g. TCP) communicate on an end-to-end basis and are not affected by the router processing.

References [2-14] through [2-16] discuss router selection requirements. Reference [2-17] is a good product comparison guide for shoppers.

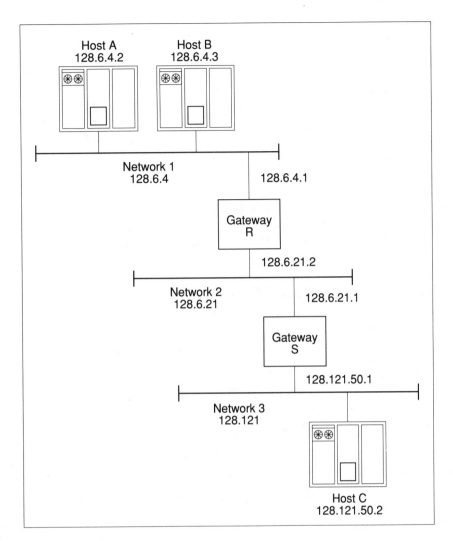

Figure 2-15. Internetwork Addressing
(Courtesy Rutgers University)

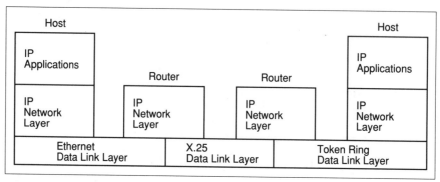

Figure 2-16. Layered Router Architecture
(Reprinted from September 21, 1989, Data Communications Magazine, © 9/21/89 McGraw-Hill, Inc. All rights reserved.)

2.5.1 Proteon p4100+ and p4200 Routers

Proteon, Inc. of Westborough, Massachusetts, which developed the first independent Token Ring network as well as the first fiber optic Token Ring, is recognized as a leader in Token Ring technology. In 1985 they developed the first multi-protocol internetworking router, and in subsequent years were the first to implement DECnet, 4/16 Mbps 802.5 connectivity, and the Open Shortest Path First (OSPF) protocol in a router. The p4100+ Bridging Router is a product that supports 16 Mbps Token Ring backbone connectivity and IBM source routing bridging in multi-protocol, multi-network internetworks. It was developed to provide an enterprise-wide solution for internetworking both IBM and non-IBM traffic over a variety of media—fiber optic cable, shielded twisted pair (STP), and unshielded twisted pair (UTP) (see Figure 2-17a).

At the LAN interface, the p4100+ supports IEEE 802.5 4/16 Token Ring, IEEE 802.3 Ethernet, ProNET-10 and Apollo Token Ring. WAN Interfaces are available for DDS (at 64 Kbps), T-1 (1.544 Mbps) and X.25. Multiple higher-layer protocols can be routed, including TCP/IP, NetWare/IPX, XNS, DECnet Phase IV (with DECnet Phase V promised), Apollo DOMAIN, OSI and AppleTalk. Proteon routers support a number of protocols for router information exchange along the internetwork. For TCP/IP internetworks, the IGP (Internal Gateway Protocol), EGP (Exterior

Gateway Protocol) and OSPF protocols are available. (Proteon led the working group which developed the proposed OSPF standard which provides fast convergence, load sharing, decreased routing traffic and least cost routing.) The p4100+ offers IBM-compatible source routing bridging for connecting IBM PC LANs to each other as well as to IBM mainframes. It also supports the spanning tree algorithm which provides transparent bridging of all protocols as well as carrying DEC LAT traffic.

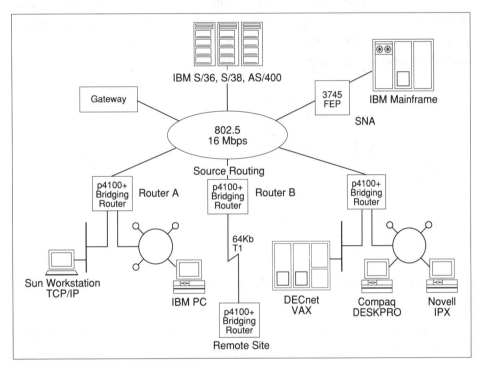

Figure 2-17a. Proteon Multivendor Token Ring Connectivity
(Courtesy Proteon)

Another example of LAN/WAN connectivity is the p4100+ X.25 Interface. Two routers may be connected with either PDN (Public Data Network) lines, such as GTE/Telenet, or DDN (Defense Data Network) links. An interesting feature of this interface is its X.25 National Personality Configuration menu. This menu automatically configures the critical Data Link and Packet Layer parameters of the X.25 protocol for the specific PDN in use, such as GTE/Telenet. Parameters can also be configured manually for private packet-switching network designs.

Proteon's p4200 FDDI Router provides a fully interoperable 100 Mbps FDDI backbone solution (see Figure 2-17b). The p4200's FDDI interface, based on the ANSI X3T9.5 standard, routes the same protocols as the p4100+ does. The interface interconnects multiple LANs and WANs using 802.6 MAN, an emerging standard that provides users with a solution for high-speed data transfer within metropolitan areas. Proteon's p4200 FDDI Router allows you to interconnect more than 1000 individual networks across the FDDI backbone.

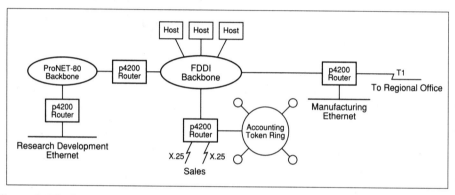

Figure 2-17b. Proteon FDDI Backbone Router Attachment
(Courtesy Proteon)

Both the p4100+ and the p4200 routers have an additional feature available to the user: standards-based network management. Proteon's OverVIEW is an icon-based network management system that supports SNMP (Simple Network Management Protocol). A migration to CMOT (the OSI Common Management Information Protocol-CMIP over TCP/IP) is also planned. OverVIEW runs in a stand-alone 80286 PC/AT or compatible, and may be located at any location in the internetwork. The SNMP engine provides equipment status and performance data for all hardware elements and transmission facilities within the internetwork. OverVIEW displays all of the Internetwork devices as icons and assigns a particular color—such as green for normal operation—to each. The health of any SNMP-compatible node can be queried at any time. OverVIEW maintains an error-log noting the critical events that might affect the health of the Internetwork.

To summarize, Proteon's p4100+ Bridging Router and p4200 FDDI Router provide product value with optimization around Token Ring internetworking and backbones. Their multiple LAN/WAN interfaces and SNMP-based network management capabilities make them excellent choices for complex internetworks.

2.5.2 ACC Series 4000 Multi-Protocol Bridge/Router

Advanced Computer Communications (ACC) of Santa Barbara, California specializes in the design and development of a family of versatile products that provide LAN-to-LAN connectivity across a variety of wide-area networks. The company's flagship product is a multi-protocol bridge/router that is available in several hardware configurations.

The ACS 4100 hardware is a tri-port bridge/router that connects one Ethernet LAN (either 10BASE5, 10BASE2, or 10BASE-T) to one or two WAN links. The two WAN ports can operate independently, and support the RS-232, RS-422/449, V.35, RS-530 or X.21 interfaces at speeds of up to 2.048 Mbps. The ports can interface to point-to-point leased lines, X.25 or Frame Relay services. Because the WAN connections are independent, they can be connected to two different locations—two links to the same location for load sharing purposes, or one primary and one standby link as shown in Figure 2-18a.

The ACS 4400 hardware unit is a rack-mounted chassis that can contain up to four ACS 4100 modules. In its maximum configuration, the ACS 4400 can accommodate four independent Ethernet LAN connections, and eight serial interfaces to the WAN facilities. The four individual platforms can be independent or interconnected as required by a particular application.

A single diskette contains application software that provides support for 802.1 Spanning Tree, Frame Compression, and Protocol Prioritization for bridging applications; IP Routing software for TCP/IP environments; DECnet Level 1 and 2 routing environments; and XNS routing software for Xerox and Ungermann-Bass environments. The SNMP management protocol is used to configure and interrogate the status of the units. This added functionality allows a user to remotely access any Series 4000 unit within their extended network.

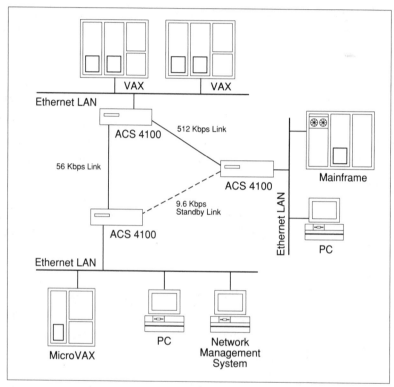

Figure 2-18a. ACC Series 4000 Tri-Port Bridge/Router
(Courtesy Advanced Computer Communications)

The great strength of the ACS Series 4000 is its ability to simultaneously bridge and route various higher-layer protocols that are typically found in most internetworks (as depicted in Figure 2-18b). The ACS 4100 router is not to be confused with a "brouter" which uses a proprietary protocol to ensure the correct "routing" of packets, but is instead a unit that provides full bridging capabilities and routing based upon network layer protocols. The unit operates by examining the protocol type contained within the Ethernet/802.3 header. Depending upon the user-defined configuration, the packet is then routed or bridged to its final destination. Both bridged and routed packets can travel over the same WAN link since appropriate packet sequencing and data integrity is maintained.

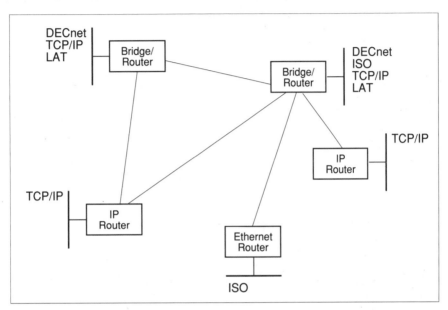

Figure 2-18b. ACC Bridging and Multiprotocol Routing
(Courtesy Advanced Computer Communications)

The Series 4000 bridge/router gives the user a tremendous amount of flexibility. For example, independent ACS 4100s in a user's network can be configured for bridge-to-bridge traffic to support the need to bridge DEC's LAT protocol; or as DECnet routers; or as combination bridge/routers for mixed-protocol environments which require the additional capabilities of routers but have traffic that is not supported by a routing protocol.

To summarize, the ACS 4000 series provides the best of both worlds: full bridging and full routing capabilities within the same hardware platform.

2.5.3 cisco TRouter

cisco Systems, Inc. of Menlo Park, California, whose founders were formerly TCP/IP researchers at Stanford University, manufactures a number of routers supporting the most popular Network Layer protocols. One example of cisco's product family is the TRouter, which combines the capabilities of a multi-protocol router and a terminal server, and performs both functions simultaneously (see Figure 2-19).

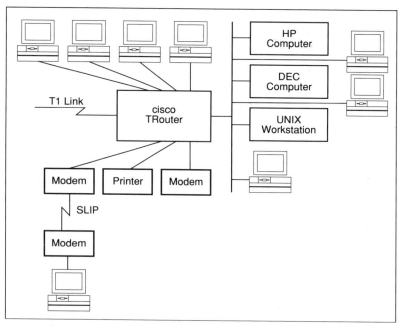

Figure 2-19. cisco TRouter Configuration
(Courtesy cisco Systems, Inc.)

The router contains a two-port interface which can connect to two Ethernet/IEEE 802.3 networks, two synchronous, serial links, or one of each. The serial ports support transmission using the HDLC, LAPB, X.25 and DDN X.25 protocols at speeds of up to 4 Mbps. They also support connections to T-1 facilities. Multiple protocols can be routed, including TCP/IP, DECnet, XNS, IPX, AppleTalk and ISO CLNS (Connectionless Network Services, ISO 8473).

The terminal server can connect up to sixteen asynchronous devices such as modems, terminals, or printers at speeds of up to 34.4 Kbps. Both incoming and outgoing connections are available. The TRouter multiplexes data from these sixteen devices onto either of the higher speed (e.g. Ethernet or T-1) interfaces. The TRouter supports the TELNET protocol (for TCP/IP applications) for access to remote hosts and the Serial Line Internet Protocol (SLIP) framing format for transmitting IP datagrams over serial connections (more on TCP/IP in Chapter 7).

Applications of the TRouter are interesting. With its support of the X.25 protocol, multiple TRouters can be connected via Public Data Networks (PDNs). Let's assume that one serial port is connected to the PDN, and the other port is connected to an Ethernet. The asynchronous ports at each TRouter connect to various terminals or PCs. With the simultaneous terminal server and router functions, a user with a terminal at one TRouter location (e.g. Denver) could log in to a remote host at a second TRouter location (e.g. San Francisco). The PDN would provide the WAN connection, although a T-1 line would work equally well. Taking this example further, it would also be possible to have a user in Colorado Springs connect to the Denver TRouter via a dial-up telephone line which is then allowed access to the San Francisco host.

To conclude, the TRouter provides unique remote access capabilities for connecting a number of asynchronous devices to a LAN or WAN.

In this chapter, we have studied some of the mathematics behind network operation, as well as various LAN-to-LAN internetworking devices that permit the extension, segmentation, or interconnection of these networks. An excellent source for those who would like further information on internetwork implementation is reference [2-18]. The mathematics behind LAN traffic models is explored in reference [2-19]. In the next two chapters, we will extend our discussion of internetwork designs to include the WAN cases as well.

2.6 References

[2-1] 3Com Corp. *Bridges, Routers, and Brouters: An Internetworking Tutorial.* Document No. 600180-002, 1990.

[2-2] Retix. *Local Bridge Application Guide.* Document 1040187-00, 1989.

[2-3] Hewlett-Packard Co. *LAN Performance Analysis Product Note.* Document 5952-5103, 1986.

[2-4] Bux, Werner. "Performance Issues in Local-Area Networks." *IBM Systems Journal* volume 23, no.4 (1984); 51–374.

[2-5] Irwin, David R. "Second-Generation Token Ring LANs: Evaluating the Need for High Speed." *Data Communications* (March 21, 1989): 47–50.

[2-6] Salamone, Salvatore ."LAN Links Boast Broader Protocol, Speed Options." *Network World* (May 7,1990): 34–61.

[2-7] Schnaidt, Patricia. "Span the LAN: Linking LANs with MAC-Layer Bridges. " *LAN Magazine* (February 1988): 28–32.

[2-8] Kousky, Ken. "Bridging the Network Gap." *LAN Technology* (January 1990): 26–34.

[2-9] King, Steven S. "Multiport Bridges." *Data Communications* (August 1990): 2–79.

[2-10] Mick, Colin. "Bridging Token-Ring, E-net LANs No Easy Task." *Network World* (June 18, 1990): 49–59.

[2-11] Hindlin, Eric M. "IBM 8209 LAN Bridge Links Ethernet to Token Ring." *Data Communications* (March 21, 1990): 75–81.

[2-12] Ullal, Jayshree. "FDDI in the Enterprise." Ungermann-Bass, Inc., Document no. PP-003-02, January 1990.

[2-13] Hedrick, Charles L. *An Introduction to the Administration of an Internet-based Local Network,* Rutgers University, 24 July 1988. Copyright Charles Hedrick, used with permission.

[2-14] Boulé, Richard and John Moy. "Inside Routers: A Technology Guide for Network Builders." *Data Communications* (September 21, 1989): 53–66.

[2-15] Spiner, Dan. "Internetwork Now." *LAN Technology* (October 1990): 33–39.

[2-16] McQuillan, John M. "Routers as Building Blocks for Robust Internetworks." *Data Communications* (September 21, 1989): 8–33.

[2-17] Teja, Edward R. "Router Roundup: Tools for Network Segmentation Come of Age." *Data Communication* (September 21, 1989): 35–40.

[2-18] Roman, Bob. "Making the Big Connection: Implementing Internetworks with Bridges, Routers, and Brouters." *3TECH* (Summer 1990): 14–25.

[2-19] Fortier, Paul J., and George R. Desrochers. *Modeling and Analysis of Local Area Networks*, CRC Press, Inc., Boca Raton, FL, 1990.

CHAPTER 3

Data Transmission Facilities for Internetworks

These days, it's rare to go to any LAN or internetworking seminar, conference, or tutorial where the presenter doesn't show a picture of a "cloud diagram" (see Figure 3-1). The cloud is used to explain the need for data transmission facilities. It is assumed that an end-user's terminal feeds data into the cloud, which mysteriously routes and switches that data to a distant location such as a host computer. The data arrives with no errors or retransmissions, and the internetwork manager lives happily ever after.

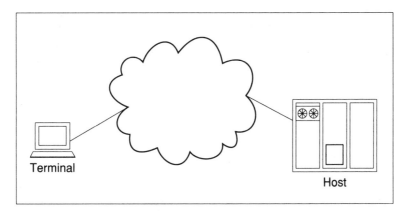

Figure 3-1. Generic Data Communications Cloud

We all know that the cloud does not appear magically to transport data. We, the internetwork designers, must specify and order the communication facility from one of a multitude of providers. This chapter will discuss typical design requirements and the different choices available. We will begin with the easiest alternative, the dial-up telephone network, and work our way up to high speed T-1/T-3 circuits. (As a reference, Appendix C lists North American Private Line Carriers, and Appendix D contains North American Public Data Networks.)

3.1   Dial-Up Telephone Network Facilities

The dial-up telephone network, also known as the Public Switched Telephone Network (PSTN), is undoubtedly the data communication facility with which we are most familiar. In North America, users have often been accused (and rightfully so) of taking basic telephone service for granted. Other areas of the world—especially some of the third-world countries—do not enjoy the reliable service that we've come to expect from the Local Exchange Carriers (LECs) and Inter-Exchange Carriers (IXCs). There are more than 250 million telephone lines in the United States, and the various switching systems that connect the voice and data calls do so with remarkable reliability. Let's begin our study of this network by looking at the characteristics of the basic telephone channel itself.

AT&T defines a channel as a "frequency band, or its equivalent in the time domain, established in order to provide a communications path between a message source and its destination" (reference [3-1], volume 1, page 23). The telephone channel is therefore a specific frequency band that has been optimized for voice communication. For a number of reasons (described in references [3-1] and [3-2]), the required channel—called a passband—must pass frequencies that range from approximately 300 to 3300 Hertz (Hz). (Figure 3-2 and other figures in this chapter will plot the signal gain or loss on the vertical y-axis as a function of frequency, which is measured in Hz and shown on the horizontal x-axis.) The bandwidth is the width, measured in Hz, of the passband, and is found by subtracting the upper and lower frequency limits (thus equalling 3000 Hz). The passband is determined by the electrical inductance and capacitance of the cable itself, and by filters connected to every analog telephone line in the telephone company's Central Offices (C.O.s).

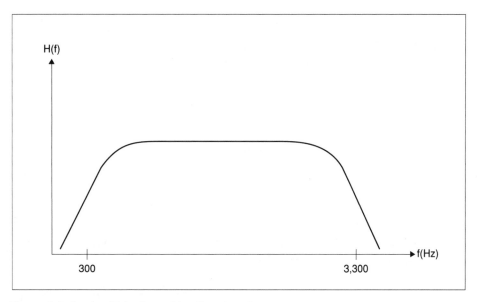

Figure 3-2. Analog Telephone Line Passband

If all we wanted to transmit was an audio signal, it's easy to see that the telephone channel characteristics would define the frequencies of interest. Frequencies below 300 Hz or above 3000 Hz would be attenuated, and not be transmitted with as great an amplitude as those frequencies within the passband.

Data communication signals, however, are measured in terms of bits per second (bps), not Hz, and therefore some mechanism must be employed to associate the transmission channel characteristic (in Hz) to the data rate (in bps). This relationship is established using two theorems that were also derived from early telegraph and telephone research (references [3-1], Volume 1, and [3-3]).

In 1928 Harry Nyquist, a researcher in the area of telegraph transmission efficiency, published an equation—called the Nyquist Rate—that measured the transmission signalling rate in baud. The Nyquist Rate equaled 2B symbols (or signals) per second, where B is the bandwith of the transmission channel. Thus, using this equation, a telephone channel bandwidth of 3000 Hz can support up to 2 x 3000, or 6000, baud.

Claude Shannon furthered Nyquist's research with his study as to how noise affects data transmission. Shannon took into account the signal-to-noise ratio of the transmission channel (measured in decibels or dB) and derived what is known as Shannon's Capacity Theorem:

$C = B \log_2 (1 + S/N)$ bps

A typical voice telephone channel has a signal-to-noise ratio of 30 dB (1000:1) and a bandwidth of 3000 Hz. If we substitute these values into Shannon's Theorem:

$C = 3000 \log_2 (1 + 1000)$

Since $\log_2 (1001)$ is approximately equal to 10, the theorem yields a maximum capacity of approximately 30,000 bps.

Three points are worth emphasizing. First, the terms "baud" and "bits per second" are often confused. Modem designers, and others who must deal with the actual signal that is placed on the telephone channel, will speak of those signals in terms of "baud." Those of us who wish to use those same channels to transfer a file, for example, will speak in terms of "bits per second." Second, upper limits to the data transmission characteristics of the telephone channel exist. These limits are 6000 baud and 30,000 bps. Thus, while it is possible to transmit data at rates greater than 30,000 bps over twisted pair transmission media, it is not possible to do so using the PSTN.

Third, it is correct to say, "I need a 9600 bps modem" instead of "I need a 9600 baud modem." Because of the Nyquist Theorem, we know that a 9600 baud modem could not transmit over the dial-up telephone network. What is probably meant when someone says "9600 baud modem" is a modem that transmits 2400 signals per second (baud) and represents each signal with 4 bits. The resulting data rate is 9600 bps (2400 signals per second x 4 bits per signal = 9600 bps).

The data rate of 9600 bps (for some modems, 14,400 bps) is a practical upper limit for data transmission via dial-up connections. The multitude of noise sources, the imperfect filters in the C.O.s, and the random selection of route through the PSTN for each call all contribute to this limit (reference [3-4]). If faster data rates are required, two options are available. The first option is to compensate for the signal degradation caused by the transmission channel through a process known as conditioning. The second is to use a digital, instead of analog, transmission facility. We will study both of these techniques in the next three sections.

3.2   Analog Leased Line Facilities

As we saw in the last section, dial-up transmission facilities are the most ubiquitous transmission option available. As we have all experienced, dial-up connections have a varying degree of quality—sometimes you get a circuit that is noisy, and sometimes you get one that sounds like the other party is next door. In other words, switched facilities have a randomness associated with them, and this is due to the switched nature of the connection itself. Every time a dial-up circuit is established, a different path is chosen. Some of those paths are noisy, some are not, and, as Shannon's Capacity Theorem illustrates, the amount of noise has a direct relationship to the maximum data rate.

An obvious improvement on this method of transmission would be to establish a constant transmission path. This path is known as a leased line or private line. The end user has access to a telephone line (either a 2-wire or 4-wire circuit) that is terminated at each end of the transmission path.

The terminations could exist within the same city or across the country, connecting different LECs via one IXC. When the transmission path is fixed, the user is then guaranteed predictable transmission parameters. Conditioning, or correction for transmission abnormalities, can be done on this fixed path.

A leased line has an economic advantage over the dial-up facility. Let's say that a leased line between two cities costs $500.00 per month. At a typical cost of $0.25 per minute, this translates to 2,000 minutes or 33.3 hours of dial-up usage. Thus, if a network requires use of the transmission facility for more than 33.3 hours per month, economics would dictate that a leased line be chosen instead of a dial-up line.

To begin our study of leased lines, let's look at the different transmission parameters that affect the quality of analog leased circuits.

3.2.1 Leased Line Transmission Parameters

A number of factors affect the quality of a leased line, and thus contribute to data transmission errors. We'll briefly summarize them here. For further details, see the AT&T standards that describe specific parameters (references [3-5], [3-6], and [3-7]).

Noise is defined as any signal that impairs or interferes with the information that we wish to convey. There are several categories of noise. Impulse noise is energy that lasts for a short duration (perhaps only a few milliseconds) and then disappears. Sources of impulse noise include lightning, power surges, and switching systems such as electromechanical C.O. switches. Gaussian noise, or white noise, is the background "hiss" that often accompanies voice telephone transmissions. Crosstalk occurs when the electromagnetic field of one transmission circuit interferes with another, similar circuit. AT&T sets limits on the amount of each type of noise allowable on each type of leased line.

Attenuation is the loss of signal strength as it travels down the telephone line. Because attenuation is measured over an analog transmission facility, the loss is always determined at a specific frequency, such as 1000 Hz. Attenuation is measured in decibels (dB).

Several frequencies are contained within the data signal. The transmission line does not react to each of these frequencies in the same manner, as a result attenuating some more than others. **Envelope Delay Distortion** is a measurement (usually given in milliseconds, or ms) of the amount of delay between these various frequency components.

Phase Jitter occurs when all the zero crossings (those points, measured in the time domain, where the signal crosses the zero axis from a negative to a positive amplitude, or vice versa) of the transmitted signal are not in phase. If viewed on an oscilloscope, the signal would appear to wiggle (or jitter) horizontally instead of showing a clean, crisp trace. **Amplitude Jitter** is similar to Phase Jitter, occurring when the signal amplitude is not constant. A vertical movement would be seen on the oscilloscope.

Nonlinear Distortion is noticed when the harmonics (or multiples) of the fundamental signal frequency are not attenuated by the same amount.

Finally, **transients** occur when the signal abruptly changes amplitude, or drops out altogether. Transients are often caused by impulse noise, and may last a few milliseconds.

Section 4.3 of reference [3-5] provides an excellent summary of these transmission impairments. Reference [3-8] discusses the effects of these impairments on transmitted signals.

3.2.2 Leased Line Conditioning

As we have seen, all telephone lines experience noise and other transmission impairments. In the case of dial-up (PSTN) lines, there is little we can do, since every connection is a random selection between the various switching centers. Leased lines are a different story, however, since the transmission path is a fixed constant. It is thus possible to "condition" that line, thus removing the negative effects of the various transmission impairments defined above.

Conditioning is defined by FCC tariffs 9,10, and 11, and specified by AT&T in AT&T PUB 43202 (reference [3-7]). These documents first identify the functional characteristics of different types of private lines. Ten different line types (1-10) are defined below:

Service Type	Description
1	Basic voice applications
2	Voice applications which require tighter control of performance specifications, i.e. tie trunks
3	Voice radio land lines that require tone control conditioning
4	Low speed data applications (less than 1200 bps)
5	Basic data applications
6	Voice and data applications on trunk circuits
7	Voice and data applications on private access lines
8	Voiceband data on intermachine trunks
9	Telephotographic or alternate voice/telephotographic transmission
10	Protective relaying applications, e.g., tone control systems

Type 5 (basic data applications) holds the greatest interest for internetwork applications. What is now called a Type 5 line was formerly defined in FCC tariff 260 as a 3002 unconditioned private line.

An unconditioned Type 5 line has no correction for the transmission impairments discussed in Section 3.2.1. To improve the line quality, five types of conditioning are available. C-conditioning corrects for attenuation distortion and envelope delay distortion. D-conditioning corrects for signal-to-C-notched noise and harmonic distortion. International, Tone Control and Special Telephoto conditioning are used for specific applications. Of these options, C and D conditioned lines are most frequently used for internetwork communication channels.

Each type of conditioning specifies parameters for and limits of the correction. Figures 3-3, 3-4, and 3-5 (taken from reference [3-7]), provide the various specifications for Type 5, C-conditioned, and D-conditioned lines, respectively. AT&T lists these specifications in tabular form. Universal Data Systems, of Huntsville, Alabama, has reduced these specifications to the charts shown in Figures 3-6 and 3-7 reference [3-8]). These two figures describe the attenuation and envelope delay distortion characteristics of C-conditioned lines. For the attenuation characteristics (see Figure 3-6), note that loss becomes less as the conditioning progresses from steps C1 to C2, and finally to C4 conditioning. The Envelope Delay Distortion characteristics (see Figure 3-7) show an additional improvement. Note that the frequency range of the minimum delay (which is close to 0 ms) becomes wider as the conditioning is increased. Notice also that C4 conditioning has almost no Envelope Delay Distortion over the range of 900-2500 Hz. (Reference [3-9], section 2-3, and reference [3-10], Appendix F have good summaries of transmission impairments and channel conditioning, respectively.)

Performance Specification Limits **Service Type 5**	
Parameter	Immediate Action Limit
1. Loss Deviation (dB)	± 4.0
2. C-Notched Noise (dBrnCO)	51

3. Attenuation Distortion
    # (dB) between:
    504 & 2504 Hz
    404 & 2804 Hz
    304 & 3004 Hz
	
	-2.0 to +8.0
	-2.0 to +10.0
	-3.0 to +12.0

4. Signal-to-C-Notched Noise Ratio (dB)	≥ 24

5. Envelope Delay Distortion (us)
    between:
    804 & 2604 Hz
	
	1750

6. Impulse Noise Threshold* (dBrnCO)	71

7. Intermodulation Distortion (dB)
    R2
    R3
	
	≥ 27
	≥ 32

8. Phase Jitter (Degrees pk-pk)
    20 - 300 Hz
    4 - 300 Hz
	
	≤10°
	≤15°

9. Frequency Shift (Hz)	± 3
# (+) means more loss. * 15 counts in 15 minutes at specified threshold.	

Figure 3-3. AT&T Private Line Type 5 Specifications
(Reproduced with permission of AT&T)

C-Conditioning Immediate Action Limits				
Conditioning	Attenuation Distortion Relative to 1004 Hz		Envelope Delay Distortion	
	Frequency Range (Hz)	Variation (dB)*	Frequency Range (Hz)	Variation (microseconds)
C1	1004-2404	-1.0 to +3.0	1004-2404	1000
	304-2704	-2.0 to +6.0	804-2604	1750
	304-3004	-3.0 to +12.0		
C2	504-2804	-1.0 to +3.0	1004-2604	500
	304-3004	-2.0 to +6.0	604-2604	1500
			504-2804	3000
C3 (access line)	504-2804	-0.5 to +1.5	1004-2604	110
	304-3004	-0.8 to +3.0	604-2604	300
			504-2804	650
C3 (trunk)	504-2804	-0.5 to +1.0	1004-2604	80
	304-3004	-0.8 to +2.0	604-2604	260
			504-2804	500
C4	504-3004	-2.0 to +3.0	1004-2604	300
	304-3204	-2.0 to +6.0	804-2804	500
			604-3004	1500
			504-3004	3000
C5	504-2804	-0.5 to +1.5	1004-2604	100
	304-3004	-1.0 to +3.0	604-2604	300
			504-2804	600
C7	404-2804	-1.0 to +4.5	1004-2604	550
C8	404-2804	-1.0 to +3.0	1004-2604	125

* (+) means loss with respect to 1004 Hz.
(-) means gain with respect to 1004 Hz.

Figure 3-4. AT&T C-Conditioned Private Line Specifications
(Reproduced with permission of AT&T)

D-Conditioning Immediate Action Limits	
Signal-to-C-Notched Noise Ratio	$\geq$ 28 dB minimum
Intermodulation Distortion (4-tone) - Signal to second order modulation products - Signal to third order modulation products	 $\geq$ 35 dB minimum $\geq$ 40 dB minimum

D6 Channel Characteristics	
Parameter	Requirement
Intermodulation Distortion (4-tone) - Signal to second order (R2) - Signal to third order (R3)	 $\geq$ 45 dB $\geq$ 46 dB
Phase Jitter 20-300 Hz	$\leq$ 7 Degree Pk-Pk
Signal to C-Notched Noise Ratio	$\geq$ 32 dB
Envelope Delay Distortion 604-2804 Hz	1400 μsec
Attenuation Distortion 404-2804 Hz	-1.0 to +4.5 dB

Figure 3-5. AT&T D-Conditioned Private Line Specifications
(Reproduced with permission of AT&T)

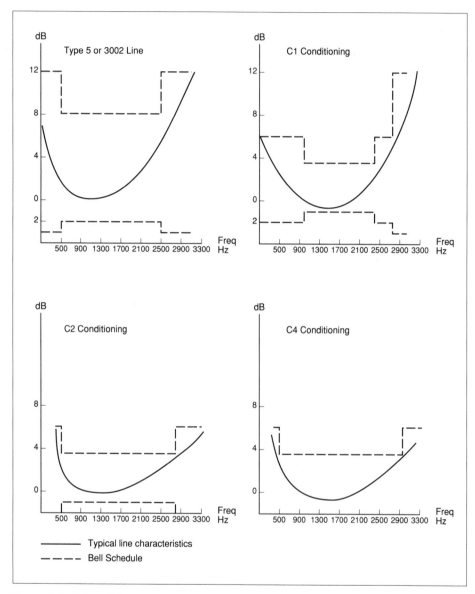

Figure 3-6. C-Conditioned Line Attenuation Characteristics
(Courtesy Universal Data Systems)

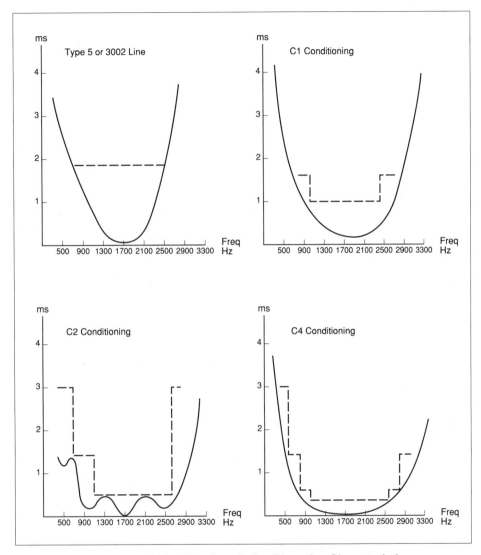

Figure 3-7. C-Conditioned Line Envelope Delay Distortion Characteristics
(Courtesy Universal Data Systems)

Fortunately, determining the means of conditioning is not always as complicated as it might sound. Transmission equipment, such as the synchronous modem, is designed to operate with a specific type of leased line, such as a C-2 conditioned line. Equipment specifications will indicate the line required, and the internetwork manager will include that information when ordering the line from the LEC and/or IXC.

Testing a private line for signal degradation and transmission impairment in order to determine conditioning is often more complicated. A device known as a TIMS (Transmission Impairment Measurement Set) is used (see Figure 3-8). The TIMS is connected to the telephone line, and can thus measure circuit noise, attenuation, envelope delay distortion and other parameters. A TIMS can be a valuable troubleshooting asset, and models are available ranging in price from $500 to $15,000. The less expensive are manually-operated units, while the high-end devices automate the tests and provide hard-copy graphical outputs. Since all LECs and IXCs specify the noise level limits for the various types of lines, the TIMS will determine if the line is functioning properly. If not, the carrier should be contacted for repair. (Reference [3-11] includes an excellent checklist to use while making TIMS measurements.)

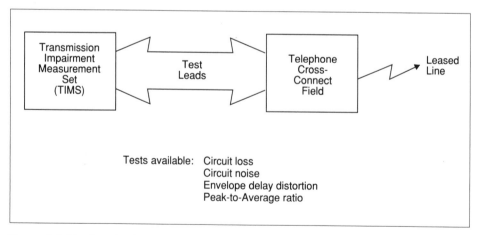

Figure 3-8. Testing the Analog Leased Line with a TIMS

3.3 Digital Leased Lines

As we saw in Section 3.2, analog leased lines are susceptible to impairments such as noise and attenuation. Digital leased facilities improve the overall channel performance by transmitting digital pulses, which are not as susceptible to those particular impairments. Digital lines are available from a number of LECs and IXCs, but are most commonly referred to by AT&T's name, DDS—short for Dataphone Digital Service or Digital Data System.

DDS is a synchronous digital transmission facility operating at 2.4, 4.8, 9.6, 19.2, or 56 kilobits per second (Kbps). The actual DDS signals are carried inside T-1 channels (discussed in section 3.4). Access to DDS facilities is available in most metropolitan locations, and connections to North American, European and Far East destinations are possible. Because of the digital nature of the transmitted signal, a modem cannot be used as the interface between the end-user's Data Terminal Equipment (DTE) and the network. Instead, a device known as a DSU/CSU (Data Service Unit/Channel Service Unit) is employed. The DSU/CSU accepts the user data via a standard interface—typically EIA-232-D at the lower data rates and V.35 at 56 Kbps (see Figure 3-9).

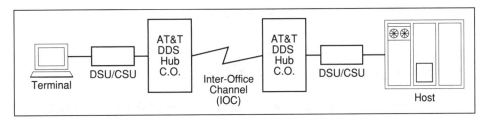

Figure 3-9. AT&T Dataphone Digital Service Network

DDS services are renowned for the high quality of their data transmission. AT&T quotes an average of 99.5% error-free seconds at 56 Kbps, and even better performance at the subrate (lower) speeds. Availability is quoted at a minimum of 99.9% on an annualized basis, resulting in an annual downtime of less than 0.1%.

Transmission capabilities allow for remote loopbacks from the central office to the customer's premises, minimizing the Mean Time to Repair (MTTR) (reference [3-12]).

AT&T provides a number of options for connection into the DDS network. ACCUNET Switched 56 service provides 56 Kbps DDS service on an as-needed, dial-up basis. Access to ACCUNET Packet Service is also available.

For users with requirements for lower data transmission rates (2.4, 4.8, 9.6, or 19.2 Kbps), AT&T provides a Subrate Data Multiplexing (SDM) service at their C.O.s. Multiplexing at the C.O. permits economies-of-scale by combining multiple lower-speed lines into one higher speed (56 Kbps) line. Three options are available: SDM-5 can multiplex a mix of five lower speed channels into one 56 Kbps channel; SDM-10 multiplexes up to ten 2.4 or 4.8 Kbps channels into one 56 Kbps channel; or SDM-20 can multiplex up to twenty 2.4 Kbps channels into one 56 Kbps channel.

Short of moving to the T-1 or Fractional T-1 speeds, many users find that the 9.6 and 56 Kbps transmission rates are the most useful. AT&T has addressed these requirements with their ACCUNET Spectrum of Digital Services (ASDS). This service offers transmission between an AT&T Point-of-Presence (POP) in one Local Access and Transport Area (LATA) and another AT&T POP in another LATA. Transmission speeds are 9.6, 56, 64, 128, 256, 384, 512 and 768 Kbps. The ASDS facilities can be accessed via DDS or analog voice-grade lines; T-1 access is available through the M24 option described in section 3.4.4.

As we have studied in the last two sections, a variety of analog and digital leased line options are available. This sector of wide-area networking is extremely competitive, and receives a great deal of attention in the press. References [3-14], [3-15], and [3-16] are examples of recent private line service comparisons.

3.4   T-Carrier Facilities

The T-carrier system was developed by Bell Telephone Laboratories in the 1960s as a means of multiplexing voice signals onto a digital transmission line. (Earlier systems such as the N-carrier multiplexed analog signals onto an analog transmission line.) The system was inspired by a telephone line capacity problem that developed in several metropolitan locations. Signals were carried between switching offices on individual pairs of copper wire, one pair per conversation. These pairs were bundled into a large cable, with up to 3000 pairs inside, and placed in a conduit under the city streets. As the city grew, so did the need for additional telephone circuits. Additional cables were placed, and conduit runs eventually became completely full of cables. When all the conduit ductwork became congested, the telephone company was left with two choices: dig up the street and place additional conduits, or figure out a way to get additional capacity out of the existing copper pairs. Bell System opted for the second alternative, and put their engineers to work to solve the problem. What we now refer to as the T-Carrier network was the result of their efforts.

The T-1 circuit is a digital, full-duplex transmission facility operating at 1.544 Mbps. It can be used to transmit digital voice, data, or video signals. The complete circuit requires a 4-wire path (of copper) and is available only for point-to-point (not multi-point) connections. The T-1 circuit, however, is not limited to copper-based, terrestrial communication channels. Many other transmission options are available, including 18- and 23-GigaHertz (GHz) microwave radio, fiber optics, infrared and coaxial cables.

At either end of the T-1 circuit is a customer-provided Channel Service Unit, or CSU (see Figure 3-10). The CSU accepts the data from the Customer Premises Equipment (CPE), and encodes that data for transmission on the T-1 circuit. Typical CPE would be a T-1 multiplexer or a LAN bridge designed for T-1 circuit rate transmission.

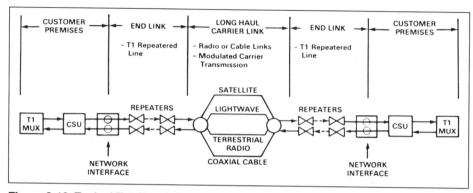

Figure 3-10. Typical T-1 Circuit Configuration
(Courtesy Telecommunications Techniques Corporation)

3.4.1   North American Digital Transmission Hierarchy

T-1 circuits are only one of a number of digital transmission facilities that are available within North America. An existing hierarchy includes a number of different transmission rates. All of these facilities contain a specific digital signal level (abbreviated DS) and are all based upon the DS-0 channel, which operates at 64 Kbps. The 64 Kbps channel is derived from a 4 KHz band limited channel that is sampled 8000 times per second. Each sample is then quantified at 1 of 256 levels (8 bits) resulting in the 64 Kbps rate (8000 samples per second x 8 bits/sample). This DS-0 channel becomes the basic building block for ISDN (Integrated Services Digital Network) transmission; although the ISDN term for the 64 Kbps unit is a B (Bearer) channel. Note that the signal is referred to as "DS-1," while the transmission channel (over a copper-based facility) is called a "T-1" circuit. The various transmission rates used within the North American hierarchy are shown below:

Signal Level	Carrier Equivalent			Data Rate (Mbps)
	System	T-1 Channels	Voice Channels	
DS-0	N/A	N/A	1	0.064
DS-1	T-1	1	24	1.544
DS-1C	T-1C	2	48	3.152
DS-2	T-2	4	96	6.312
DS-3	T-3	28	672	44.736
DS-4	T-4	168	4032	274.760

The hierarchy is derived using a series of digital, time domain multiplexers (see Figure 3-11, and reference [3-17]). The DS-1 signal is generated by combining 24 of the individual DS-0 channels. Two DS-1s can be multiplexed into a DS-1C, and two DS-1CS can become a DS-2. Seven DS-2s are combined for a DS-3. Finally, six DS-3s are multiplexed to generate a DS-4 signal. The DS-1 (1.544 Mbps) and DS-3 (44.736 Mbps) rates are of greatest interest to LAN and WAN designers.

Those of you with calculators in hand will immediately notice that all the numbers, when multiplexed together, do not add up. For example, the DS-1 rate contains 24 DS-0 channels, but 24 x 64 Kbps yields 1.536 Mbps, not 1.544 Mbps. The numerical difference is in the framing information, which is the subject of the next section.

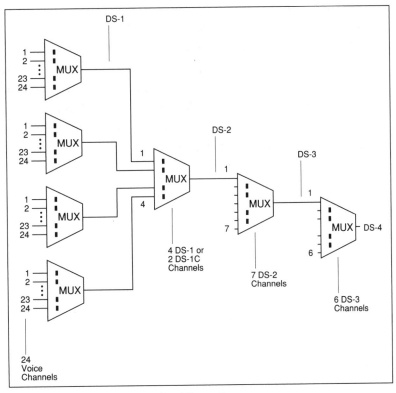

Figure 3-11. Digital Signal Multiplexing Hierarchy

3.4.2   DS-1 Framing

All DS-level transmissions use Alternate Bipolar (ABP)—which is also called Alternate Mark Inversion (AMI)—signal encoding (see Figure 3-12). The signal has three different levels: a positive voltage (+V), a negative voltage (-V), and a ground reference (0). The signal is called "alternate" because successive "1"'s alternate in polarity. The first "1" is transmitted as a +V pulse, and the next "1" is transmitted as a -V pulse. Zeros are transmitted as a 0. The signal transmissions (+V and -V) are used to regenerate the timing information, since all T-carrier circuits are synchronous facilities and must be referenced from a master clock source. As a result, constraints may be placed on the data so that it contains enough 1s to regenerate the clock information. Those constraints are referred to as "pulse density" or "1s richness" requirements, and are often quoted at 12.5% (one 1 for every 8 bits). Since the pulse density is a requirement of the network (not the end equipment), users do not appreciate these constraints being placed on their data. As a result, carriers accept the user's data as is and modify its pulse stream to satisfy the ones constraints. These modifications are done in such a way that they are transparent to the end user. The technique that is commonly used is B8ZS (Bipolar with 8 zero substitution), described in references [3-18] and [3-19]. With B8ZS, a special code is placed in and then removed from the pulse stream in substitution for a zero byte (all eight bits are equal to zero) that has been transmitted by the user's equipment.

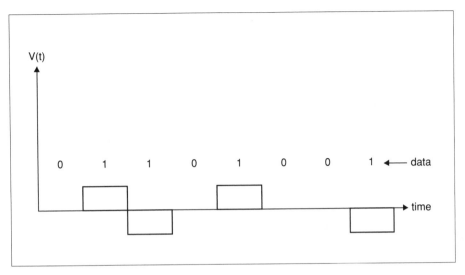

Figure 3-12. Alternate Bipolar Signal

After the format of the data is specified, a method of distinguishing between the individual channels (which may be distinct telephone conversations or data circuits) must be established. For DS-1 signals, this framing is accomplished by adding one additional bit, dubbed the 193rd bit, to each frame (see Figure 3-13). The mystery of the DS-1 transmission rate is solved thus:

24 DS-0 channels at 64 Kbps	= 1.536 Mbps
1 framing bit at 8 Kbps	= 0.008 Mbps
Resulting DS-1 data rate	= 1.544 Mbps

Two different framing techniques for DS-level transmission—D4 and ESF—are available. We'll look more closely at each.

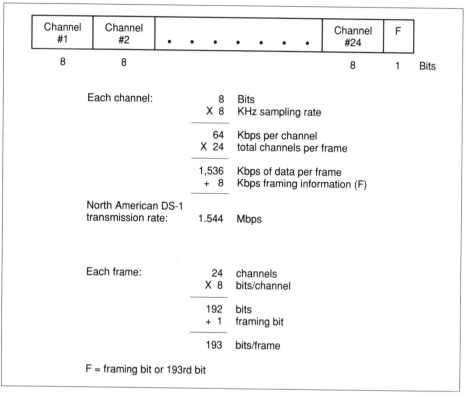

Figure 3-13. DS-1 Frame Format

3.4.2.1 D-4 Framing

D-4 framing (see Figure 3-14) uses the 193rd bit strictly for framing purposes. A total of 12 individual frames are combined into a D-4 "superframe." A pattern of the sampled 193rd bits (bit numbers 193, 386, 579, etc.) are used to identify individual DS-0 channels within each DS-1 frame. This framing pattern (100011011100) is repeated every 12 frames (or superframe). Signaling information (used for central office-to-central office messages) appears in bit 8 of frames 6 and 12. AT&T PUB 43801 (reference [3-20]) provides additional details.

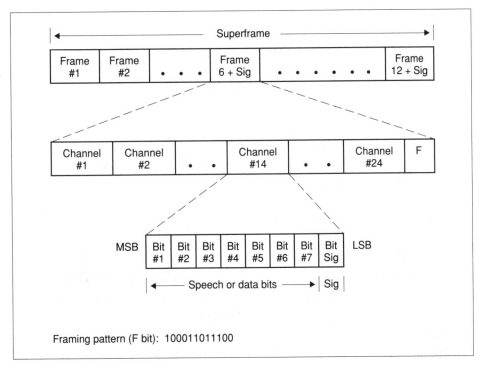

Figure 3-14. AT&T D4 Framing Format

3.4.2.2 ESF Framing

In 1979, AT&T proposed a new DS-1 framing format known as the Extended Superframe Format (ESF) (described in reference [3-21], and shown in Figure 3-15). ESF extended the superframe from 12 to 24 DS-1 frames, which resulted in a total of 24 of the framing (or 193rd) bits. With 24 bits instead of 12 to work with, two additional capabilities became available (see Figure 3-16). The signaling capabilities were expanded to four options (T, 2, 4, 16) and are shown in the traffic and signaling columns in Figure 3-16. Signaling information (if used), is present in frames 6, 12, 18 and 24.

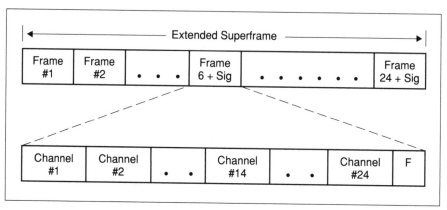

Figure 3-15. AT&T ESF Framing Format

There are three uses for the framing function (shown as S in Figure 3-16): Framing itself (Fe); Data Link (DL); and Block Check (BC). The Data Link function provides a 4 Kbps communications link between circuit end points. Transmissions on this data link would typically consist of maintenance and performance messages. Two different standards exist for the use of these maintenance messages. The AT&T 54016 standard specifies that the CSU store up to 24 hours of statistics, and transmit those results over the Data Link to network management stations upon request. The ANSI T1.403 standard requires that the CSU transmit performance data on a continuous basis. Since the AT&T and ANSI standards govern the way the collected data is disseminated, not collected, both techniques can coexist on the same transmission facility. AT&T, US Sprint, and MCI Communications support the ANSI standard, and are expected to migrate to that implementation in the future. Reference [3-22] describes these functions further.

The Block Check framing function (BC) provides a six-bit Cyclic Redundancy Check (CRC-6), which is used to verify the accuracy of the entire superframe. Any individual line errors would cause a violation of the CRC-6, thus alerting the intermediate transmission equipment of the problem. The CRC-6 is 98.4% accurate (63/64) in detecting burst errors that occur on the transmission line (reference [3-23]).

The advantage of the ESF framing format over that of the D-4 is its ability to monitor the network and then notify a network management console of any difficulties. This communication path is often implemented via a serial (EIA- 232) port on an intelligent CSU. Data from a number of CSUs can be accumulated and then presented in a centralized format.

3.4.2.3 T-1 Network Management

With the complexities of the framing patterns and other related technical issues, the management of a T-1-based network becomes a strategic issue as well. Many of the multiplexer vendors have begun to incorporate network management software into their products to facilitate the reporting of configuration, performance, and administrative information. Telco Systems Network Access Corporation of Fremont, California incorporates a number of management functions into their Muxview system, which runs with their Route 24 T-1 multiplexer. The Route 24 product can incorporate a number of digital inputs for transmission on a T-1 circuit, including facsimile, video and LAN traffic.

	S BITS			BIT USE IN EACH CHANNEL TIME SLOT		SIGNALING-BIT USE OPTIONS			
FRAME NUMBER	Fe	DL	BC	TRAFFIC	SIGNALING	T	2	4	16
1	-	m	-	BITS 1-8					
2	-	-	C1	BITS 1-8					
3	-	m	-	BITS 1-8					
4	0	-	-	BITS 1-8					
5	-	m	-	BITS 1-8					
6	-	-	C2	BITS 1-7	BIT 8	-	A	A	A
7	-	m	-	BITS 1-8					
8	0	-	-	BITS 1-8					
9	-	m	-	BITS 1-8					
10	-	-	C3	BITS 1-8					
11	-	m	-	BITS 1-8					
12	1	-	-	BITS 1-7	BIT 8	-	A	B	B
13	-	m	-	BITS 1-8					
14	-	-	C4	BITS 1-8					
15	-	m	-	BITS 1-8					
16	0	-	-	BITS 1-8					
17	-	m	-	BITS 1-8					
18	-	-	C5	BITS 1-7	BIT 8	-	A	A	C
19	-	m	-	BITS 1-8					
20	1	-	-	BITS 1-8					
21	-	m	-	BITS 1-8					
22	-	-	C6	BITS 1-8					
23	-	m	-	BITS 1-8					
24	1	-	-	BITS 1-7	BIT 8	-	A	B	D

NOTES: Fe – Extended Framing (sequence...001011...)
DL – 4 kb/s Data Link (message bits m)
BC – Block-Check Field (check bits C1-C6)
Option T – Transparent (bit 8 for traffic)
Option 2 – 2-State Signaling (channel 4)
Option 4 – 4-State Signaling (channels A, B)
Option 16 – 16-State Signaling (channels A, B, C, D)

Figure 3-16. AT&T ESF Frame Coding
(Reproduced with permission of AT&T)

124

MuxView is a system that runs under Microsoft Windows, and provides a number of graphical outputs. The MuxConf screen (see Figure 3-17a) identifies the locations that are being managed. Information on a site-by-site basis details various options, such as D-4 framing, and maintenance functions, such as loopback conditions (see Figure 3-17b). The exact equipment configuration at that location is information that can be accessed from the Mux screen (see Figure 3-17c). Trouble tickets (see Figure 3-17d) can also be generated to track the performance difficulties. With the trend towards all-digital backbones for internetwork communication, look for more network management capabilities to be built into multiplexers and LAN hardware. For further details, see reference [3-24].

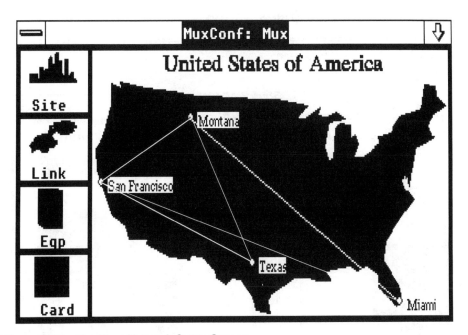

Figure 3-17a. MuxView Network Setup Screen
(Courtesy Telco Systems)

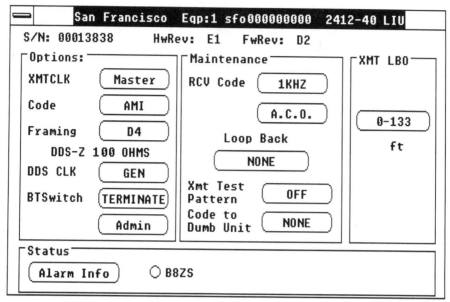

Figure 3-17b. MuxView Site Screen
(Courtesy Telco Systems)

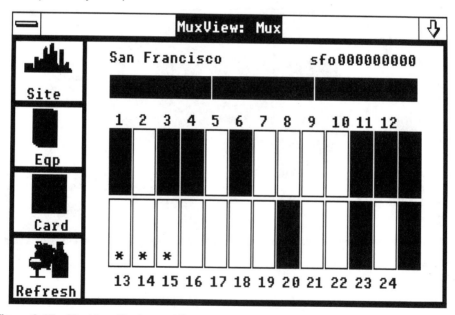

Figure 3-17c. MuxView Equipment Screen
(Courtesy Telco Systems)

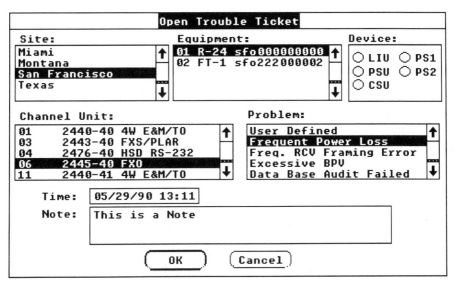

Figure 3-17d. MuxView Trouble Ticket Screen
(Courtesy Telco Systems)

3.4.3   Fractional T-1

Fractional T-1 (FT-1), as its name implies, offers the network manager a range of digital bandwidth choices that are a fraction of a full T-1 link. The service is designed for applications that have requirements greater than those provided by analog or DDS private lines, but perhaps less than a full T-1 circuit. Fractional T-1 circuits are thus configured in 64 Kbps segments, up to the maximum 1.544 Mbps. Cost savings follow as well (reference [3-25]). Previously offered only by Canadian carriers, Cable and Wireless became the first U.S. IXC to offer the service in 1987 (reference [3-26]). Since then a number of other IXCs, including AT&T, MCI, US Sprint, and Williams Telecommunications have added FT-1 services (reference [3-27]).

RBOCs (Regional Bell Operating Companies) and LECs (Local Exchange Carriers) have been slower to offer comparable service, with NYNEX Corporation the only provider as of this writing. An example of FT-1 access, taken from reference [3-25], is shown in Figure 3-18. In this example, the FT-1 circuit terminates in the IXC's Point of Presence (POP) within that LATA, and may be connected to other AT&T Inter-Office Channels (IOCs). A digital trunk circuit connects the IXC and LEC Central Offices (C.O.s). If the LEC does not offer FT-1 service, a voice-grade private line (VGPL), or a digital private line (DDS), another T-1 circuit will be used to connect to the customer location.

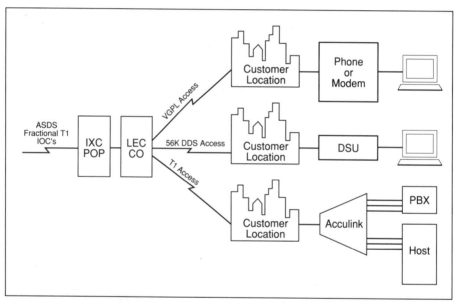

Figure 3-18. AT&T Fractional T-1 Access Methods
(Reproduced with permission of AT&T)

A number of T-1 multiplexer vendors, including Timeplex, Inc., Infotron Systems, Network Equipment Technologies, Codex Corporation, and Larse Corporation, support FT-1 service in their products. Look for a gradual migration of analog and digital (DDS) lines to fractional T-1, plus increased interest among LAN vendors, as bandwidth requirements increase and digital transmission facility costs decrease (reference [3-28]). The financial implications of FT-1 service must be considered along with the alternative voice-grade or digital private lines. Reference [3-29] provides an economic comparison between FT-1, voice-grade, DDS, and T-1 lines for the reader's consideration.

3.4.4   T-1 Service Example

ALL RBOCs and some LECs offer T-1 service to end users. In addition, some RBOCs, LECs, and IXCs offer T-3 service. As the major vendor, AT&T's offerings will be profiled here; Appendix C lists names and phone numbers of many other private line vendors.

ACCUNET T1.5 is the name of AT&T's terrestrial T-1 service. In addition to this, AT&T offers a central office-based service option known as M24. The M24 Multiplexing office function combines up to 24 voice-grade or 56 Kbps switched channels into one T-1 circuit for transmission. AT&T's network supports both ESF and B8ZS formats.

ACCUNET T45 is AT&T's T-3 circuit offering. Several service options are available here as well. The ACCUNET T45 channelized services require all 28 DS-1 signals with the DS-3 to support ESF. A non-channelized version is also available for high-speed data transfers. The M28 Multiplexing Office function combines or divides 28 DS-1 signals into a DS-3. The M28 function can also be combined with the M24 function for a total T-3 to T-1 to subrate service connection.

The prices of T-1 and T-3 services are based upon several components. A Local Channel (LC) provided by the LEC connects the customer's premises to the AT&T central office at each end of the facility. The Inter-Office Channel (IOC), provided by AT&T, is charged on a per-mile basis. Central Office functions such as M24 or M28 are also priced individually. Contact AT&T for current information and individual circuit pricing, and see reference [3-13] for technical details.

3.5   Public Data Networks

Public Data Networks (PDNs), sometimes called Value Added Networks (VANs), have been popular data-transmission facilities since their inception in the early 1970s (reference [3-30]). PDNs are often referred to as "X.25 networks." This statement (as we will study in Chapter 5) is clearly false. PDNs are, in fact, packet switched networks, and X.25 is the protocol of choice between most DTEs (Data Terminal Equipment) and the network. The misconception lies in the fact that the X.25 protocols define an interface *into* the PDN, not the internal protocols *within* the PDN. This is a subtle but important point. The internal protocols and architecture of the PDN may be considered proprietary to the network provider, as well as the manner in which they route, switch and store their customer's packets of information. PDNs operate by accepting fixed-length packets of information (usually 128 octets in length) and routing these through the network to the desired location. To begin our discussion of PDNs, we'll look at the network access techniques and then discuss value-added services and pricing.

3.5.1   PDN Access

Network users can access the PDN "cloud" (see Figure 3-19) in several different ways. For high-speed applications, a synchronous leased line is provided between the customer's premises and the local PDN node (see Figure 3-20). Typical transmission rates are 9.6, 14.4, 19.2, and 56 Kbps. Since most of the North American PDNs have access nodes in all major cities, the leased line becomes a local rather than a long-distance facility. Either the end-user or the PDN can contract with the LEC for the leased line. The terminal equipment (synchronous modems or CSUs) required by the type of facility (analog or digital) must also be obtained.

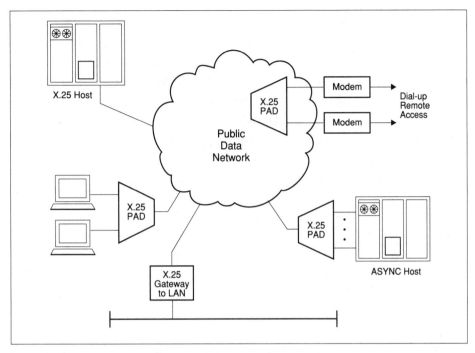

Figure 3-19. Public Data Network Access Options

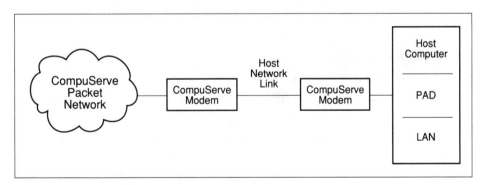

Figure 3-20. CompuServe Host Network Link Configuration
(Courtesy CompuServe)

Dial-up access is also available and can be provided in two different ways. The first method assumes that the user wishes to transmit asynchronous data, typically ASCII characters. The PDN publishes a list of access telephone numbers, along with the port speeds (1.2, 2.4 Kbps, etc.) associated with those ports. The user dials into the port with an asynchronous modem and then connects into another device, known as a PAD (Packet Assembler and Disassembler). The PAD functions similarly to a statistical multiplexer, taking the asynchronous characters and placing them in the appropriate length (e.g. 128 octet) packets. At the receiving end, the PAD performs the opposite function, decomposing the packet and generating characters.

The second alternative is dial-up access using the X.32 protocol, which provides synchronous X.25 service over dial-up lines. This alternative is often used when the traffic volumes don't warrant a dedicated connection, but the error control capabilities of the X.25 protocol are still required or desired.

3.5.2 PDN Rate Structures

PDNs have different rate structures for dial-up and leased access ports. Dial-up access charges are based upon connect time and are typically in the $5.00–10.00 per hour range. Leased line connections into a PDN are typically charged on a two-tier basis. The first component is a link charge and is based upon the speed (9.6–56 Kbps) of the leased line port. This charge may range from a few hundred to a few thousand dollars per month. The second component is a traffic charge, based on the volume of data transmitted into the network. The typical metric is the kilocharacter (1000 characters) or kilopacket (1000 of the 128 octet packets). The traffic charge typically ranges from $0.50–1.00 per kilopacket, or roughly $0.001 per packet (reference [3-31]). (As pricing techniques vary among the various PDNs, consult the vendors listed in Appendix D for exact price quotations.)

3.5.3 Value-Added Network Services

One of the advantages of a PDN is its ability to connect host computers that have dissimilar hardware and software platforms. A number of value-added network services, some of which are described below, are often incorporated into the PDN offering (reference [3-32]). Speed and format conversion are fundamental, as PCs or Macintoshes transmitting ASCII characters at 1.2 or 2.4 Kbps may need to access a much faster IBM mainframe that uses the EBCDIC character formats. Protocol conversion is a frequent requirement for PDNs to offer, with IBM's 3270 and 5250 protocols among the most popular for access to IBM 30xx, 43xx, 93xx, AS/400 or S/3x processors. Electronic mail, a feature that allows users across the country to communicate with each other on a store-and-forward basis, is especially useful for those who travel and are difficult to reach. The public databases are also good features; they have capabilities for home shopping, airline reservations, and stock market quotations, and they provide access to research databases such as encyclopedias and magazine-article abstracts. An excellent summary of international VAN services is given in reference [3-33].

3.5.4 PDN Example

CompuServe of Columbus, Ohio is a good example of a PDN that also provides a wide variety of VAN services. Currently, CompuServe has over 2300 commercial clients, and its VAN, CompuServe Information Service, has over 600,000 subscribers. Local dial-up and leased-line access is available in over 650 U.S. cities, reaching over 85 percent of the U.S. population.

LAN to WAN internetworking is supported with the FIXED-X25 service shown in Figure 3-21. Links are available at speeds from 9.6 to 19.2 Kbps over either analog or digital leased lines. Up to 32 logical channels can be supported per link. A number of devices can access the network via the X.25 protocol. These include LAN bridges and gateways, hosts having X.25 interfaces, customer-supplied Packet Assembler/ Disassemblers (PADs), and CompuServe-supplied PADs or switches. Chapter 5 is devoted to further applications of these devices and the X.25 protocol.

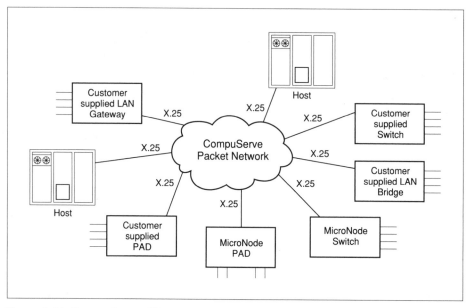

Figure 3-21. CompuServe FIXED-X25 Network Configuration
(Courtesy CompuServe)

3.6 Optimizing Transmission Facilities

A growing trend in the telecommunications arena is the use of software tools to simulate network performance and calculate optimum costs. References [3-34] and [3-35] are recent summaries of available products, and [3-36] is an excellent book on network design techniques. We'll look at two illustrative products here.

3.6.1 Comdisco BONeS

Comdisco Systems, Inc. of Foster City, California has developed a network modeling and simulation tool known as BONeS (Block Oriented Network Simulator). BONeS operates on Sun Workstations, running under UNIX. A number of networks can be simulated, including LANs and WANs, packet and circuit switched networks, and computer buses and architectures. A model library is contained within BONeS and includes a number of building blocks for X.25, IEEE 802.3, IEEE 802.5,

FDDI, and HDLC protocols. Using the model library, a user builds a network to be simulated employing a number of building blocks (Figure 3-22) that specify the desired input and output parameters. The software then performs the simulation, computing the statistical performance of the network, and displays the results in a graphical format.

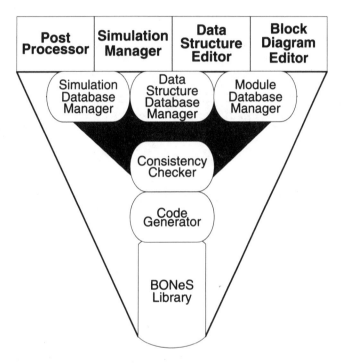

Figure 3-22. Key Components of BONeS
(Courtesy Comdisco Systems, Inc.)

Example outputs from the BONeS environment are shown in Figure 3-23. The first network simulated is an Ethernet that uses TCP and is comprised of six stations: one fileserver, two stand-alone workstations, two diskless workstations, and one dataless workstation (indicating that the local disk was small, and only used for swapping). Each workstation has three different applications running, with each application generating disk requests at random times and on random disks. Diskless

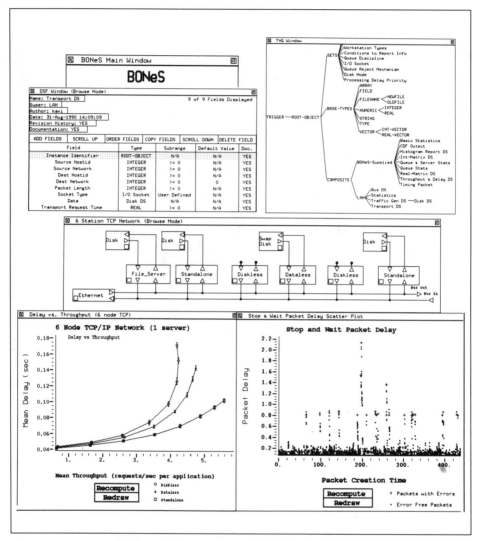

Figure 3-23. BONeS Environment
(Courtesy Comdisco Systems, Inc.)

workstations always use the file server; dataless workstations use the file server for 70 percent of their requests; and stand-alone workstations use the file server for 30 percent of their requests. The results (in the lower left window) plot the mean delay versus mean throughput. It shows that the mean delay is smallest for stand-alones (due mostly to local requests) and highest for diskless workstations (which had all remote requests). In any case, the system can not handle the number of requests that are specified, which results in applications waiting longer for disk access.

A second example (from a completely different network) models a simple two-node network operating a Stop and Wait Data Link Layer protocol. The plot is a measured history of the delay incurred by each transmitted frame. The model for the channel introduces random errors, which results in retransmissions. Most of the frames have delays of less than 0.2 seconds. Some of the frames (denoted by +) have to be transmitted more than once, and so their delay is higher (at least 0.8 seconds, which is very close to the time-out period specified for the protocol). Notice that frames with errors also cause the next few frames to be delayed (those with good eyesight can see that the dots that are stacked up actually come right after the +). Also, notice that some frames have to be transmitted three or four times.

The BONeS simulator has a number of other outputs and simulations that can be generated from the model. For network designers, this tool is a valuable resource for predicting network performance before investing in components.

3.6.2 Quintessential Solutions WAN Design Tools

If you have an existing WAN or LAN topology defined, there are a number of transmission facility options available to the internetwork manager. However, keeping track of the changes in the rate and tariff structures of the various LEC and IXC carriers can be a monumental task. As a result, a number of companies market software packages that will minimize WAN facility costs. Quintessential Solutions, Inc. of San Diego, California has developed wide-area network modeling, pricing, analysis and design tools (shown in Figure 3-24). This product runs on a PC/XT/AT or compatible under DOS, or on a Sun workstation under UNIX.

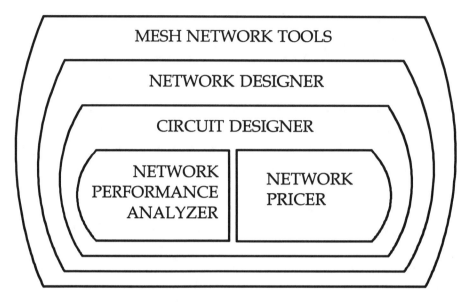

Figure 3-24. Quintessential Solutions System
(Courtesy Quintessential Solutions)

WAN Design Tools is made up of a number of modules which address specific tasks. The Network Performance Analyzer is used to analyze bandwidth requirements and processing delays. The Pricer is a cost analysis module that contains monthly updates of current tariff information. Design tools include the Circuit Designer, which determines the network topology, and the Network Designer, which determines multiplexer and concentrator locations. In addition, the suite of Mesh tools can be used to design and analyze the backbone network that interconnects multiplexers, concentrators, switches and hosts. These tools provide backbone or mesh pricing, line loading and throughput analysis, traffic routing, link design, and switch placement—all in a cost-effective manner that satisfies the performance criteria.

Let's assume that a communication facility is needed between Broomfield, Colorado and San Diego, California. Several different carriers may provide that service, but who are they, and which one is the least expensive? The Point-to-Point pricer module reveals the answer. The summary report (Figure 3-25a) compares five IXCs: AT&T, MCI, Cable & Wireless, National Telecommunications Network, and US Sprint. Of these five, three (AT&T, MCI, and NTN) provide 56 Kbps via FT-1, one (CWC) operates at 64 Kbps, and the last (USS) has a 112 Kbps circuit available. Details of the monthly circuit costs are given in Figure 3-25b. Note that the prices are broken down into Local, IOC, and Installation costs for a valid comparison. Also note that local access for the NTN circuit is not available, thus precluding its use even though the tariffs rate it as the least-cost carrier. Other factors—such as the available service options—should also be considered as part of the total bid package.

```
                      QUINTESSENTIAL SOLUTIONS, INC
                              PRICER (4.08)
                             MODEL: DIGINT
                      SAMPLE PRICER REPORT—DIGINET

                              BRIEF REPORT
                         ---------------------
```

CIRCUIT	TARIFF	LINE SPEED	IOC COST	LOCAL COST	TOTAL COST	INSTALL
CKT3	USS FT1	112000	811.40	1,439.34	2,250.74	3,260.00
CKT4	CWC FT1	64000	482.00	1,317.31	1,799.31	3,822.32
CKT1	ATT FT1	56000	512.96	345.21	858.17	1,770.85
CKT2	MCI FT1	56000	449.28	441.36	890.64	1,481.06
CKT5	NTN FT1	56000	413.28	394.55	807.83	983.06
TOTAL COSTS			2,668.92	3937.77	6,606.69	11,317.29

Figure 3-25a. Pricer Brief Report
(Courtesy Quintessential Solutions)

```
+----------------------------------------------------------------------------------+
|                        QUINTESSENTIAL SOLUTIONS, INC                              |
|                              PRICER (4.08)                                        |
|                             MODEL: DIGINT                                         |
|                      SAMPLE PRICER REPORT—DIGINET                                 |
|                            SUMMARY REPORT                                         |
+----------------------------------------------------------------------------------+
| CIRCUIT NAME: CKT3        FROM Page:    2 TARRIFF: USS FT1  SPEED: 112000         |
| IOC TOTALS                                           IOC Miles     IOC C ost      |
|                                                         830   $      811.40       |
| LC TOTALS       LC Cost     COC Cost    ACF Cost                  LOCAL Cost      |
|                 1271.34     124.00      44.00                 $    1,439.34       |
| TOTAL COSTS                                                   $    2,250.74       |
|                                                                  ----------       |
| INSTALL         LC Cost     COC Cost    ACF Cost                   INSTALL        |
|                 2330.00     558.00      372.00               $    3,260.00        |
+----------------------------------------------------------------------------------+
| CIRCUIT NAME: CKT4        FROM Page:    3 TARRIFF: CWC FT1  SPEED: 64000          |
| IOC TOTALS                                           IOC Miles     IOC Cost       |
|                                                         828   $      482.00       |
| LC TOTALS       LC Cost     COC Cost    ACF Cost                  LOCAL Cost      |
|                 871.31      .00         500.00               $    1,317.31        |
| TOTAL COSTS                                                  $    1,799.31        |
|                                                                  ----------       |
| INSTALL         LC Cost     COC Cost    ACF Cost                   INSTALL        |
|                 2622.32     200.00      1000.00             $    3,822.32         |
+----------------------------------------------------------------------------------+
| CIRCUIT NAME: CKT1        FROM Page:    4 TARRIFF: ATT FT1  SPEED: 56000          |
| IOC TOTALS                                           IOC Miles     IOC Cost       |
|                                                         828   $      512.96       |
| LC TOTALS     LC Cost   COC Cost   ACF Cost   DDA Cost           LOCAL Cost       |
|               187.03    40.00      57.30      60.88          $      345.21        |
| TOTAL COSTS                                                  $      858.17        |
|                                                                  ----------       |
| INSTALL       LC Cost   COC Cost   ACF Cost                        INSTALL        |
|               826.85    392.00     552.00                   $    1,770.85         |
+----------------------------------------------------------------------------------+
| CIRCUIT NAME: CKT2        FROM Page:    5 TARRIFF: MCI FT1  SPEED: 56000          |
| IOC TOTALS                                           IOC Miles     IOC Cost       |
|                                                         826   $      449.28       |
| LC TOTALS     LC Cost   COC Cost   ACF Cost   DDA Cost           LOCAL Cost       |
|               244.06    40.00      57.30      100.00         $      441.36        |
| TOTAL COSTS                                                  $      890.64        |
|                                                                  ----------       |
| INSTALL       LC Cost   COC Cost   ACF Cost                        INSTALL        |
|               633.06    352.00     496.00                   $    1,481.06         |
+----------------------------------------------------------------------------------+
| CIRCUIT NAME: CKT5        FROM Page:    6 TARRIFF: USS FT1  SPEED: 56000          |
| ***** WARNING: Access for NTN FT1 is not available in this LATA. *****            |
| IOC TOTALS                                           IOC Miles     IOC Cost       |
|                                                         828   $      413.28       |
| LC TOTALS     LC Cost   COC Cost   ACF Cost   DDA Cost           LOCAL Cost       |
|               154.55    90.00      .00        150.00         $      394.55        |
| TOTAL COSTS                                                  $      807.83        |
|                                                                  ----------       |
| INSTALL       LC Cost   COC Cost   ACF Cost                        INSTALL        |
|               633.06    350.00     .00                      $      983.06         |
+----------------------------------------------------------------------------------+
```

Figure 3-25b. Pricer Summary Report

(Courtesy Quintessential Solutions)

```
                    QUINTESSENTIAL SOLUTIONS, INC
                           PRICER (4.08)
                         MODEL: DIGINT
                   SAMPLE PRICER REPORT—DIGINET

                           (CONTINUED)
                         SUMMARY REPORT
                   ----------------------------
=========================NETWORK SUMMARY====================

IXC TOTALS                    IXC 1/4s    IXC Miles        IXC Cost
                                     0            0  $         0.00

IWC TOTALS                    IWC 1/4s    IWC Miles        IWC Cost
                                     0            0  $         0.00

IOC TOTALS                    IOC 1/4s    IOC Miles        IOC Cost
                                     0            0  $         0.00

LC TOTALS  IW Cost   CT Cost        CND Cost
              .00       .00
LC TOTALS  IO Cost   LL Cost        DND Cost
              .00       .00
LC TOTALS  LC Cost COC Cost ACF Cost DDA Cost BRG Cost  SIG Cost  LOCAL Cost
           2674.29   294.00   658.60   310.88                   $   3,937.77
                                                                 =========
TOTAL COSTS                                                     $   6,606.69
                                                                 =========
INSTALL    IW Cost   CT Cost        CND Cost
              .00       .00
INSTALL    IO Cost   LL Cost        DND Cost
              .00       .00
INSTALL    LC Cost COC Cost ACF Cost DDA Cost BRG Cost  SIG Cost    INSTALL
           7045.29  1852.00  2420.00                            $  11,317.29
                                                                 =========
TOTAL LC 1/4 s  = 0
TOTAL LC Miles  = 62      TOTAL CIRCUITS       = 5
TOTAL SITES     = 5       TOTAL TERMINATIONS   = 10
  0 ERROR (S) & 1 WARNING (S)
```

Figure 3-25b. Pricer Summary Report, cont.

(Courtesy Quintessential Solutions)

3.7   Future Transmission Facility Trends

Data-communication facilities can be a major expense of the total internetwork. Frequently, multi-year leases are required when the facility is installed, so the design decision has long-term implications. In view of the long term, it is vital for the internetwork manager to be aware of future trends in the telecommunications industry. Let's take a brief look into the future.

The first telecommunications trend is the gradual replacement of analog facilities with digital facilities. The increased reliability of DDS, FT-1, and T-1/T-3 circuits makes them an obvious choice, with all other factors (such as cost and existing equipment) being equal. A second, related trend is the increasing speed of transmission. We have seen LANs, such as the Token Ring, increase from 4 to 16 Mbps. When the speeds of the LAN backbones increase, the internetwork transmission facilities must increase in speed as well. We will look at these growth trends in more detail in Chapter 4.

The third, and probably most important, trend is the emergence in the next few years of network-to-network communication technologies. One of these is the ISDN (Integrated Services Digital Network). As its name implies, the ISDN is an all-digital transmission facility that will gradually replace the analog PSTN on a worldwide basis. ISDN services to residences and small business is known as the basic rate, offering a data throughput of 144 Kbps. The transmission pipeline is divided into two B (Bearer) channels offering 64 Kbps throughput each, plus one D channel operating at 16 Mbps. The B channels are for user information, carrying voice, data, or image communication. The D channel is used for signaling on behalf of the B channel, plus packet switched data transmission.

The primary rate has a data throughput of 1.536 Mbps. It has the same structure as the DS-1 frame, providing 24 of the 64 Kbps channels. In most configurations, 23 of the channels are B channels, with the last channel designated a D (signaling) channel. Primary rate interfaces are designed for businesses requiring higher bandwidth voice and data facilities. Two internetworking applications would be interfaces to digital PBXs (currently available from AT&T) or LANs (references [3-37] and [3-38]). Look for LAN-to-ISDN connections via bridges or routers to be available in the near future. (An excellent text on ISDN is reference [3-39].)

A second emerging transmission facility is SONET, the Synchronous Optical Network. Originally proposed by Bell Communications Research (Bellcore), SONET is also a proposed CCITT/ANSI standard (reference [3-39]). The basic signal is known as Synchronous Transport Signal Level One (STS-1), which operates at 51.84 Mbps. Higher transmission rates are obtained by interleaving the lower rates, which is similar to the North American T-carrier network hierarchy. SONET signals are transmitted via single mode fiber optic cables and are being tested by the various IXCs. Because of the high transmission speeds, SONET users will undoubtedly be internetworks with extremely high throughput requirements. Managers having a requirement in the DS-3 (44.736 Mbps) range should investigate the possibilities of the SONET alternative.

The third emerging technology is known as frame relay. Frame relay is a Data Link Layer protocol that is built upon the existing CCITT X.25 and ISDN standards. New standards from ANSI (T1S1) and CCITT (I.122) are expected in the 1991–1992 timeframe (reference [3-41]). Several improvements to the existing X.25 technologies are present in frame relay.

Frame relay gets its name because it defines a method for efficiently relaying frames of information across a packet-switched network. Efficiencies are realized by reducing the overhead in each packet and making error calculations at source and destination, instead of at each individual switching node. The most interesting aspect of frame relay is the way it will internetwork LAN and WAN technologies. Bridges and routers are internal packet switches, making them an ideal candidate for frame-relay technology. On the WAN side, most backbones are constructed using T-1 multiplexers or nodal switches. Their architecture also lends itself to frame-relay technology. Not surprisingly, a number of LAN, WAN, and internetworking vendors are collaborating to various degrees on the development of frame-relay standards and products. Key players include AT&T, Advanced Computer Communications, cisco Systems Inc., Digital Equipment Corp. (DEC), US Sprint/Telenet, Vitalink Communications Corp., and Wellfleet Communications, Inc.

In summary, this chapter has covered a number of transmission facilities for LAN-to-WAN internetworking. Some of these, such as dial-up or analog leased lines, have been in service for years; LAN requirements have merely provided a new application for existing transmission technologies. Other WAN facilities, such as ISDN and frame relay (which employ digital transmission), are creating the all-digital enterprise network. The wise network manager will keep abreast of these emerging trends and technologies. References [3-42] through [3-44] are examples of articles that provide further glimpses into the future.

3.8 References

[3-1] AT&T. *Telecommunications Transmission Engineering.* 2d ed., vol. 1-3, 1977.

[3-2] Bell Telephone Laboratories, Inc. *Transmission Systems for Communications.* 5th ed. 1982.

[3-3] Freeman, Roger L. *Telecommunication System Engineering—Analog and Digital Network Design.* John Wiley & Sons, 1980.

[3-4] AT&T. *Data Communications Using the Switched Telecommunications Network.* PUB 41005, May 1971.

[3-5] AT&T. *Data Communications Using Voiceband Private Line Channels.* PUB 41004, October 1973.

[3-6] AT&T. *Transmission Parameters Affecting Voiceband Data Transmission—Description of Parameters.* PUB 41008, July 1974.

[3-7] AT&T. *Analog Voice—Total and Coordinated Services.* PUB 43202, May 1985, and addendum 1, August 1988.

[3-8] Douglass, Jack L. *Applied Data Communications Handbook.* Universal Data Systems, 1987.

[3-9] Stallings, William. *Data and Computer Communications.* 2d ed. Macmillan, 1988.

[3-10] McNamara, John E. *Technical Aspects of Data Communication.* 3d ed. Digital Press, 1988.

[3-11] Douglass, Jack . "How to Find Phone-line Faults and What to Do About Them." *Data Communications* (September 1988): 179–197.

[3-12] AT&T. *Digital Data System Channel Interface Specification.* PUB 62310, September 1983.

[3-13] AT&T. *Accunet Spectrum of Digital Services*. TR 62421, December 1989.

[3-14] Jander, Mary. "User's Rate Long-Distance Carriers." *Data Communications* (August 1990): 91–96.

[3-15] Briere, Daniel . "Private Line Services, Parts I and II." *Network World* (December 25, 1989): 29–39 and (January 8, 1990): 29–38.

[3-16] Lippis, Nick. "At AT&T, Much Ado About Switched Services." *Data Communications* (August 1990): 29 –30.

[3-17] AT&T. *Digital Multiplexes Requirements and Objectives*. PUB 43802, July 1982.

[3-18] Flanagan, William A. *The Teleconnect Guide to T-1 Networking*. Telecom Library, Inc., 1986.

[3-19] Bellamy, John C. *Digital Telephony*. John Wiley & Sons, 1982.

[3-20] AT&T. *Digital Channel Bank Requirements and Objectives*. PUB 43801, November 1982.

[3-21] AT&T. *Requirements for Interfacing Digital Terminal Equipment to Services Employing the Extended Superframe Format*. TR 54016, September 1989.

[3-22] Rux , Peter T. and Clifford V. Ciles. "ESF Rx for Healthy T1 Nets." *Data Communications* (May 1990): 81–94.

[3-23] Verilink Corporation. *The Book on ESF*. 1986.

[3-24] Telco Systems Network Access Corporation. *T-1 Application Guide*. 1989.

[3-25] AT&T Paradyne. *Fractional T1 Your Pipeline to Network Savings*. 1990. MUX-BKT1-0-0590.

[3-26] Edwards, Morris. "F-T1: Buy Only What You Need." *Communications News* (June 1990): 35–38.

[3-27] "Carriers with Fractional T1 by LATA." *Data Communications* (May 1990): 25.

[3-28] Miller, C. Kenneth. "Fractional T-1, An Idea Whose Time Has Come." *LAN Times* (June 1990): 47.

[3-29] Mier, Edwin E. "Fractional T1: Carriers Carve Out Bandwidth for Users." *Data Communication* (November 1989): 84–98.

[3-30] Halsey, J. R, et.al. "Public Data Networks: Their Evolution, Interfaces and Status." *IBM System Journal* Vol. 18, no. 2 (1979): 223–243.

[3-31] Schlar, Sherman K. "Shopping Smart to Save on Packet Networks." *Data Communications* (March 1990); 77–86.

[3-32] Schlar, Sharman K. *Inside X.25: A Manager's Guide.* New York: McGraw-Hill, Inc., 1990.

[3-33] Crockett, Barton. "Good News on the Global Front." *Network World* (May 21, 1990): 81–94.

[3-34] Van Norman, Harrell J. "A User's Guide to Network Design Tools." *Data Communications* (April 1988): 115-133.

[3-35] Salamone, Salvatore. "Network By Design." *Network World* (March 12, 1990): 45–57.

[3-36] Ellis, Robert L. *Designing Data Networks.* Prentice-Hall, 1986.

[3-37] Duncanson, Jay and Joe Chew. "The Ultimate Link?" *Byte* (July 1988): 278-286.

[3-38] Kessler, Gary C. "ISDNs and LANs Unite." *LAN Magazine* (October 1990): 117–126.

[3-39] Kessler, Gary C. *ISDN*, McGraw-Hill, 1990.

[3-40] Mulqueen, John. "Carriers Ready Their Networks for SONET." *Data Communications* (August 1990): 52–55.

[3-41] Lippis, Nick. "Frame Relay Redraws to Map for Wide Area Networks." *Data Communications* (July 1990): 80–94.

[3-42] Carr, Jim. "Wide Area Wonders." *LAN Magazine* (October 1990): 40–50.

[3-43] Briere, Daniel. "Fractional T-1 Services Drive Hardware Market." *Network World* (September 24, 1990): 1–87.

[3-44] Smith, Gail P. "Foundations for Tomorrow's Private Network." *Business Communication Review* (July 1990): 35-40.

CHAPTER 4

LAN to WAN Internetworking

With our study of the various transmission facilities completed, we'll look next at specific applications for these facilities in an internetworking environment.

To begin, let's assume that we have a system where the network resources are located at different sites. The network may not have started out that way, however, since most LANs installed in the mid-1980s were designed for small workgroups with 10 to 20 workstations per network. Since that initial installation, new network requirements have evolved: expansion, access to new resources, and different platform connectivity. First, the network has invariably grown. A growth rate of 100–200 percent in the first year is not uncommon. Second, the network now needs to access other identified resources (at separate locations). These other resources may be another LAN or a host computer, or a remote workstation—such as a salesperson who is travelling. Third, the platforms requiring connectivity might not be the same, e.g. Macintosh to UNIX. All of these user requirements will invariably require the use of WAN facilities. (This subject has received much publicity lately— see references [4-1] through [4-4] for examples of LAN-WAN applications and current issues.) We'll study some of these challenges in Chapter 9.

The topic of LAN-WAN interconnection is a broad one. Many fine products are available. In order to put some structure into our study, we will first investigate the design issues of LAN-WAN interconnectivity, answering the question of how to determine the type of transmission facility that is required for a particular application. Next, we will study products that are used with the various transmission facilities. As we did in Chapter 3, we'll begin with the lower-speed, dial-up lines, and conclude with the high-speed T-1 products.

4.1   Designing the LAN-WAN Connection

Let's assume that the internet contains segments (or subnetworks) in dissimilar locations. The objective is to design the LAN/WAN transmission facilities required for this internetwork. Since this can be an involved process, let's break it down into a number of smaller steps.

Define the Goals. Determine the functional goals for the internetwork. Write these down as a statement of objective, so that all parties associated with the internet are aware of what is being attempted. Reference [4-5], Chapter 5, includes an excellent tutorial on design goals. The issues discussed include cost, performance, maintenance and support, reliability, redundancy, and robustness. The last issue, robustness, is especially critical for LAN/WAN integration, as it addresses the ability of the internetwork to handle periods of heavy usage or peak activity.

Identify the Components. Identify the hardware/software components at each location that must be incorporated into the internetwork. Specifically address two issues. First: Which LAN hardware architectures (e.g. Ethernet, Token Ring) must be connected? If a long-range plan exists to convert one architecture to another (e.g. replacing Ethernet with Token Ring), make sure that these long-term objectives are considered as well. (Reference [4-6] is a good overview of the various LAN/WAN topologies to consider.) Second: Which LAN operating systems (e.g. Novell's NetWare, 3Com's 3+Open, Banyan's VINES) are implemented at each location? It is considerably easier to connect dissimilar systems if they have some degree of commonality in either their hardware or software platforms.

Understand the Applications. Consider the applications that are to be internetworked—such as electronic messaging using the CCITT X.400 standard, or file transfer using the Sun Microsystems NFS (Network File System). As with the hardware/software platforms, if there are common denominators at the Application Layer, the design job is that much easier.

Project the Growth. Make a projection of the growth that is expected to occur between various locations in the internet in the next 1,3, and 5 years. Consider three growth areas: at individual locations, in the number of locations, and as a result of mergers or acquisitions that may occur during the projected period.

Analyze the Traffic. Determine the amount of network traffic between various internetwork locations. This study will begin by measuring the network traffic on each segment, and will then calculate the amount of inter-segment traffic. (Reference [4-7] discusses link capacity requirements in general, reference [4-8] discusses the StarLAN/Ethernet design case, and [4-9] provides a Token Ring example.)

An excellent template for a traffic analysis is shown in Figures 4-1a through 4-1e, taken from Appendix A of reference [4-10]. While originally designed for Ethernet networks, many of the principles could be applied to other network designs. The analysis is broken down into five different worksheets:

Worksheet number 1, the "Host Resource Worksheet," is designed to give a clear understanding of the host resources that are available to the remote user community. The parameters examined include:

- Host Type: The manufacturer's designation for the host or workstation.
- Protocols: The protocols that are actively implemented on the hosts.
- Applications Running: These should be categorized as interactive, program compilation, file transfer, word processing, database, graphics oriented, etc.

- Max Users: Either the maximum simultaneous users as stipulated by the manufacturer, or the number of users that will cause throughput to drop to an unacceptable level for your environment.

- Current Users: The average number of people simultaneously logged into a host.

- Resources Left: The delta between maximum users and current users. The amount of resource remaining for remote user load.

By completing Worksheet number 1, you detail the host resources that are available for sharing by any remote devices and users of the wide area network.

Worksheet number 2, the "Peripheral Resource Worksheet," provides a list of all nodes other than host nodes that exist on the network segments. This worksheet will indicate the growth permitted at this site by the existing hardware. Worksheet number 2 is also valuable if there are no tools to monitor the traffic, leaving traffic estimation to averages established by protocol and peripheral type.

Worksheet numbers 3 and 4 are for those who choose to closely monitor their Ethernet traffic with hardware and software. If you are not interested in doing this, skip to Worksheet number 5.

Worksheet number 3, the "Traffic Worksheet," will prove helpful to those who choose to monitor their Ethernet traffic at each site with Ethernet monitoring devices, such as LAN analyzers and network management hardware and software. Samples of traffic should be taken on the production network at a time of day that most accurately represents the typical amount of traffic on each segment. Multiple samples should be taken to establish trends in traffic flow, user activity, and traffic rates. When this has been accomplished, Worksheet number 3 should then be completed using the averages of these samples to derive numbers that are representative of the Ethernet environment. (The worksheet applies simple mathematics to arrive at the average number of bytes per user for the specific protocol.)

Host Resource Worksheet #1

Host Type	Protocols	Applications Running	Max Users	Current Users	Resources Left
_____	_____ _____ _____	_____ _____	_____	_____	_____
Host Type	Protocols	Applications Running	Max Users	Current Users	Resources Left
_____	_____ _____ _____	_____ _____	_____	_____	_____
Host Type	Protocols	Applications Running	Max Users	Current Users	Resources Left
_____	_____ _____ _____	_____ _____	_____	_____	_____
Host Type	Protocols	Applications Running	Max Users	Current Users	Resources Left
_____	_____ _____ _____	_____ _____	_____	_____	_____
Host Type	Protocols	Applications Running	Max Users	Current Users	Resources Left
_____	_____ _____ _____	_____ _____	_____	_____	_____

Figure 4-1a. Host Resource Worksheet #1
(Courtesy Vitalink Communications Corporation)

Peripheral Resource Worksheet #2

Terminal Server	Protocol	Total Ports	Ports Used
_____	_____	_____	_____
_____	_____	_____	_____
_____	_____	_____	_____
_____	_____	_____	_____
_____	_____	_____	_____
_____	_____	_____	_____
_____	_____	_____	_____
_____	_____	_____	_____
_____	_____	_____	_____
_____	_____	_____	_____
_____	_____	_____	_____
_____	_____	_____	_____
_____	_____	_____	_____
_____	_____	_____	_____

Other Devices	Protocol
_____	_____
_____	_____
_____	_____
_____	_____
_____	_____

Figure 4-1b. Peripheral Resource Worksheet #2
(Courtesy Vitalink Communications Corp.)

Traffic Worksheet #3

Site Name _____

Protocol _____

A. Number of Users _____
B. # of Packets per Sample _____
C. % of Total Ethernet Traffic _____

MULTICAST TRAFFIC

D. # of Multicast Packets per Sample _____
C. % of Total Ethernet Traffic _____
F. % of Protocol Traffic _____
G. Average Packet Size _____

USER TRAFFIC

H. # of Data Packets per Sample _____
I. % of Total Ethernet Traffic _____
J. Average Large Ethernet Packet Size _____
K. % of Large Packet Traffic _____
L. Average Medium Packet Size _____
M. % of Medium Packet Traffic _____
N. Average Small Packet Traffic _____
O. % of Small Packet Traffic _____

AVERAGE TRAFFIC PER USER PER PROTOCOL

B/A = *Total Number of Packets / Number of Protocol Users*
G*F = *Average Multicast Packet Size * % of Protocol Traffic*
J*K = *Average Large Data Packet Size * % of Large Packet Traffic*
L*M = *Average Medium Data Packet Size * % of Medium Packet Traffic*
N*O = *Average Small Data Packet Size * % of Small Packet Traffic*

P   = *Average Number of Bytes per User for this Protocol*
P   = *[(B/A)((G*F) + (J*K) + (L*M) + (N*O))]*

Average Number of Bytes per User for this Protocol _____

Figure 4-1c. Traffic Worksheet #3
(Courtesy Vitalink Communications Corp.)

Remote Traffic Worksheet #4

Link Name _____

Site Name _____ to Site Name _____

In this section, the traffic per user for a specific protocol (taken from worksheet 3) is converted from the time unit of the sample to the time unit of one second (e.g. if the sample was 1 minute, then x would equal 60 for the conversion factor to seconds). This number is then multiplied by 8 to convert from bytes per second to bits per second. When multiplied by the number of remote users, this becomes the amount of bandwidth needed for this protocol in a remote environment.

Protocol	Traffic/User	Traffic/User/Sec	Bps/User	Remote	Bandwidth
_____	_____ /x	_____ *8	_____ *	_____ =	_____
_____	_____ /x	_____ *8	_____ *	_____ =	_____
_____	_____ /x	_____ *8	_____ *	_____ =	_____
_____	_____ /x	_____ *8	_____ *	_____ =	_____
_____	_____ /x	_____ *8	_____ *	_____ =	_____
_____	_____ /x	_____ *8	_____ *	_____ =	_____
_____	_____ /x	_____ *8	_____ *	_____ =	_____
_____	_____ /x	_____ *8	_____ *	_____ =	_____
_____	_____ /x	_____ *8	_____ *	_____ =	_____

Bandwidth Needed = _____

It is advisable for reasons of throughput and ease of management to multiply the bandwidth needed by 1.30 to ensure that the link will have a 30% buffer to maximize throughput with bandwidth utilization at 70%.

Suggested Bandwidth = 1.30 * Bandwidth Needed

Figure 4-1d. Remote Traffic Worksheet #4
(Courtesy Vitalink Communications Corp.)

Network Growth Worksheet #5

Link Name _____

Site Name _____ to Site Name _____

A = Peak Bandwidth Utilization of Link   _____

B = # of Current Users   _____

C = Peak Bandwidth per User   _____

C = A/B

D = Additional Future Users   _____

E = Future Bandwidth Requirements   _____

E = C*(B+D)

Future Bandwidth Requirements =   _____

Figure 4-1e. Network Growth Worksheet #5
(Courtesy Vitalink Communications Corp.)

The information from Worksheet number 3 is used on Worksheet number 4, the "Remote Traffic Worksheet," which is a guide to estimating the bandwidth needed for effective throughput between two specific sites. By entering the information about each protocol operating at each site that will traverse the link between the two sites, the required bandwidth can be adequately estimated. Parameters on Worksheets 3 and 4 may vary depending upon the network architecture and LAN analysis tool that is used to gather the statistics. Here are some general guidelines to assist in completing the worksheet:

- Protocol: the operating standard that is being analyzed.

- Number of Users (A): the number of users who were using the above protocol at the time the sample was taken.

- % of Total Ethernet Traffic (C): the percentage of that protocol traffic.

- # of Multi-cast Packets (D): number of Multi-cast packets for this protocol.

- % of Protocol Traffic (F): the percentage of total protocol traffic for each type of packet.

- # of Data Packets (H): number of packets containing user information.

- Average Packet Size (J): mean packet size for this packet type. Suggested ranges: Large—1000 to 1518 bytes; Medium—400 to 999 bytes; Small—64 to 99 bytes.

Worksheet number 5, the "Network Growth Worksheet," takes information compiled on the preceding worksheets and allows the internetwork designer to use it to make a projection of the future requirements. The analysis is based upon the current Peak Bandwidth Required per user, and the future need is projected with a straightforward calculation that yields the Future Bandwidth Requirements. The designer can use this result to determine the transmission speed of the link between the two distant locations. The growth calculation is important to avoid obsolescence in the transmission facility hardware. (For further details, see reference [4-10].)

Don't forget the 80/20 rule, however (given in reference [4-8]), which estimates that 80 percent of a network's traffic remains local to that segment, while 20 percent of the traffic is directed to other segments. Use the results of the internetwork traffic study to make a preliminary assessment of the transmission facility type and speed requirements. Also consider segments that will require redundant transmission paths for greater reliability.

Solicit Vendor Input. Solicit input from both WAN facility providers (e.g. AT&T and CompuServe) and internetworking equipment vendors. These services are usually available free-of-charge, and may identify alternatives that have not been considered.

Develop a Plan. Develop an internetwork implementation plan. This would include establishing specific milestones for network design, equipment procurement, installation, cutover, and documentation elements. We will discuss implementation issues in greater detail in Chapter 10.

Finally, remember that the internetwork design will, by its nature, be a multi-vendor network. We are all familiar with the finger-pointing that can occur between different vendors in these situations. Your best defense here is a strong offense: a thorough design, a well-thought out implementation plan, and reputable vendors. With these goals in mind, let's look at some representative products that can solve the LAN/WAN connectivity challenge.

4.2   Asynchronous Communication Servers

Asynchronous Communication Servers (ACSs) go by a variety of other names, including "communications servers" and "asynchronous gateways." The ACSs are used to access the LAN via the dial-up telephone network, or to share a modem on the LAN for outgoing data calls among various workstations. An ACS can be either dedicated (with multiple ports) or non-dedicated (typically with one modem in a workstation). The practicality of the ACS lies in its ability to reduce the recurring monthly phone line charges. With network hardware costs dropping dramatically, a strong business case cannot be made for simply reducing the number of modems on the LAN. Eliminating extra phone lines to the network is another matter, however.

Since we are all intimately familiar with using communication software to access a bulletin board system or remote asynchronous host, the operation of an ACS would appear to be equally straightforward. References [4-11] and [4-12] shed some light on why this function is more difficult than it may initially appear. A serial port is driven by an LSI device known as a UART (Universal Asynchronous Receiver/Transmitter), such as the Western Digital 8250. The PC controls this 8250 with ROM BIOS routines that are addressed through Interrupt 14 (INT 14 H). For speed, however, most communication programs are written to address the 8250 directly, thus bypassing INT 14 H. With a networked communication requirement, the data that was intended to go to/from the serial port must be placed on the LAN instead. According to reference [4-12], several such Application Program Interfaces (APIs) can be used for this purpose.

The first API is the NCSI/NASI (Network Communications Services Interface/ Network Asynchronous Services Interface) developed by Network Products Corporation. Novell uses this interface in their NASC (NetWare Asynchronous Communication Server) product. This interface utilizes DOS interrupt vector 6BH to send and receive its information to and from the communication application in each workstation. A number of communication software packages—such as Crosstalk Mk.4 (Digital Communication Associates of Roswell, Georgia), Procomm Plus Network (Datastorm Technologies, Inc. of Columbia, MO) and Reflection (Walker, Richer, and Quinn, Inc. of Seattle, Washington)—support NCSI (reference [4-12]). The second type of API are interfaces that send and receive their information via INT 14H calls that conform to IBM's standard INT 14H (a specification has been published in every IBM PC communications book since the early 80s), as well as IBM's Extended 14H BIOS (EBIOS). These interfaces redirect the calls away from the PC's BIOS to themselves. In addition to being slow, another reason many developers don't call the PC's INT 14H to send/receive characters is that the standard specification does not give them a way to control the line signals. The application must be able to raise and lower Data Terminal Ready (DTR) as well as Request To Send (RTS), or to send a break function to the Host. IBM's EBIOS provides a mechanism to do these much-needed functions. The third type of API is the NetBIOS API (INT 5CH) used by IBM as well as others.

The fourth API alternative is a hardware redirector card installed in each workstation needing to run non-network modified software (i.e. the application reads and writes information directly to a COM hardware address). This card intercepts the write, sends the information down the network to the communication server, and then makes the received data available to the application to read as if it just came in from the local COM port (which, of course, does not have to be present in this workstation).

With this overview of the ACS architectural challenge, let's begin to look at some solutions. A number of these ACS devices are available from third-party vendors and Network Operating System (NOS) designers. In this section we'll look at one software-only product (LAN+MODEM) and one integrated hardware/software solution (the Chatterbox). In Chapter 8, we will study the communications capabilities of the major LAN NOSs, such as Novell, 3Com, and Banyan. (Because of the popularity of ACSs, they receive lots of attention in the press. References [4-13] and [4-14] are examples of recent product reviews.)

4.2.1 Cross Information LAN+MODEM

Cross Information Company of Boulder, Colorado—widely known for its office-automation software CROSS+POINT—enhanced its product line with its LAN+MODEM outbound modem sharing software. The package works with internal and external modems, transmitting at 300-19,200 bps. It can also be used to share other serial devices on a LAN, such as printers or plotters. Two versions of the software are available: a Novell NetWare version supporting the IPX/SPX protocol, and a second version that supports the NetBIOS interface for non-Novell networks. The 20-modem version of LAN+MODEM supports up to 16 modems on a single PC. This option is unique since it does not require a dedicated PC and is achieved by using multi-port serial cards manufactured by Digiboard (Digi International, Inc. of Minneapolis, Minnesota) or Stargate Technologies of Solon, Ohio. Almost all LAN operating systems will work with the product, including 3Com 3+Open, DCA 10-Net, AT&T StarLAN, CBIS Network-OS, and Artisoft LANtastic.

One major strength of the software is its background operation with a workstation RAM requirement of under 10 Kbytes. A workstation can be operated by one user while another user accesses the attached modem. No dedicated communication server is required, and all existing modems remain in place. LAN+MODEM can support up to 20 modems per file server and two modems per PC. With the multi-com (twenty-modem) version, LAN+MODEM supports up to 16 modems on a single PC.

A number of application and utility files are used within LAN+MODEM. MCOM.EXE is the TSR modem driver, and is loaded on to any PC that will be sharing a modem. UCOM.EXE is the user interface that features several file transfer protocols, as well as ANSI, VT52, and VT100 terminal emulation.

NETDEV.COM is an INT 14 driver that allows other third party communication programs to work with LAN+MODEM. These communication programs include Procomm Plus Network Version, Crosstalk Mk.4, Reflection, Lexis/Nexis, Westmate, and others. Utilities are included for NetBIOS and Novell IPX/SPX support.

Cross Information has also released two enhancements to LAN+MODEM: IN+TOUCH, an incoming remote control communication package, and CROSS+CONNECT, an integration of products that offers a total communications solution.

A quick peek into how LAN+MODEM works may prove educational. When MCOM is loaded into the PC containing a modem, it looks for the UART that indicates the presence of a serial device. MCOM then attaches to this UART, and creates a network name for itself, e.g. COMM01. When a user executes UCOM, that program searches the network name tables for an MCOM-designated modem driver (e.g. COMM01 and COMM02). Once the UCOM driver connects with the MCOM-designated name, communications between the workstation and modem begin.

LAN+MODEM is an extremely easy-to-use solution for both outbound modem sharing and inbound communications, and may well be one of the most economical LAN communications products available.

4.2.2   J & L Information Systems Network Communications Server

In contrast to the simplicity of a software-only solution, J&L Information Systems of Chatsworth, California markets a variety of hardware and software products for a dedicated ACS. The Network Communication Server is available in three different forms. The first, software-only product uses the standard COM ports in a PC/AT or PS/2, generally one to four medium speed ports each. The second version packages the software with an intelligent card from Digiboard that has four, eight, or sixteen asynchronous ports. This solution may be installed in a standard PC/ AT workstation on the LAN, and will then function as the Asynchronous Gateway. A third option, known as the Network Communication Gateway, is a complete unit in that only a Network Interface Card (NIC) is required to install it on the Network.

The gateway software uses one of two techniques to communicate with the network operating system as it sends and receives information between each workstation and the Network Communication Server. The first technique is called Internet Packet Exchange (IPX), which is the protocol specific to Novell LANs, and the second is NetBIOS, which is used to talk to most other LANs (e.g. Banyan, 3Com, Microsoft, IBM, and Network O/S).

J&L's product line is complemented by their flagship product known as the Chatterbox. This unit is a tower or 19" rack mount chassis with multiple slot groups which are functionally equivalent to multiple network workstations in a single box and include features that J&L has found are required for the routine and dependable operation of dial-in and dial-out services. Each user cluster (or group of slots equivalent to a workstation) is a 100% IBM PC-compatible workstation, and most clusters have additional slots for ISA bus cards to be installed. (One of the additional cards is always an industry-standard NIC that ensures compatible operation with the other workstations on the LAN.) These clusters perform a combination of services like a 3270 or X.25 gateway, or J&L's Network Communication Server. Most often they are run as a dial-in processor with the assurance that any program that runs on other workstations on the LAN will run on the Chatterbox user clusters. The Chatterbox is currently shipping with a mini-site license of CO/SESSION remote communication software included.

The J&L Chatterbox is a communications platform for dial-in as well as dial-out service. Outgoing calls are handled by the dedicated ACS running the Network Communication Server software (see Figure 4-2). Three different options are available to allow each workstation's software to communicate with the Network Communication Server. One is the INT 6BH, another is the INT 14H, and a third way is the hardware redirector card known as the Network Communication Adapter (NCA). When a workstation wishes to access the ACS (generally from a batch file called from a menu system), it exercises the resident program requesting a type of service, and upon successful connection, proceeds to use the communication software as a stand-alone application. When the application is finished, or if the user re-boots the workstation, the port is returned to an inactive state, awaiting another outgoing call request. Until recently, each user would require their own asynchronous connection (i.e. cable, or modem and phone line). J&L's Network Communication Server for X.25 allows up to four users to utilize the same connection into a public network, thus allowing up to 64 network users to simultaneously share 16 connections. Incorporation of a protocol known as Autostream permits this "multiplexing" of asynchronous cables. This protocol was developed by Hayes Microcomputers and is part of their Ultra 9600 modem. The modem includes a four-port X.25 PAD, and the Autostream protocol allows J&L's gateway software to keep track of which information is destined for the four different users. Each user can communicate with a different Host on the public data network.

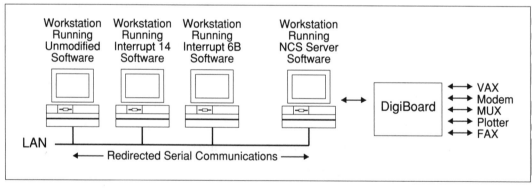

Figure 4-2. J & L Information Systems NCS Outgoing Operation
(Courtesy J & L Information Systems)

Incoming calls are handled exclusively with the Chatterbox hardware by connecting each incoming line to the COM port of the individual processors. A remote-control software package such as Dynamic Microprocessor Associates' pcAnywhere, Triton Technologies' Co/Session, or Norton-Lambert's Close-Up runs on the Chatterbox processor, waiting for an incoming call. When the remote user dials in, the program takes control of the Chatterbox processor attached to that incoming line. Since the processor is also connected to the LAN via the NIC, the remote user has assumed control of a network-attached workstation. File access, printing, etc. can then proceed as if the remote user's PC was physically attached to the LAN. There are two main advantages to this approach. First, all of the screen and keyboard traffic generated by the remote program (updating the remote user's screen) does travel over the LAN cable, thus needlessly adding to the network traffic. Second, and more important, if the remote user commands a combination of programs to execute on the LAN workstation's processor, it is likely that the processor may lockup due to collisions of Terminate and Stay Resident (TRS) programs. Additional circuitry on each Chatterbox processor will detect the remote user's hang-up and issue a hardware reset to the processor. This ensures dependable operation without administrative intervention.

In summary, J&L has an impressive array of products for both outgoing and incoming LAN access. Their greatest strength lies in their ability to handle both the "ins" and the "outs" from the same Chatterbox platform.

4.3   Analog Leased Line Connections

As we studied in Section 3.2, analog leased line facilities provide an optimized transmission path (via conditioning), thus permitting higher transmission rates and lower errors. For LAN-to-LAN traffic that requires higher throughput and longer connect times, leased lines may be preferred over dial-up PSTN connections. We'll look at two products, the Microcom LAN Bridge and the Hayes InterBridge, as examples of products using leased lines to connect LANs.

4.3.1 Microcom LAN Bridge

Microcom Inc. of Norwood, Massachusetts has long been known for its expertise in dial-up and leased-line modems, and is also known as the inventor of the Microcom Networking Protocol (MNP) used for data compression and error correction (reference [4-15]). The Microcom LAN Bridge (MLB) is a MAC-layer bridge for connecting geographically separate Ethernet or Token Ring LANs. What makes the MLB unique are its numerous options for the WAN facility interface. Four different models are available. The MLB/5000 series connects to dial-up lines at 9.6 Kbps. The MLB/5500 series is used for ISDN Basic Rate Interface (BRI) access at 64 Kbps. The MLB/6000 connects to analog or digital private lines at speeds from 9.6 Kbps to 2.048 Mbps. Finally, the MLB/6500 series connects to PDNs via the X.25 protocol with links of up to 500 Kbps in speed.

The architecture that provides this flexibility is shown in Figure 4-3a. The hardware consists of full-size add-in cards which require an 80286 or 80386 CPU. The bridge software supplies the core bridging functions as well as network management capabilities using SNMP (Simple Network Management Protocol). The LAN processing module supports Ethernet (versions 1 and 2) as well as IEEE 802.3 and Token Ring (IEEE 802.5) networks. The Module consists of a two-board set (but is not limited to two slots) that provides address filtering and forwards the selected frames to the WAN Interface Module. Every conceivable WAN facility for either dial-up (see Figure 4-3b) or leased lines (see Figure 4-3c) is available. The dial-up WAN interface transmits at 9.6 Kbps using a V.32 modem, and incorporates MNP data compression. The synchronous interface for analog or digital leased lines uses the HDLC protocol for enhanced reliability. The X.25 WAN interface transmits over links at up to 500 Kbps with the recent addition of 2:1 compression, and supports a maximum of 15 virtual circuits. The ISDN WAN module provides a single BRI, for both circuit switched and X.25 connections at 64 Kbps. The modular design allows an easy upgrade path as the network transmission requirements increase. Additional links can be added by incorporating additional WAN interface modules into the PC/AT platform.

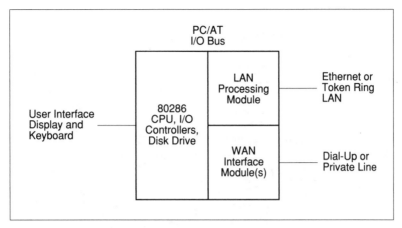

Figure 4-3a. Microcom LAN Bridge Functional Block Diagram
(Courtesy Microcom, Inc.)

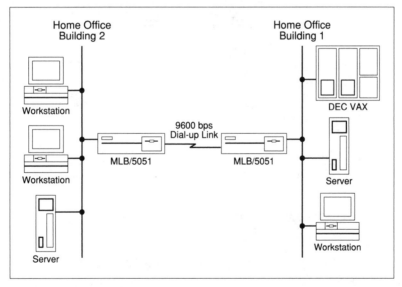

Figure 4-3b. Microcom LAN Bridge Dial-up Bridging Application
(Courtesy Microcom, Inc.)

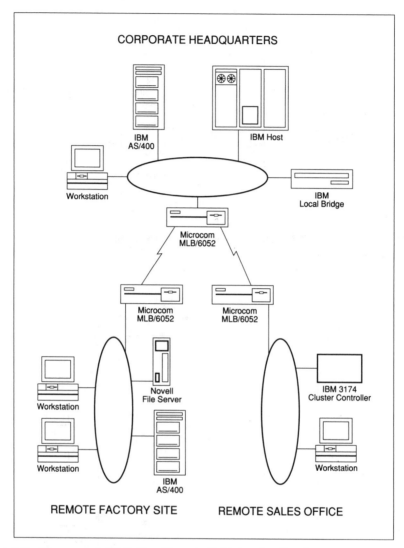

Figure 4-3c. Microcom LAN Bridge Remote Bridging Application
(Courtesy Microcom, Inc.)

A third component of the MLB architecture is the Microcom Management Station (MMS) software. The MMS allows a network manager to maintain statistics and alarm information on all MLBs within the network. The MMS implements SNMP for control of the various bridge parameters.

In summary, the MLB series is an extremely flexible remote bridge platform. Its uniqueness is in the number of WAN interfaces, ranging from dial-up to ISDN connections, that are available.

4.3.2   Hayes InterBridge

Hayes Microcomputer Products, Inc. of Norcross, Georgia is probably best known for its intelligent modems and the Hayes Standard AT Command Set, which has become a de facto standard within the data communications industry. The InterBridge is a complement to that technology, and is used specifically to connect both local and remote LocalTalk networks using Apple Computer Inc.'s AppleTalk Phase 1 and Phase 2 protocols. The InterBridge can connect several LocalTalk networks in either a local or remote configuration, thus enabling a workstation on one network to access files and peripherals on another network. (As an aside, while Hayes calls the product a bridge, Apple refers to it as an internet router.)

The InterBridge hardware can connect up to two local and two remote AppleTalk networks. The device has a total of four ports: two for LocalTalk (DB-9 connectors) and two for serial communication (RS-232 with DB-25 connectors). The LocalTalk connectors allow the InterBridge to connect two local AppleTalk networks in order to optimize the network traffic, or to permit the network to extend beyond the 1000 foot and 32 node limitation. The number of cascaded AppleTalk networks is limited by a hop counter field within AppleTalk's Datagram Delivery Protocol (DDP) header, and has a maximum value of fifteen. For local connections, the InterBridge examines the AppleTalk network address which is also contained within the DDP header. If that packet has a destination outside of the local network, the Interbridge forwards that packet. Otherwise, the packet is ignored by the InterBridge and remains on that network.

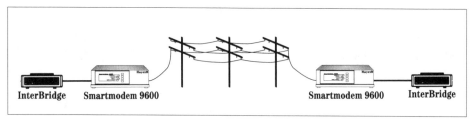

Figure 4-4. Hayes InterBridge Remote Bridging Application
(Courtesy Hayes Microcomputer Products, Inc.)

The remote InterBridge configuration provides AppleTalk WAN support (see Figure 4-4). For remote applications, the serial ports on the InterBridge are connected to any serial transmission device, such as asynchronous or synchronous modems, X.25 PADs or PBX ports. Transmission speeds of up to 4.8 Kbps synchronous or 19.2 Kbps asynchronous are supported, and either dial-up or leased telephone lines can be used depending upon the modems chosen. The protocol used between the two InterBridges is the LocalTalk Link Access Protocol (LLAP). Similar to the Local bridging configuration, the remote application is constrained by the hop count within the DDP header. In addition, the transmission speed of the WAN facility has an impact here, as slower speeds (1.2–4.8 Kbps) add delay to the data transmission. The length (speed) plus number of hops must not exceed fifteen; Hayes provides tables to facilitate these calculations.

The InterBridge Manager software is provided with the hardware, and is used for internetwork configuration, communications and diagnostics. The software is icon-driven, and is first used to configure the four ports for function and address (network number and zone). Remote bridge ports also require communication parameters, such as transmission mode and type to be defined for both ends of the communication path. The software also includes a diagnostic package that maintains the status of the hardware ports, as well as information on network traffic, such as bad packets and communication line congestion. A Routing Table is available, and provides a complete map of the internet. The remote bridge link can be initiated through the Macintosh Chooser, or from the Hayes InterBridge Manager.

In summary, the InterBridge is a straightforward device for connecting local and remote AppleTalk networks. It combines both the simplicity of the LocalTalk architecture with the experience of Hayes' data communication products.

4.4   Digital Leased Line Connections

Digital (or DDS) lines further improve on their analog counterparts in two ways, as we studied in Section 3.3. First, the digital nature of the transmission is less susceptible to noise and is therefore more error-free. Secondly, digital lines are available at speeds of up to 56 Kbps, more than doubling the practical upper limit (19.2 Kbps) of the analog lines. Let's look at two product examples here, Micom's Marathon 5K and Vitalink's Dial 56.

4.4.1   Micom Marathon 5K

Micom Communications Corporation of Simi Valley, California has recently added the Marathon series of Data/Voice Network Servers to their product line. The Marathon 5K Server (see Figure 4-5) integrates a number of dissimilar inputs for transmission on a single 9.6 - 19.2 Kbps analog or 56 Kbps digital leased line. Data inputs can be any combination of asynchronous or synchronous terminal-to-host traffic, digital voice between PBX and Key systems, facsimile transmissions, or LAN traffic between two remote bridges.

Signal bandwidth is reduced by combining four different technologies: data compression, speech compression, facsimile demodulation, and Fast Packet Multiplexing (FPM). Micom describes FPM as a generic term for remote networking that meets three criteria: transport of a combination of signals (e.g. voice, data, fax); high network efficiency (quoted at 90% or greater); and fast, predictable delivery of that data. Micom further contrasts FPM as an emerging technology that improves on existing Frequency Division Multiplexing (FDM), Time Division Multiplexing (TDM), Packet Multiplexing, such as X.25, or statistical multiplexing technologies. FPM operates on a dynamic basis, dividing the incoming datastreams into small cells ranging from 9 to 125 bits in length (with lower link speeds requiring smaller cells). The FDM process can interrupt one transmission on a cell boundary, inserting another, as required by the nature of the data (e.g. voice and video) itself. For this reason, FPM is often referred to as cell-relay technology (reference [4-16]).

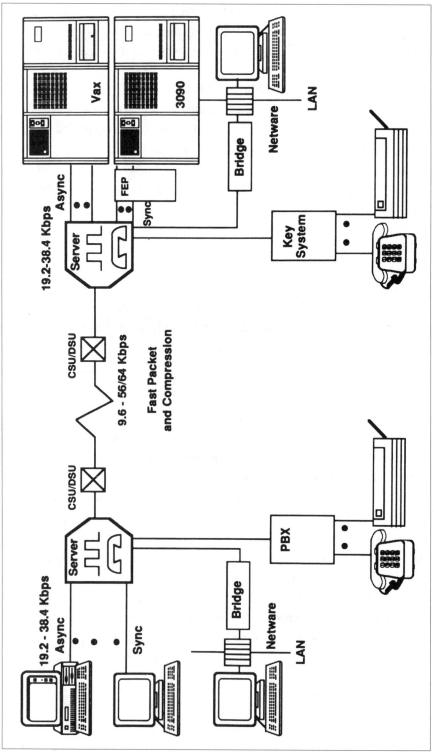

Figure 4-5. Micom Marathon 5K Communication Server
(Courtesy Micom Communications Corporation)

The Marathon 5K product is a 6 to 40-port device, supporting 3 to 37 data devices (e.g. bridge, asynchronous data, voice) and three network facility ports. One of these ports can operate at 56/64 Kbps (DDS) and the other two operate at 19.2 Kbps. Planned future additions include network management, FT1 interfaces, and integral bridging and routing modules.

The Marathon 5K is a unique product, integrating a number of low-speed signal inputs for transmission onto one low-speed analog or digital leased line. For LAN applications requiring low throughputs, this is a solution worth considering.

4.4.2   Vitalink TransLAN and TransRING

Vitalink Communications Corporation of Fremont, California builds a number of products for remote bridging of IEEE 802.3 and 802.5 LANs. A number of models are available. The TransLAN family is used for Ethernet/IEEE 802.3 bridging. The TransRING family bridges Token Ring networks. The TransPATH family is a combined TCP/IP XNS and IPX router plus a bridge, and can operate on either Ethernet/IEEE 802.3 or Token Ring networks. Data links between the various devices can operate from 9.6 Kbps up to 1.544 Mbps. Multiple output links are also possible (see Figure 4-6a).

One very unique feature of the Vitalink products is their dial-up support for the Switched 56 Service, available from AT&T and other vendors. This feature has two clear applications. First, extra bandwidth can be provided for peak traffic periods. Secondly, a backup path is available in the event that the primary path fails.

The Switched 56 service is a 56 Kbps DDS line that is provided on an as-needed, rather than a leased line, basis. As such, users pay for the (length of) time of use, rather than a flat rate per month regardless of use.

Both the TransLAN (Ethernet) and TransRING (Token Ring) products support Switched 56 service. One of the bridge ports is configured for a V.35 interface, and connected to a DSU/CSU (see Figure 4-6b). The DSU/CSU will automatically dial the Switched 56 service when one of three conditions occurs: the failure of a leased line; the detection of a congestion threshold on a leased line; or a specific time and/ or day requiring additional bandwidth. The link failure case is illustrated in Figure 4-6c. The Switched 56 facility is automatically accessed if either link A or link B fails.

While many products support DDS and T-1 digital leased lines, Vitalink's products are distinguished by their support of the Switched 56 service for redundancy.

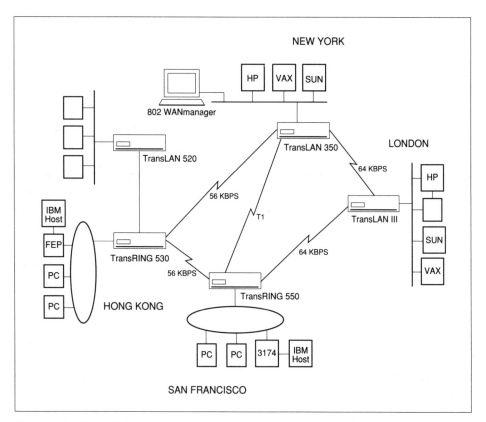

Figure 4-6a. Vitalink TransLAN/TransRING Connectivity
(Courtesy Vitalink Communications Corp.)

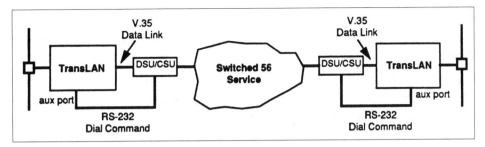

Figure 4-6b. Vitalink TransLAN Switched 56 Service Access
(Courtesy Vitalink Communications Corp.)

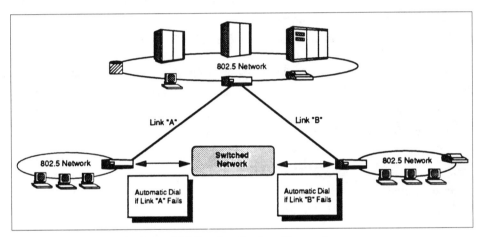

Figure 4-6c. Vitalink Switched 56 Service Backup Support
(Courtesy Vitalink Communications Corp.)

4.5 Access to Public Data Networks (PDNs)

Public Data Networks (PDNs) provide packet-switched data communication facilities between dissimilar locations. PDNs are most useful when a number of locations require interconnection. These locations may have a range of host processors, from PCs to LANs to mainframes. We'll look at the PC and LAN examples here, and examine the mini/mainframe case in Chapter 5.

4.5.1 TIL Systems "Office On the Go"

TIL Systems, Ltd. of Toronto, Ontario (a Canadian firm with U.S. headquarters in Lowell, Massachusetts) is best known for its XPERT PC card, an add-in that turns a PC into an X.25 PAD. A new enhancement to the XPERT product line is the XPERT/Office on the Go, which allows a laptop or PC to connect to a PDN via the dial-up telephone network (see Figure 4-7). The system consists of a PC half card plus a software driver. The communications adapter contains an integrated V.22 bit modem operating at 2.4 Kbps, which is Hayes AT command set-compatible. The software is called XPERT/Emulate and it provides terminal emulations for micro to mainframe communications. Support of the X.32 protocol is also included, and is the standard for dial-up (PSTN) access to a PDN. The system is compatible with most PC/XT/AT bus computers, and requires DOS 3.3 or higher.

The Terminal Emulation software supports a number of options. IBM 3270 SNA uses the QLLC (Qualified Logical Link Control) procedures for communications with IBM 37XX front-end processors. This emulation includes support for the 3270 file transfer program IND$FILE. The 3270 DSI/DSP emulation provides IBM 3278/ 3279 terminal support. IBM 3780 file transfer program is used for communication with a 3780 RJE device. DEC VT100 and VT220 support is also included for communication with most minicomputers. All terminal emulations function as Terminate and Stay Resident (TSR) programs, allowing background operation.

The Office on the Go adheres to CCITT's 1988 X.25, X.3, X.28, and X.29 standards (more on these in Chapter 5). At the packet level, modulo 8 packet sequencing, a packet size of 128 or 256 octets, and eight switched virtual circuits (SVCs) are supported, allowing simultaneous connections to multiple hosts. A number of optional X.25 facilities are supported as well. Examples include reverse charging, packet size negotiation, multiple closed-user groups, and throughput class negotiation.

Extensive capabilities are built into the communications adapter. These include XID exchange, DES encryption and built-in diagnostics. Both synchronous and asynchronous transmission are supported.

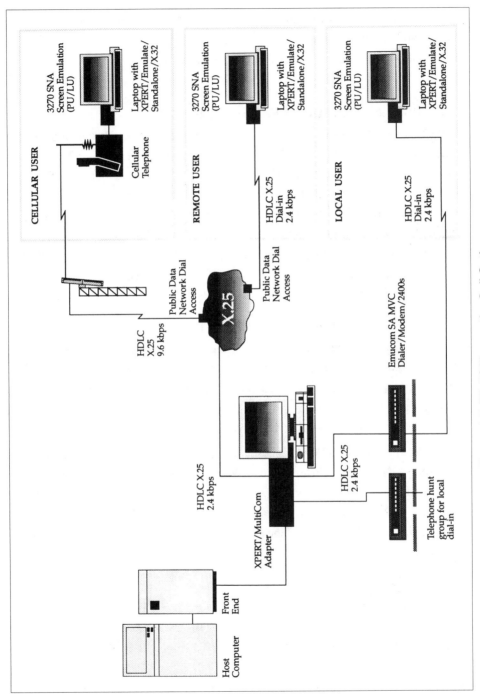

Figure 4-7. TIL "Office on the Go" Options
(Courtesy TIL Systems, Ltd.)

177

The Office on the Go is a unique solution for laptop or PC users requiring remote access to an X.25 host. The ability to combine the reliability of the X.25 protocol with a LAN gateway makes for a powerful remote access device.

4.5.2 RAD Network Devices REB/XEB and RTB/XTB

RAD Network Devices, Inc. of Huntington Beach, California provides a number of LAN/WAN connectivity products that support both Ethernet and Token Ring networks. The Remote Ethernet Bridge (REB) is a protocol-independent bridge/router (brouter) that makes its routing decision based upon several user-defined criteria. These include protocol type, Network Layer Address, message type or arbitrary bit and byte assignments. Three models are available, supporting one, two, or four remote links. Link options include analog leased lines, DDS or T-1/CEPT circuits, or fiber optic modems. The REB is a PC-AT based device, requiring three full-sized add-in cards plus software.

The X.25 Ethernet Bridge/Router (XEB) is the member of the RAD family that is designed for PDN applications (see Figure 4-8). Each XEB supports up to 32 virtual circuits, with up to 250 of the devices allowed on a single network. Like its REB counterpart, the XEB is protocol independent, allowing transparent operation with any higher-layer protocol such as TCP/IP, DECnet or XNS. The XEB supports Novell's NetWare, 3Com's 3+, Banyan's VINES, and other network operating systems.

The XEB hardware is PC-AT based, and supports up to four serial links and one X.25 link per device. The different links (WAN and X.25) are integrated within the XEB, permitting both X.25 and serial link connections within the same hardware platform. The X.25 connection operates between 4.8 and 128 Kbps, and the other links operate up to 2.048 Mbps. The aggregate data rate of the device must be less than 3.0 Mbps.

Two other members of the RAD family support Token Ring networks. The RTB (Remote Token Ring Bridge/Router) is similar to the REB. It uses a proprietary "STRING" routing algorithm that combines both Source and Transparent routing techniques. RAD plans to be fully compliant with the IEEE 802.1 SRT (Source

Routing Transparent) algorithm discussed in section 1.7.3, when that standard is finalized. The XTB (X.25 Token Ring Bridge) is similar to the XEB, providing a combination of X.25 and serial links in a LAN/WAN bridge/router.

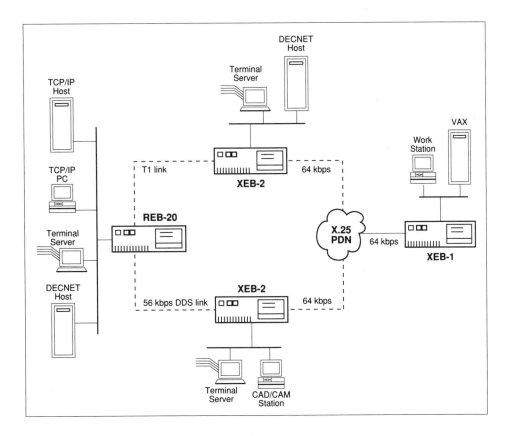

Figure 4-8. RAD Ethernet to WAN Connections
(Courtesy RAD Network Devices)

    In review, the RAD remote bridge/routers provide a very flexible mechanism to integrate Ethernet and Token Ring networks into a PDN environment.

4.6   Integrating LANs into T-1 Networks

As LANs increase in their backbone transmission rate from 1 to 10 Mbps (StarLAN and Ethernet, respectively) or 4 to 16 Mbps (the two Token Ring transmission rates), the amount of aggregate network traffic increases as well. When the LAN traffic increases, an increase in any LAN-to-LAN traffic follows. Therefore, a need for higher bandwidth LAN to WAN channels will also exist. When these high-capacity channels are called for, there are two choices available: FT-1 and T-1 (reference [4-17]), and T-3 (reference [4-18]). We'll study three examples: Newport Systems' LAN²LAN/FT1, CrossComm's ILAN, and Wellfleet's Link Node.

4.6.1   Newport Systems Solutions LAN²LAN/FT1

Newport Systems Solutions of Newport Beach, California manufactures a number of multi-port routers for Novell NetWare networks, designated the LAN²LAN family. Because of their close tie to the NetWare operating system, the Newport products can also support any LAN hardware that is NetWare supported. These include Ethernet, StarLAN, Token Ring and ARCNET. There are four members of the product family, all using the same hardware and software. Functionality and performance are controlled by a field-upgradable plug-in chip. The LAN²PC product connects remote PCs to analog or digital leased lines. LAN²LAN/64 is a 2-4 port NetWare router available in either dedicated or non-dedicated versions. It operates at speeds of between 9.6 and 56 Kbps per port. The LAN²LAN/FT1 is a 4-port product, operating at line speeds between 9.6 and 768 Kbps per port. The high-performance product is the LAN²LAN/Mega that supports T-1 links at 1.544 Mbps or CEPT links at 2.048 Mbps. Let's look in detail at the LAN²LAN/FT1 offering.

The LAN²LAN/FT1 is a single NetWare router node that consists of an internal hardware interface plus software. The hardware is designated the Wide Area Network Interface Co-Processor (WNIC) and is a high-performance communications controller for PC/AT, PS/2, and compatible computers. Either two or four-port versions of the WNIC are available. Port interfaces support RS-232, RS-422, V.35 and X.21 standards. An optional daughter board for data compression is also available and can increase data throughput up to fourfold. The software is available for both NetWare 286 and NetWare 386, and is fully compatible with Novell's IPX/SPX protocols.

An example of the LAN²LAN/FT1 is shown in Figure 4-9, illustrating the flexibility associated with the Fractional T-1 links. When 56 Kbps is inadequate, but a full T-1 link is overkill, Newport's product fits the bill. At the center of the figure, the NetWare 386 internal router is connected to four other networks in addition to the Ethernet on which it resides. Note the multiple links between the lower two routers for redundancy and load balancing. Should the 768 Kbps rate (half a T-1) prove inadequate, a field upgrade to the LAN²LAN/Mega is available.

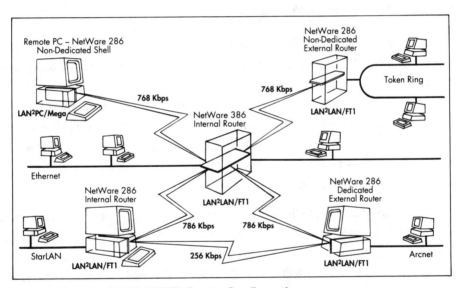

Figure 4-9. Newport LAN²LAN/FT1 Router Configurations
(Courtesy Newport Systems Solutions)

If what you need to connect is remote, dissimilar NetWare LANs, Newport Systems has solutions that use the "pay as you go" philosophy.

4.6.2   CrossComm ILAN

CrossComm Corporation's ILAN is a product family specializing in LAN to LAN connectivity devices for Ethernet, StarLAN or Token Ring networks. A number of WAN transmission facilities are also permissible. The heart of CrossComm's architecture is the ILAN Internetwork Server. It is a modular device consisting of a base unit and a number of plug-in LAN and WAN interface modules. A maximum of four of these LAN/WAN modules can be added in any combination. The four slots are designated by a four-letter code. Letters are inserted into the code as various interfaces are added.

The LAN choices are Ethernet (E), Token Ring (R), StarLAN (S), twisted pair (P) or fiber optics (F). The WAN interfaces are T1, FT-1, CEPT, V.35, X.21 or RS-422 (T), or 56/64 Kbps, V.35, or RS- 232 (L).

A number of different ILAN configurations can be used in a mixed LAN environment (see Figure 4-10). In the upper left-hand corner, the ILAN designated RRRO is bridging three Token Rings. The upper right-hand corner connects a Token Ring, Ethernet and StarLAN to a T-1 link (RTES). At the center, another ILAN (RTTT) connects a single Token Ring to the T-1 links. Source routing, transparent routing, and source routing transparent (SRT) are supported within the ILAN server. Note that the ILAN product is, in fact, a brouter, operating independently of the higher-layer protocols in use.

Unique to CrossComm is the ILAN-H that bridges either local or remote Ethernet and Token Ring networks. Allowable connections include Token Ring to Ethernet, IEEE 802.3, StarLAN (1BASE5), Ethernet or twisted pair (10BASE-T), Ethernet or broadband (10BROAD36) Ethernet or Ethernet over fiber optic cable. Of greatest interest is the remote Ethernet to Token Ring bridging via T-1 links which, as of this writing, is only available in the ILAN-H.

In summary, CrossComm provides a modular approach to LAN/WAN bridging, thus providing the ultimate in internetworking flexibility.

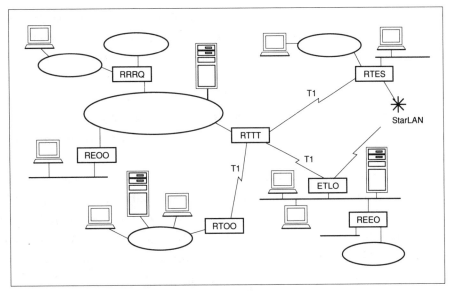

Figure 4-10. CrossComm ILAN Mixed LAN Environment
(Courtesy CrossComm Corporation)

4.6.3   Wellfleet Link Node

Wellfleet Communications, Inc. of Bedford, Massachusetts has designed three high-performance internetworking products that allow a great deal of flexibility in their LAN and WAN connections. The Feeder Node (FN) permits up to two LAN and two WAN interfaces. The Link Node (LN) provides up to eight LAN or eight WAN links. The larger Concentrator Node (CN) handles up to 26 LAN or 26 WAN connections. All are based upon a VME bus architecture, and contain multiple 68020 processors. The multiprocessor design permits several flexible options. First, concurrent multi-protocol routing and bridging is possible using dissimilar protocols such as TCP/IP and DECnet. Secondly, both LAN (802.3) and WAN (T-1) interfaces are available. Third, and probably most interesting, the integration of digital voice (e.g. digital PBX traffic) and LAN data is possible. Let's look at this architecture in more detail.

The FN, LN, and CN models are similar in that they all contain the VME bus controller and I/O modules. They differ in the number of link interface slots allowed: the FN has one and the LAN can accommodate four, while the CN can handle up to 13. The different link interfaces are a major strength of WellFleet's architecture. Several different interfaces are available. The Dual Port Ethernet/IEEE 802.3 interface connects to two LANs. The Dual Port T-1 Framer/Multiplexer is both D4 and ESF framing compatible, and can provide connections to two different DS-1 signals. If used for a WAN application, the interface can connect to two DS-1 signals. If used in an integrated voice/data environment, one channel connects to a DS-1 WAN facility, while the other connects to a local DS-1 facility such as a digital PBX. The third type, Quad Port Synchronous V.35/RS449/442, provides four full-duplex synchronous ports that can accommodate data transmitted at 1.2 Kbps to 2.048 Mbps. The Dual Ethernet/ Dual Port Synchronous interface combines the LAN and serial data input capabilities. Several Token Ring module types are provided, and a separate FDDI interface is also offered.

An example of Wellfleet's LAN/WAN connectivity is shown in Figure 4-11. LAN traffic from a Link Node (upper right corner in the figure) is transmitted over a 56 Kbps link to a DDS Mux. Voice or data signals from a PBX can be multiplexed at the LN for transmission via another DS-1 link. An IXC facility can also perform the routing of individual DS-0 channels. An example of this is AT&T's Digital Access and Cross Connect System (DACS) with the Customer Controllable Reconfiguration (CCR) Option.

Wellfleet demonstrates a great deal of flexibility in its FN, CN and LN product lines, and is worthy of consideration for internetworks with a mixture of voice, data and LAN traffic that require DS-1 transmission rates.

As the products in this chapter have demonstrated, there are many ways to connect a LAN into a WAN facility. The key to success, however, is an overall plan that incorporates both voice and data communication requirements. We will study the implementation issues in greater detail in Chapter 10. In the next three chapters, we will continue our journey up the OSI Reference Model stack by looking at three specific protocol suites: X.25, TCP/IP, and XNS.

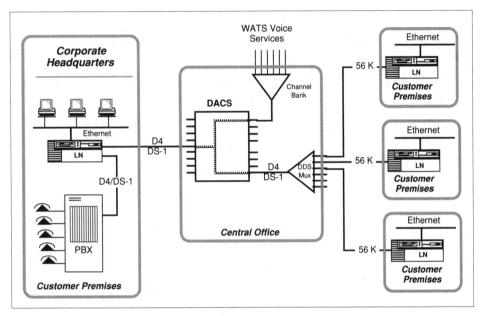

Figure 4-11. Wellfleet Integrated Voice/Data Services
(Courtesy Wellfleet Communications, Inc.)

4.7 References

[4-1] Nolle, Thomas. "Making the LAN-to-WAN Connection." *LAN Technology* (September 1989): 24–33.

[4-2] Weiss, Jeffrey. "High-Speed LAN Internetworking." *Networking Management* (December 1989): 66–72.

[4-3] Miller, Darrell. "Hooking Your LAN to a WAN." *TPT/Networking Management* (January 1989): 40–43.

[4-4] Lenko, John A. "LAN-WAN Issues." *Telecommunications* (December 1989): 67–69.

[4-5] Ellis, Robert L. *Designing Data Networks*. Prentice-Hall, Inc., 1986.

[4-6] Day, Michael. "Segmenting the WAN." *LAN Times* (October 1989): 118–120.

[4-7] Kornblum, Deborah F. "Interconnecting Remote LANs to Build Wide Area Networks." *Journal of Network Management* (Summer 1990): 26–37.

[4-8] Retix. *Local Bridge Application Guide*. Document 1040187-00, 1989.

[4-9] Irvin, David R. "Second-Generation Token Ring LANs: Evaluating the Need for High Speed." *Data Communications* (March 21, 1989): 47–50.

[4-10] Vitalink Communications Corp. *Wide Area Network Configuration Guidelines*. Technical Note 013581F, *April 1988*.

[4-11] Freed, Les. "Asynchronous Communication Servers." *PC Magazine* (May 16, 1989): 227–228

[4-12] Marks, Howard. "Asynchronous Communication Servers." *LAN Technology* (January 1990): 7–46.

[4-13] Hinners, Bonny. "Help Wanted Looking For Asynchronous Communication Servers." *LAN Magazine* (July 1990): 135–146.

[4-14] Hurwicz, Michael. "Novell's Access Server: Dial-In Made Easy." *LAN Technology* (August 1990); 66–75.

[4-15] Microcom, Inc. *A Guide to LAN Internetworking.* December 1989.

[4-16] Guy, Ken. "Fast Packet Multiplexing: A Technical Overview." Micom Communications Corp., 1990.

[4-17] Mier, Edwin E. "Adding to Your Net Worth with T1-to-LAN Devices." *Data Communications* (September 1989): 103–118.

[4-18] Lippis, Nick. "Linking LANs and WANs with T3." *Data Communications* (July 1990) 37–38.

CHAPTER 5

X.25 Protocols

Research into the technologies currently known as packet switching began in the 1960s and was dictated by U.S. military requirements. Behind the research conducted in the United States at that time was a basic understanding that, in a wartime environment, it is essential to provide secure communications links between various command posts. The military always considered the possibility that the enemy could tap into a secure communications link and capture sensitive information. To reduce this risk, researchers proposed that a sensitive message could be divided into a number of small elements, called packets, and each of these elements could then be transmitted using a different communication path. Should the enemy tap any single channel, they would receive only a portion of the overall message. Major contributions to fundamental packet switching technology were also made in Europe thanks to the work of Englishmen Donald Davies and Derek Barber at the National Physical Laboratory at Teddington. From their packet-switching research came the development of public data networks (PDNs), which made the researched technology available for commercial use.

Before long, it became clear that an interface standard was required to provide a common access method to these PDNs. The result was the CCITT X.25 standard. Reference [5-1] provides some interesting historical and architectural information about these early projects. To begin our study of the X.25 protocols, we will first investigate the development of commercial PDNs.

5.1   Public Data Networks Development

In 1969, the Advanced Research Projects Agency Network (ARPANET)—
sponsored by the U.S. Defense Department—became operational with four nodes
(reference [5-2]), and led to three significant internetworking developments.

First, a worldwide family of Public Data Networks (PDNs) were made operational. Early PDNs included Telenet (U.S.A.), established in 1975; Datapac (Canada)
and Tymnet (U.S.A.), created in 1977; and Transpac (France) and Accunet (U.S.A.),
placed into operation in 1978. (Appendix D lists addresses and phone numbers for
many North American PDNs.)

Second, the CCITT, driven by the need to create an interface for these PDNs,
adopted in 1976 the X.25 recommendation entitled "Interface Between Data
Terminal Equipment (DTE) and Data Circuit-Terminating Equipment (DCE) For
Terminals Operating In The Packet Mode and Connected To Public Data Networks
By Dedicated Circuit" (reference [5-3]). X.25 is a suite of protocols that provide an
interface between a synchronous packet-mode host (or other device) and a PDN,
over a dedicated (or leased-line) circuit.

Third, the interconnection between Telenet (U.S.A.) and Datapac (Canada),
established in 1978, pointed to the need for PDN internetworking. Thus the X.25
recommendation "Packet-Switched Signalling System Between Public Networks
Providing Data Transmission Services" was also released in 1978 (reference [5-4]).
CCITT conventions in 1980, 1984, and 1988 have helped these protocols mature to
the point where today the X.25 technology is well-understood and implemented by
a large number of PC, minicomputer, mainframe, LAN, and WAN vendors.

Before we study the protocols and examples of LAN implementations, let's look
at the architecture of a PDN.

5.2   PDN Architecture

First, let's define what the X.25 protocols do—and do not—provide. X.25 defines the interface to a PDN, or more specifically, it defines the Data Terminal Equipment/Data Circuit Terminating Equipment (DTE/DCE) interface between a synchronous (as opposed to an asynchronous) packet-mode host and the PDN. The X.25 protocol suite does not, however, define the internal architecture of the PDN, nor does it define the PDN's operation. That function is the responsibility of the PDN designers, who may, in fact, consider the internal PDN architecture to be proprietary.

This DTE/DCE interface and the internal structure of the PDN are shown in Figure 5-1. Three different types of DTEs are displayed here. The first is a host computer with an X.25 interface. The second is a PAD (Packet Assembler/ Disassembler). The PAD accepts asynchronous characters input from low-speed terminals, and assembles these characters into packets to be transmitted to the network. Conversely, the PAD also disassembles packets from the network so the data can be delivered as characters to terminals. The third type of DTE, and perhaps the one of greatest interest for LAN applications, is the gateway between a PDN and the LAN. We will look at some applications of these gateways in Section 5.8.

Access between the DTE and DCE is typically maintained by means of a synchronous leased line operating at 9.6, 19.2, or 56 Kbps. Either analog or digital lines can be used, depending upon transmission requirements and local availability. In addition, a pair of synchronous modems, or DSUs, is required to complete the connection. Most PDNs can be locally accessed in all major cities, making the leased lines a local communication facility rather than a long-distance connection.

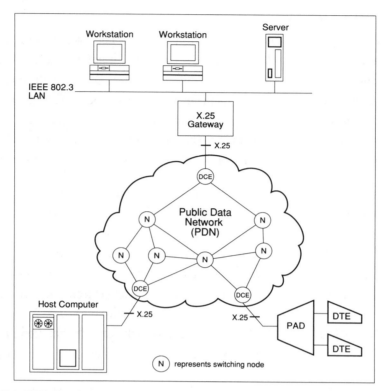

Figure 5-1. PDN Architecture

A PDN can implement one of two methods for internal communications. One method is the datagram, where every packet is given a complete source and destination address, and "dropped" into the network (much like you would mail a letter by dropping it into the mailbox). With a datagram, every packet finds its own route through the PDN so that it ends up at the destination host, although delivery of that packet is not guaranteed. One example of datagram service is Ethernet. In an Ethernet network, collisions may occur that prevent a packet (actually a frame) from being delivered. Datagram service was eliminated from the X.25 standard in 1980 and replaced with an optional facility known as Fast Select, although a number of other network architectures (such as Ethernet) continue to use the datagram technique very effectively.

The second method of internal communication is the virtual circuit, shown in Figure 5-2. The circuit is a DTE-to-DTE (end-to-end) connection, established by Call Request and Call Accept packets that function very similarly to the way in which a telephone call is placed. The circuit connection is established prior to the transfer of any data, and the connection provides a fixed route through the PDN for all packets associated with that virtual circuit. All packets experience a delay through the various networks' nodes, but they arrive in sequence, without duplication. The "virtual" part of the virtual circuit definition comes from the fact that the connection appears to be a circuit. In reality, it is a series of routing table entries within the various switching nodes. These table entries change on a dynamic basis as virtual calls are established or disconnected. We'll discuss the virtual call establishment process in Section 5.7.

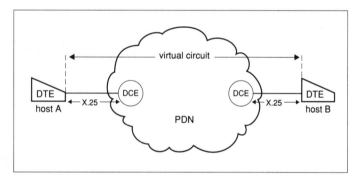

Figure 5-2. Virtual Circuit Connections
(Courtesy Hewlett-Packard Company)

To gain a better perspective on the PDN architecture, let's consider the three layers of protocols that make up the X.25 protocol suite. Recall from our discussion in Chapter 1 that a host (that is responsible for running application programs) interfaces with the communications subnetwork (or subnet), which in turn provides the WAN facilities and connection. The host implements all seven layers of the OSI model, but the subnet only implements the lower three. It is at these lower three layers that we find the X.25 protocol suite (see Figure 5-3)—the Physical Layer protocol transmits bits; the Data Link Layer protocol transmits frames; and the Network Layer protocol transmits packets. We'll look at the individual layers of X.25, in detail, beginning in Section 5.3.

In addition to the CCITT standard, three references provide good background reading on X.25. Reference [5-5] explores the protocols in detail. Reference [5-6] is an application-oriented approach to X.25, with many design examples. Reference [5-7] discusses the DTE/DCE interface to PDNs. Reference [5-8] is the workbook from a vendor's hands-on training course on X.25 protocol analysis and contains extremely practical information from both a user's and designer's perspective. References [5-9] and [5-10] discuss IBM's SNA support of the X. 25 protocols.

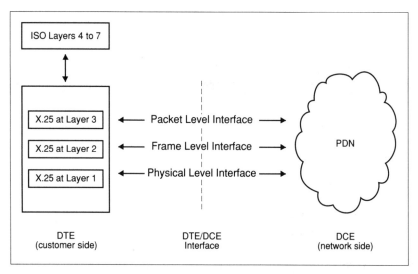

Figure 5-3. X.25 DTE/DCE Protocols
(Courtesy Hewlett-Packard Company)

5.3   The X.25 Physical Layer

The X.25 Physical Layer offers several standards options, choices that are the result of the CCITT's attempt to accommodate hardware options used on several different continents.

European networks use the X.21 interface, which is an electrically balanced interface similar to EIA-422. Interface X.21 is used in countries where the PDN can be accessed by digital (rather than analog) lines. The X.21 interface uses a DB-15 connector, supports a maximum DTE-DCE cable distance of 1,000 meters, and can operate in synchronous, half-, or full-duplex modes with transmission rates up to 10 Mbps.

The second standard is known as X.21 bis. ("Bis" is a French word meaning "alternate.") The X.21 bis standard specifies the use of V.24/V.28 interfaces, which are very similar to EIA-232-D. Most PDN applications in the United States do, in fact, use EIA-232-D (or the earlier RS-232-C) as the Physical Layer interface. (For further details on these interfaces, refer to Appendix 3A of the *LAN Troubleshooting Handbook*, the companion volume to this book.

The third interface option, V.35, is used for transmissions with speeds of 48 Kbps in Europe, or 56 Kbps in the United States. The V.35 interface uses a rectangular 34-pin connector and is electrically balanced. V.35 is typically used with DSU/CSUs connected to 56 Kbps digital (or DDS) leased lines.

5.4   The X.25 Data Link Layer

The X.25 Link Access Procedure Balanced (LAPB) protocol is structured after the well-known ISO HDLC (High Level Data Link Control) format. LAPB was designed to be used in a point-to-point connection between the DTE (host) and the DCE (attaching network node). The transmission is serial, synchronous, and full-duplex. The "balanced" designation within LAPB indicates that the control of the link is balanced between the DTE and the DCE; either end can initiate a link-setup or link-disconnect command.

Flag characters (01111110) begin and end the frame. The frame header consists of Address and Control fields (one octet each), and the frame trailer contains a 16-bit Frame Check Sequence, specified as the CRC-CCITT (two octets). Within the frame Information field is the packet as prescribed by the X.25 Packet Layer Protocol. Note, in Figure 5-4, that one packet fits inside each frame.

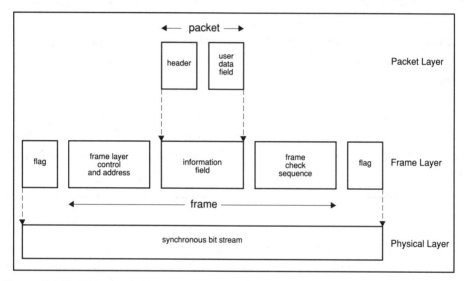

Figure 5-4. X.25 Packet Within an LAPB Frame
(Courtesy Hewlett-Packard Company)

As shown in Figure 5-5, the Address field contains one of two possible addresses: a (03H) for the DTE, or B (01H) for the DCE. Command (C) frames contain the address of the opposite device; for example, if the DTE initiates the command, the address field must contain a 01H (DCE). Response (R) frames contain the address of the responder; for instance, if the DCE issues a response, it would put a 01H in the Address field.

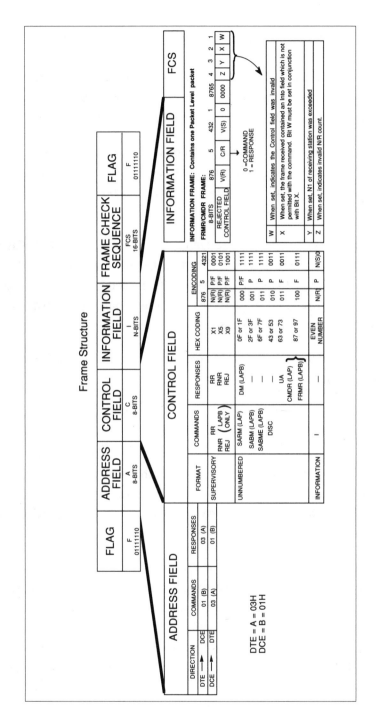

Figure 5-5. X.25 LAPB Protocol Encoding
© 1987, Hill Associates, Inc.

The Control field specifies which of three frame formats this frame contains. Information (I) frames are used for the sequenced transfer of data between DTE and DCE. The Least Significant Bit (LSB) of the Control field is set to zero (to indicate the I format). Two frame sequence counters—N(S) for sending and N(R) for receiving or acknowledgment—are also included within the Control field.

Supervisory (S) frames are used to supervise the exchange of I frames by acknowledging good frames and rejecting bad ones. The two LSBs of the S frame Control field are set to 01, and the remaining bits carry a code indicating the frame type and the acknowledgment number N(R).

Unnumbered (U) frames are used to establish and disconnect the DTE/DCE link. U frames are indicated when the two LSBs of the Control field are set to 11. The remaining bits are encoded to indicate the type of frame being sent (see the chart in Figure 5-5). Common to all three frame types is the Poll/Final bit (P/F) that indicates the urgency of the command or response.

The Information field of the LAPB I frames contain one X.25 packet. We'll look at the structure of this packet next.

5.5   The X.25 Network Layer

The Packet Layer Protocol (PLP) defines the format for the packet that is to be sent into the PDN by the local DTE for delivery to the remote DTE. The protocol defines seventeen different packet types, which are designated by the third octet (Packet Type field) of the packet itself. These seventeen packets can be divided into six categories (see Figure 5-6).

Call Setup packets are used to establish the virtual circuits (end-to-end connections via the PDN) between DTEs. Data and Interrupt packets are used to transfer information. Expedited data, such as an urgent message from a higher layer protocol, uses the Interrupt packet format, and routine information is transferred in Data packets. The Flow Control and Reset packets provide control mechanisms for the virtual circuits. The Restart packet is used to re-initialize the DTE/DCE interface following the occurrence of an error condition. Diagnostic packets are generated by the network (DCE) in response to an erroneous packet received from a DTE, or if one of the PLP watchdog timers expires. Finally, Registration packets are used to request or obtain specific parameters of user facilities, such as a non-default packet size or window size. The service provided can either be a virtual circuit or a permanent virtual circuit (PVC). We'll look at these in detail in section 5.7.

Packet Type		Service	
From DCE to DTE	From DTE to DCE	VC	PVC
Call set-up and clearing			
Incoming Call	Call request	X	
Call connected	Call accepted	X	
Clear indication	Clear request	X	
DCE clear confirmation	DTE clear confirmation	X	
Data and interrupt			
DCE data	DTE data	X	X
DCE interrupt	DTE interrupt	X	X
DCE interrupt confirmation	DTE interrupt confirmation	X	X
Flow control and reset			
DCE RR	DTE RR	X	X
DCE RNR	DTE RNR	X	X
	DTE REJ	X	X
Reset indication	Reset request	X	X
DCE reset confirmation	DTE reset confirmation	X	X
Restart			
Restart indicaiton	Restart request	X	X
DCE restart confirmation	DTE restart confirmation	X	X
Diagnostic			
Diagnostic		X	X
Registration			
Registration Confirmation		X	X
	Registration Request	X	X

Figure 5-6. X.25 Packet Types *(Courtesy International Telecommunication Union)*

The format of the first two octets of each packet type is identical (see Figure 5-7). The first four bits are known as the General Format Identifier (GFI) which determines data packet formats, acknowledgment parameters, and sequence counter sizes. The next twelve bits are the Logical Channel Identifier, which indicates which of the 4,096 possible logical channels is currently being used for this packet. This LCI includes the Logical Group Number (LGN), which is four bits, and the Logical Channel Number, (LCN) which is 8 bits .

A detailed description of each packet type is available in references [5-4], [5-5], and [5-6], and interested readers are directed to those sources for more information. The Data packet, however, is of interest to internetwork designers, so we will spend some time investigating its characteristics.

The Data packet sets the LSB=0 of the third octet (Packet Type field) to distinguish it from other packets used for control purposes. (These control packets always have LSB=1.) The user data begins in octet four, which may be negotiated by the communicating parties to quantities from 64 to 4,096 octets, incremented in powers of two. The default is 128 octets, which is also the packet size supported by most PDNs in the United States. The user data is actually higher-layer information that has been downloaded from the Network Operating System.

Consider the Banyan VINES internetwork shown in Figure 5-8. The Banyan servers have a variety of LAN and WAN connectivity options (discussed in Section 8.5), including an X.25 interface for server-to-server communication at speeds of up to 64 Kbps. Each side of the internet is an IEEE 802.X LAN connected over an X.25 PDN to form a LAN-WAN-LAN connection. The VINES frame structure is shown in Figure 5-9. (A complete description of the frame is available in reference [5-11], or Chapter 6 of the *LAN Protocol Handbook*. We'll summarize it here.)

The frame header and trailer are specific to the LAN hardware used (e.g. IEEE 802.3, 802.5, and ARCNET), and Banyan supports a variety of frame header and trailer options. The VINES Fragmentation Protocol (VFRP) header is next, and is used to segment or reassemble the VINES packets into multiple frames. The VINES

Internet Protocol (VIP) and Transport Layer headers precede the NetRPC header, which provides Session and Presentation Layer services. The Application data (e.g. electronic mail, and file transfer) completes the frame. Note that the VINES packet is defined beginning with the VINES IP header and ending with the Application data.

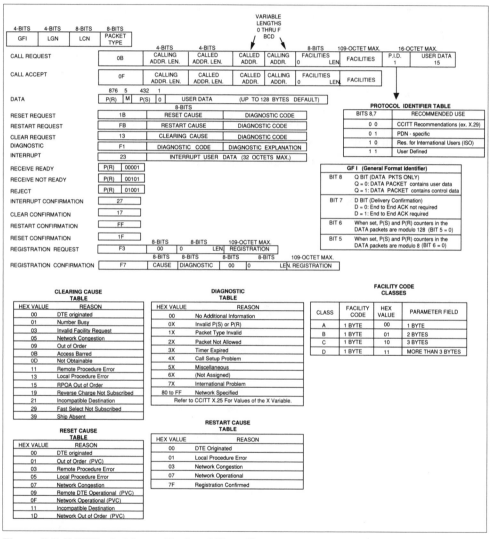

Figure 5-7. X.25 Packet Layer Protocol Encoding

© 1987, Hill Associates, Inc.

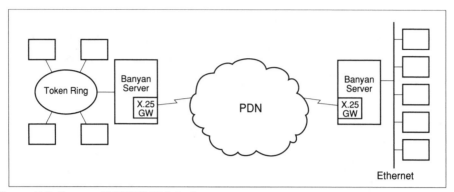

Figure 5-8. Banyan VINES X.25 Interface

When a WAN facility is used to internetwork two Banyan servers, the VINES packet (shown in Figure 5-9) must be encapsulated within the X.25 LAPB frame (see Figure 5-10). Also added will be the X.25 Packet Layer Protocol Header. When converted into an X.25 packet, a fragmentation is required to match the maximum packet size of the PDN (i.e. 128 octets). This function is performed by the VINES X .25 driver software, not VFRP. See reference [5-12] for more information on the VINES X.25 options.

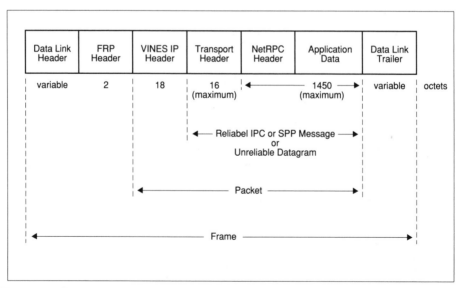

Figure 5-9. Banyan VINES Data Link Layer Frame

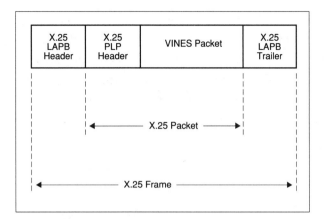

Figure 5-10. Banyan VINES Protocol Encapsulation

5.6   X.25 Related Protocols

Recall that the X.25 Standard specifies a synchronous connection between a DTE and DCE for PDN transport. DTE devices that do not have the X.25 protocols built into their software may transmit data to a PAD, which will then convert that data to an X.25 packet. Many X.25 gateways function as a PAD by taking the LAN frame, stripping the LAN Data Link Layer header and trailer, and adding the X.25 LAPB header and trailer as well as the X.25 PLP header.

A number of additional protocols are required to support the PAD and its access to a PDN. We'll look at each of these briefly, but for a complete explanation refer to the respective CCITT standards.

Recommendation X.3 defines the operation of a PAD (see Figure 5-11). The PAD must handle the setup and clearing of the virtual call, assemble packets for transmission to the PDN, and disassemble packets for delivery to the attached terminal(s). Included in X.3 are twenty-two parameters that specify the PAD's profile. These parameters specify transmission speed and parity, flow control between terminal and PAD, and line-feed treatment.

203

Recommendation X.28 defines the interface between a start-stop (asynchronous) terminal and a PAD, and the manner in which the PAD will interact with that terminal. This interface requires a bi-directional control path. Commands are sent from the terminal to the PAD to read or modify the X.3 parameters, or initiate or disconnect a virtual call. Messages from the PAD to the terminal are responses to the terminal commands, and are known as PAD Service signals. Figure 5-12 summarizes these X.28 commands.

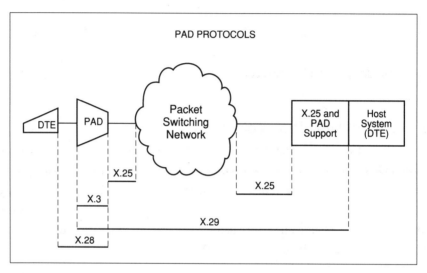

Figure 5-11. Protocols Related to X.25
(Courtesy Hewlett-Packard Company)

Recommendation X.29 is used by a remote DTE to communicate with a PAD. For example, a remote host may need to communicate with a PAD in order to read and/or set various PAD parameters, such as the BREAK signal between the remote DTE and the local terminal. Protocol X.29 is a layer above the X.25 PLP, but it uses the X.25 packet (and the PDN) as the transmission path between host and PAD. Figure 5-12 also summarizes the X.29 messages.

X.3 PARAMETERS

PARAMETER NUMBER	PARAMETER FUNCTION	CCITT VALUES*
1	PAD Recall Character	0 or 1 32 - 126
2	Local Echo	0 or 1
3	Data Forwarding Characters	0, 2, 6, 18, 126
4	Idle Timer Delay	0 - 255
5	PAD to Terminal Flow Control	0 - 2
6	Control of PAD Service Signals	0, 1, 5, 8 - 15
7	PAD Action on Receipt of Break from Term	0, 1, 2, 5, 8, 21
8	Discard Output	0 or 1
9	Padding after Carriage Return	0 - 255
10	Line Folding	0 - 255
11	Async Speed (Read Only parameter)	0 - 18
12	Terminal to PAD Flow Control	0 or 1
13	Line Feed Insertion	0, 1, 4 - 7
14	Padding After Line Feed	0 - 255
15	Editing	0 or 1
16	Character Delete Defined Character	0 - 127
17	Buffer Delete Defined Character	0 - 127
18	Buffer Display Defined Character	0 - 127
19	Editing Service Signals	0, 1, 2, 8 , 32 - 126
20	Echo Mask	0 - 128
21	Parity Treatment	0 - 3
22	Page Wait	0 - 255

* Both mandatory and optional values included

X.28 COMMAND SUMMARY

FUNCTION	COMMAND
Establish Call	**Call Selection**
	[optional_facilities] - address [user_data]
	[optional_facilities] - .abbrviated_address [user*data]
	Optional_facilities precede address:
	N(NUI), T(RPOA), G(CUG), R(Reverse
	Charging), C(Charging Information)
	User_data follows address: Character P or D,
	followed by up to 12 characters
	These two fields are optional.
Clear call	CLR
Check user profile	PROF
Set user profile	PROF n
Set PAD parameter(s)	SET para_ #:value
Set & read PAD parameter(s)	SET? para_ #:value
Display PAD parameter(s)	PAR?
Display call status	STAT
Reset virtual call	RESET
Send INTERRUPT packet	INT

X.29 MESSAGES

4 - BITS	4 - BITS	8 - BITS	8 - BITS			
GF I	LGN	LCN	P(R)	M	P(S)	0

SET	02	PARM	VALUE
SET & READ	06	PARM	VALUE
PARAMETER INDICATION	00	PARM	VALUE
READ	04	PARM	00
INVITATION TO CLEAR	01		
ERROR	05	TYPE	CODE
INDICATION OF BREAK	03	08 *	01 *
RESELECTION	07	ADDRESS	FACILITIES

* optional

Figure 5-12. X.3, X.28 and X.29 Protocol Encoding

5.7 Virtual Call Establishment

Reviewing Figure 5-6, we see that the X.25 Packet Layer Protocol defines seventeen different packet types. We will look at three of these packets—the Call Request, Call Accept, and Data packets—in detail as we discuss how a virtual call or virtual circuit is established.

There are actually two different types of virtual circuits: permanent virtual circuits (PVCs), which are established by the network and are analogous to a leased telephone line; and switched virtual circuits (SVCs), which are analogous to a dial-up connection. Both PVCs and SVCs could be used in an internetwork environment, but the SVC is more common. An SVC connection is also referred to as a virtual call.

To establish the virtual call, we first assume that two DTEs need to communicate. These two DTEs are attached to their respective DCEs via the X.25 interface, as shown in Figure 5-13. Let's further assume that DTE 1193 wishes to contact DTE 1440. Establishing the call begins when DTE 1193 transmits a Call Request packet to its attached DCE. An unused logical channel, selected by DTE 1193, is used for that DTE/DCE communication. The network then processes the Call Request, and transmits it to the Destination DCE, which is attached to DTE 1440. That remote DCE also selects an unused logical channel for communication, and delivers an Incoming Call packet to DTE 1440.

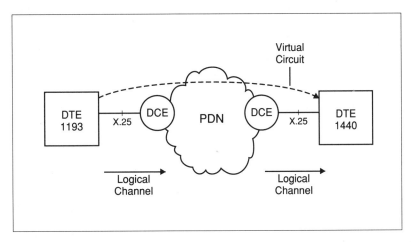

Figure 5-13. Virtual Call Establishment

Two points are noteworthy here. First, a logical channel is a DTE/DCE definition and is not likely to have the same number at each DTE/DCE pair. Second, the Call Request packet initiated by DTE 1193 undergoes a change when it is transmitted from the remote DCE to DTE 1440. Although transmitted as a Call Request packet, it is delivered as an Incoming Call packet. These packets are shown in Figure 5-14. The third octet (Packet Type field) of the Call Request/Incoming Call packet is set to 0BH. It is understood within the PLP that a Call Request is initiated by the DTE and an Incoming Call is initiated by a DCE, so no confusion occurs.

If the remote DTE (1440) is willing to accept the call, it transmits a Call Accepted packet (see Figure 5-15) which is next delivered by the local DCE to DTE 1193 as a Call Connected packet. Both of these packets assign Packet Type equal to 0FH. A full-duplex data exchange can then occur using the Data packet format (Figure 5-16) that was established by the Call Request. At the end of the session, Clear Request/ Clear Indication packets (see Figure 5-17) are used to signal termination.

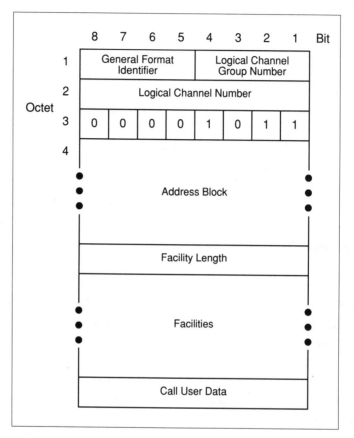

Figure 5-14. X.25 Call Request / Incoming Call Packet *(Courtesy International Telecommunication Union)*

If DTE 1440 is initially unable to accept the Call Request, a Clear Request/Clear Indication packet will be returned. The Clearing Cause field elaborates on the reason—such as a remote DTE that was busy or out-of-order—that the call did not go through.

With this background on the X.25 protocols and their use, let's next examine products that implement these protocols.

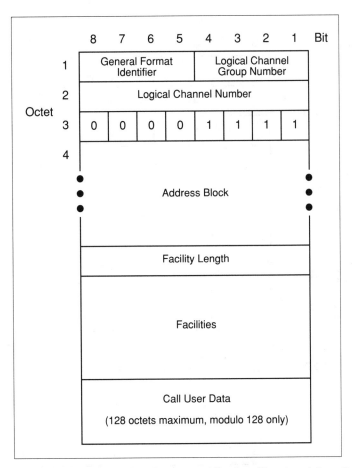

Figure 5-15. X.25 Call Accepted / Call Connected Packet *(Courtesy International Telecommunication Union)*

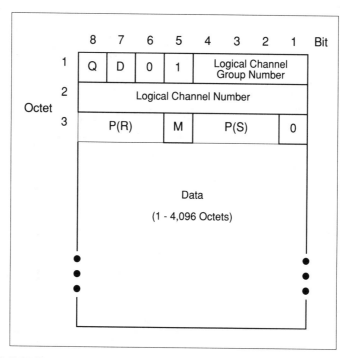

Figure 5-16. X.25 Data Packet (modulo 8) *(courtesy International Telecommunication Union)*

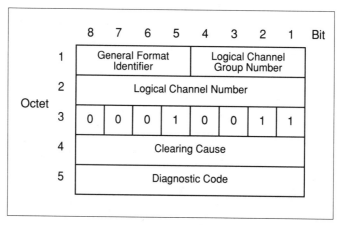

Figure 5-17. X.25 Clear Request / Clear Indication Packet (modulo 8) *(courtesy International Telecommunication Union)*

5.8   X.25 Internetworking Examples

The X.25 protocols lend themselves quite readily to remote LAN interconnections. The device that is typically used on the LAN is called an X.25 gateway—
although from the OSI point of view, it is actually a router.

We'll look at three different products that address differing user requirements.

5.8.1   Symicron DTSX

Symicron, Inc. of Torrance, California, a relative newcomer to the United States,
is a well-established English firm that provides both hardware and software X.25
solutions. The heart of the Symicron X.25 interface is the DTSX (Data Transport
Station for X.25) communications processor. Five different versions of the DTSX
are available, each supporting a different bus—the PC/XT/AT (DTSX-8); DEC
VME (DTSX-10); Micro Channel (DTSX-12); Apple Macintosh II (DTSX-14); and
PC/AT compatibles with the ISA and EISA bus (DTSX-30).

All DTSX's are intelligent co-processor cards that run under Symicron's STS
software. STS is certified for X.25 connectivity on packet-switched networks
throughout the world. By using shared memory on the card (64 kilobytes) that is
directly accessible to both the DTSX co-processor and the workstation's own
processor, and high-speed direct memory access (DMA) I/O to the X.25 port, each
of the four DTSX cards is capable of achieving throughput rates in excess of 150
Kbps. The latest addition to the family, the DTSX-30, supports either 2 or 4 ports,
and is capable of throughput greater than 2 Mbps. The DTSX allows up to 254 virtual
circuits (either SVC or PVC) to be established between the workstation and the PDN.

Different versions of the STS software support three different X.25 applications:
stand-alone workstation access to remote host computers, LAN gateway access to
remote hosts, or bridging between two or more remote LANs.

The first application, access to host computers through terminal emulation, uses the SYMCOM software, an application program that provides emulation for a variety of different terminal types, including IBM 3278, DEC VT100, and Videotex. SYMCOM runs in conjunction with the DTSX card to provide remote access to one or more host computers (see Figure 5-18a). Up to eight sessions may be run concurrently, each utilizing a separate virtual circuit. Three versions of SYMCOM are available to support DOS, OS/2, or UNIX/XENIX workstations.

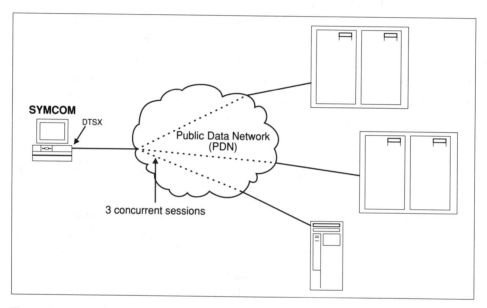

Figure 5-18a. Symicron Terminal Emulation
(Courtesy Symicron Computer Communications)

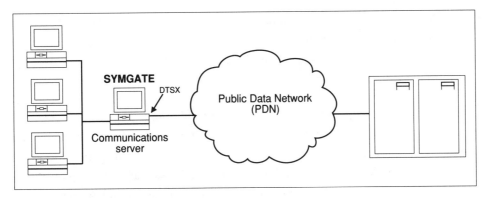

Figure 5-18b. Symicron X.25 Gateway
(Courtesy Symicron Computer Communications)

The second X.25 application supported is the gateway application, which is comprised of SYMGATE software running in conjunction with one or more DTSX cards installed in a PC on the LAN (see Figure 5-18b). SYMGATE effectively couples workstation applications and X.25 virtual circuits. Each workstation can access multiple virtual circuits, as long as the aggregate number for all workstations does not exceed 254. When transmitted through a PDN, these virtual circuits may be routed to multiple remote hosts. However, if only access to a single host is required, a point-to-point dedicated line may be used instead of a network. Two versions of the gateway software are available: SYMGATE-S for Novell NetWare LANs, and SYMGATE-N for NetBIOS-based LANs such as those from 3Com and Banyan.

The third STS X.25 application, SYMBRIDGE-S, provides a powerful means of bridging between multiple Novell NetWare LANs across a common PDN. Using standard DOS commands, a user on any LAN can access servers on the same LAN, or, using SYMBRIDGE, on any of the other remote LANs. For example, a workstation user in Los Angeles can access files on a file server in New York, and can direct output to a print server in Seattle (see Figure 5-18c).

Each communications server includes a Symicron DTSX Data Transport Station card and SYMBRIDGE software. For bridging between any pair of LANs, only one virtual circuit is required. Up to thirty-two virtual circuits may be allocated for use by SYMBRIDGE at each communications server, thus allowing many LANs to be interconnected for concurrent bridging. In the event that only two LANs are to be bridged, a point-to-point dedicated line—instead of the PDN—may be used between the communications servers.

SYMSHELL is an additional component of the bridging system that provides extended connectivity capability. It allows a single, isolated personal computer connected to the PDN to appear to be a LAN workstation, thereby gaining access to all the services offered by SYMBRIDGE. In Figure 5-18c, the user in San Francisco can also access files on a file server in New York, and send output to a print server in Seattle.

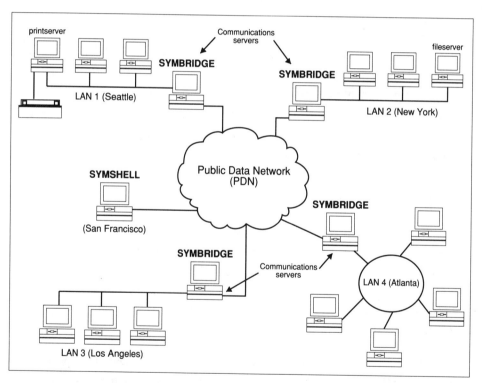

Figure 5-18c. Symicron LAN-WAN-LAN Bridge
(Courtesy Symicron Computer Communications)

In summary, Symicron's products provide many different options that provide remote LAN access and LAN-WAN-LAN connections by means of PDN facilities.

5.8.2 Gateway Communications ComSystem

Gateway Communications, Inc. of Irvine, California, a company well-known for its X.25 gateways, has incorporated a number of powerful features into its ComSystem. The ComSystem is based on the 80286 hardware platform, and includes expansion capabilities for a variety of communications co-processors. It can be installed on any Advanced NetWare or NetBIOS-compatible LAN, and supports all NetWare-compatible network hardware.

Four different communication co-processor options are available (see Figure 5-19). The SNA 64 Gateway supports synchronous, SDLC connections to IBM SNA environments at speeds of up to 64 Kbps. Both 3270 and 3770 (RJE) terminal emulation capabilities are available to LAN workstations. Up to thirty-two Logical Units (LUs) are supported.

The X.25 64 option provides X.25 PAD support. Up to 128 user sessions are available, with four concurrent sessions per PC. Transmission speeds in ranges up to 64 Kbps are available over V.35 or RS-232-C physical interfaces.

The IPX Router 64 provides LAN-WAN-LAN connectivity and can connect up to 128 remote NetWare network locations. A combination of the X.25 Gateway and Router 64 within the same hardware platform is also available to support the X.25 host as well as LAN-WAN-LAN connections over the same dial-up or leased line.

The ComSystem provides a unified platform to maintain connections between LANs and other networks.

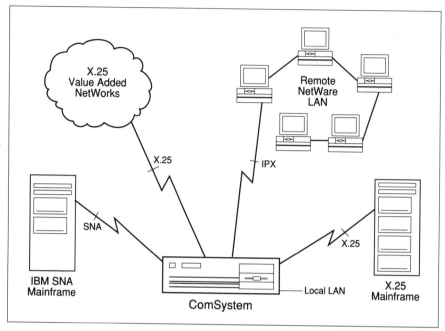

Figure 5-19. Gateway Communications ComSystem
(Reprinted with permission. © 1990 Gateway Communications, Inc.)

5.8.3   Eicon Access/X.25

Eicon Technology Corporation of Lachine, Quebec offers a broad range of connectivity options built around the EiconCard family of intelligent communications co-processor cards.

EiconCards support HDLC, X.25, and SDLC protocols at line speeds of up to 128 Kbps. IBM, 3270, 5250, APPC, DEC, VT100, and TTY are just a few of the protocols and emulations supported in order to provide LAN-to-mainframe, LAN-to-minicomputer, and LAN-to-LAN communications (see Figure 5-20a). Platform independence means that EiconCards may be installed in industry standard bus, Micro Channel bus, and Macintosh NuBus PCs. EiconCards support DOS, UNIX, Xenix, AIX, OS/2, Windows, or Macintosh operating systems. In addition, support for both NetBIOS and NetWare LANs ensures optimized workstation-to-communications server transmissions, as well as compatibility with virtually every network operating system available.

Access/QLLC with EiconAPPC and LAN Bridging allows users to connect to IBM mainframes, IBM minicomputers (System 3X and AS/400), non-IBM minicomputers (e.g., Tandem, Hewlett Packard, AT&T, and Data General), PDNs, and other LANs through a single physical connection. Up to 254 simultaneous sessions can be supported through one EiconCard, with a maximum of nine concurrent sessions on any one PC. Users may install up to four EiconCards in a single PC to create a high-end communications server with built-in redundancy.

One application of the EiconCard is to provide APPC (Advanced Program-to-Program Communication) support between a workstation and a remote host by means of an X.25 or SDLC link (see Figure 5-20b).

EiconAPPC performs all LU 6.2 verb processing within the EiconCard. A resident program translates the IBM APPC/PC requests to the EiconCard, thus minimizing communication-processing overhead. It supports all IBM-defined Basic and Mapped Conversation verbs, as well as Control Operator verbs. EiconAPPC supports up to 254 Logical Units (LUs) through a single Physical Unit (PU), thus allowing users to run up to 254 parallel sessions. Up to sixteen Transaction Programs can be activated per LU 6.2 session. The software can maintain up to thirty-two concurrent PU emulations, supporting either PU 2.0 or PU 2.1. EiconAPPC can also be used on any NetBIOS or NetWare-compatible LANs (including Novell NetWare, 3Com 3+, IBM PC LAN Support Program, and others) using any topology such as Ethernet, ARCNET, or StarLAN.

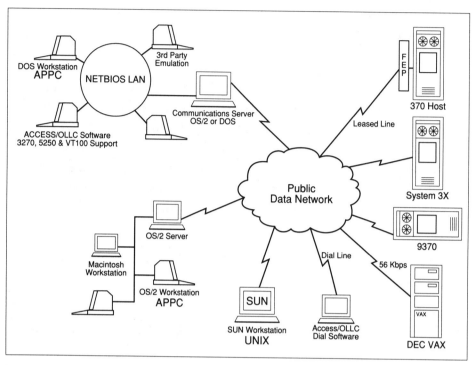

Figure 5-20a. Eicon X.25 Connectivity Options
(Courtesy Eicon Technology)

EiconAPPC consists of two components. First, the EiconAPPC Program provides an interface so that both EiconAPPC and IBM APPC/PC applications can run in conjunction with Eicon Technology communications products. Second, the EiconAPPC Developer's Toolkit provides a development environment to create custom applications that will execute with the EiconAPPC Program. The toolkit includes a programming interface, specifications, and examples. EiconAPPC is offered as a software option for stand-alone or LAN versions of Eicon Technology's Access/X.25, Access/QLLC, or Access/SDLC programs.

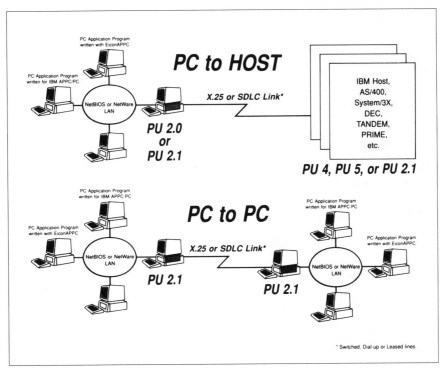

Figure 5-20b. Eicon APPC Connectivity
(Courtesy Eicon Technology)

In summary, the EiconCard provides a base hardware platform for a number of X.25 connectivity options, including LAN-to-minicomputer, LAN-to-mainframe, or LAN-to-LAN connections.

As we have seen, the X.25 protocols provide an extremely versatile option for LAN-to-host and LAN-to-remote LAN communications. The wide international acceptance of these protocols and their implementation techniques makes X.25 an excellent choice for both enterprise-wide and international internetworking.

5.9 References

[5-1] Rosner, Roy D. *Packet Switching*. Belmont, CA.: Language Learning Press, 1982.

[5-2] BBN Communications. *ARPANET, The First Decade*. NTIS Document no. ADA115440, April 1981.

[5-3] The International Telegraph and Telephone Consultative Committee. Blue Book Volume VIII, Fascicle VIII.2. Recommendation X.25, 1988.

[5-4] The International Telegraph and Telephone Consultative Committee. Blue Book Volume VIII, Fascicle VIII.3. Recommendation X.75, 1988.

[5-5] Deasington, R. J. *X.25 Explained: Protocols for Packet Switching Networks*. 2d ed., New York: John Wiley & Sons, 1984.

[5-6] Schlar, Sherman K. *Inside X.25: A Manager's Guide*. New York: McGraw-Hill, 1990.

[5-7] Dhas , C. R. and V. K. Konangi. "X.25: An Interface to Public Packet Networks." *IEEE Communications Magazine* (September 1986): 18–25.

[5-8] Hewlett-Packard Company. *X.25: The PSN Connection*. 1987.

[5-9] Matusow, David G. "BTAM, VTAM, X.25: Uneasy Alliance." *Data Communications* (March 1987): 191–197.

[5-10] Routt, Thomas J. "From Out of the Blue: Interfaces from SNA to X.25." *Data Communications* (June 1987): 183–205.

[5-11] Banyan Systems, Inc. *VINES Protocol Definition*. Document no. DA254-00, December 1989.

[5-12] Banyan Systems, Inc. *VINES X.25 Option Guide*. Document no. DA184-03, November 1989.

CHAPTER 6

TCP/IP Protocols

The Transmission Control Protocol/Internet Protocol (TCP/IP) suite are perhaps the best known of all the internetworking protocols. TCP/IP was developed in the 1970s, and funded by the U.S. Government's Defense Advanced Research Projects Agency (DARPA). The government's objective was to develop a mechanism to link the dissimilar computers of the various military agencies, defense and research contractors, and universities into a wide area network. (Preceding the TCP/IP development was the establishment of the ARPANET [Advanced Research Projects Agency Network], also funded by DARPA. ARPANET demonstrated the first available application of packed switching technologies. Some interesting background information on ARPANET is found in references [6-1] and [6-2].)

Today, well over 150 hardware and software vendors incorporate the TCP/IP into their products, which range in size from PCs to mainframes. One example of the variety of TCP/IP connectivity options is shown in Figure 6-1, taken from reference [6-3]. Note the wide variety of hardware platforms and operating systems represented in the drawing.

We'll begin our study of TCP/IP by looking at the history of the Internet.

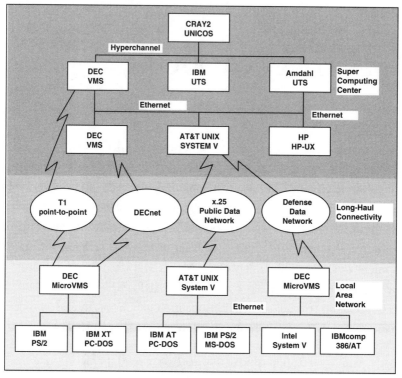

Figure 6-1. TCP/IP Connectivity Options
(Courtesy The Wollongong Group, Inc.)

6.1   The Department of Defense Internet

The history of the TCP/IP protocols dates back to the mid 1960s when DARPA initiated research into the viability of packet switching technology. A contract was awarded to Bolt, Baranek and Newman (BBN) of Cambridge, Massachusetts to develop ARPANET. The project proved successful, and ARPANET began operation in 1969 connecting four locations: the University of California at Los Angeles (UCLA), the University of California at Santa Barbara (UCSB), the University of Utah, and Stanford Research Institute (SRI). From that beginning, ARPANET developed into a worldwide packet switching network connecting hundreds of dissimilar computers. In addition, BBN in 1975 initiated Telenet (currently owned by Sprint International) which became the first commercial packet switching network.

The ARPANET research engendered additional networks that are collectively referred to as the DARPA Internet, TCP/IP Internet, or simply the Internet (reference [6-4]). (Following conventional nomenclature, we will use the term Internet [capital I] when referring to the DARPA Internet, and the term internet [small i] when discussing generic internetworks.) The collection of interconnected networks within the Internet is now quite diverse (see Figure 6-2). ARPANET was dismantled in June 1990, and replaced with the Defense Research Internet (DRI) which is based upon a T-1 (1.544 Mbps) backbone instead of ARPANET's 56 Kbps transmission rate; military traffic now has its own network (MILNET), which is part of the Defense Data Network (DDN); the National Science Foundation Network (NSFNET) was originally built to provide access to the NSF supercomputers; the Corporation for Research and Educational Networking sponsors two networks; the Computer Science Network (CSNET) is a network of universities, government agencies and private corporations engaged in various research projects; the Because It's Time Network (BITNET) is a network supporting a variety of educational users, and sponsors a number of discussion topics, ranging from Agriculture to World Politics (reference [6-5]).

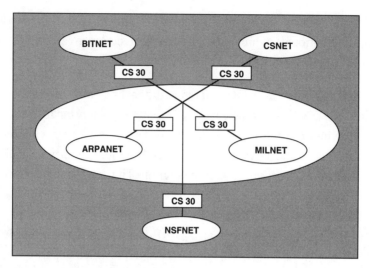

Figure 6-2. The Internet
(Courtesy The Wollongong Group, Inc.)

The diversity of ARPANET node locations and organizations necessarily brought with it a diversity of hardware platforms and operating systems. Research into the development of a protocol suite that would overcome these differences began in the mid-1970s with papers on the subject published by Vincent Cerf in 1974 (reference [6-6]). Implementation of these protocols throughout the Internet was mandated by DARPA in 1983; if you wanted to do business with the U.S. Government over the ARPANET, your computer needed to implement TCP/IP. Thus, a commercial interest in the TCP/IP protocols was born (reference [6-7]).

The architectural model of the Internet protocols uses terminology that is a slight variation from the OSI Reference Model [6-8]. Hosts (which run application programs) connect to a local network (either LAN or WAN) by means of a network access protocol. Each network connects to at least one gateway (actually a router in the OSI terminology, but old names are difficult to revise) which connects to other networks, as shown in Figure 6-3.

Gateways must contain at least three protocols: two to connect to each of the attached networks (e.g. LAN and WAN), and another (an internet protocol) which relays the network-to-network information.

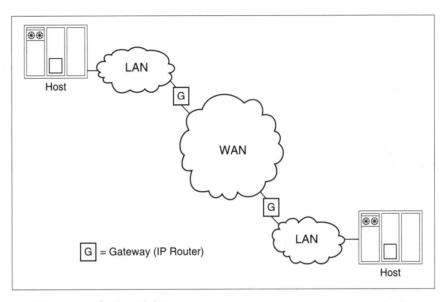

Figure 6-3. Internet Connectivity

Hosts are more complex, and must have at least four distinct protocols. The network access and internet protocols are required to communicate with the routers. A Transport Layer protocol must assure reliable communication between hosts, since neither the network access nor internet protocols are of an end-to-end nature. Finally, the Host Application protocols—such as file transfer or electronic mail— are required for actual communication. We'll look at the details of these protocols in Section 6.2.

Information on the Internet architecture and related protocols are published in reports known as Request for Comments, or RFCs, that are circulated among the Internet community. These RFCs are available electronically via the Internet, or in hard copy from the DDN Network Information Center (reference [6-9]).

Of special interest is RFC 1000, a topical index to the RFCs. For those readers needing assistance with Internet installation and management tools, RFC 1147 (reference [6-10]) is helpful.

6.2   The DoD Internet Protocol Suite

The Department of Defense (DoD) protocols follow a four-layer architecture. This includes the Network Access (or Local Network Layer), the Internet Layer, the Host-to-Host Layer, and the Process Application Layer. When comparing DoD and OSI Reference Model architectures (Figure 6-4), the Network Access Layer includes the Physical and Data Link Layers. The Internet Layer includes the OSI Network Layer functions. The Host-to-Host Layer provides OSI Transport Layer functions, and the DoD Application/Utility Layer includes the Session, Presentation, and Application Layer functions.

Of specific interest to our study of internetworking is the manner in which these layers are implemented. The Network Access Layer, as its name implies, controls access to the locally-attached LAN or WAN. This layer is network- specific, and may have multiple implementations throughout the internet. (We will look at Network Access protocols specific to LANs in Section 6.3.) The Internet Protocol (IP) resides on both hosts and gateways (actually routers) and relays data from the source host to the destination host. The Transmission Control Protocol (TCP) resides only on the hosts, and assures reliable data delivery. The various utilities and applications such as the File Transfer Protocol (FTP) and Simple Mail Transfer Protocol (SMTP) also reside only on the hosts.

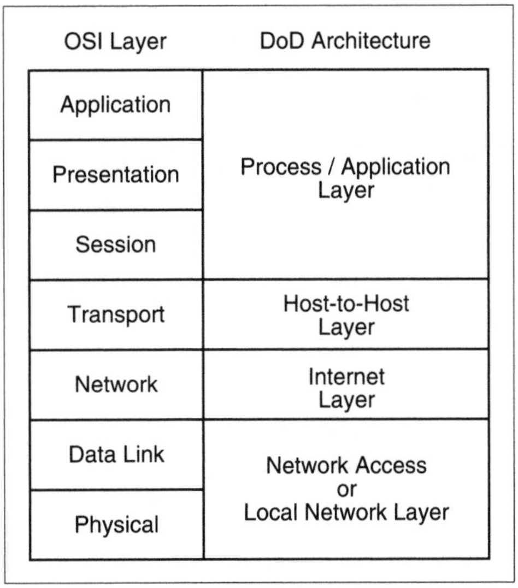

OSI Layer	DoD Architecture
Application	Process / Application Layer
Presentation	
Session	
Transport	Host-to-Host Layer
Network	Internet Layer
Data Link	Network Access or Local Network Layer
Physical	

Figure 6-4. Comparing OSI and DoD Models

As we discussed in Section 6.1, all of the DoD protocols are specified by Request for Comments (RFC) documents published by the Defense Data Network Information Center. The most prevalent of these protocols are shown in Figure 6-5 in relationship to the OSI model. Also shown are the associated RFC numbers, which are referenced throughout the remainder of this chapter. Excellent documents on the various protocols and their operation are references [6-11], [6-12], and [6-13].

OSI Layer	Protocol Implementation			
Application	File Transfer	Electronic Mail	Terminal Emulation	Network Management
Presentation	File Transfer Protocol (FTP)	Simple Mail Transfer Protocol (SMTP)	TELNET Protocol	Simple Network Management Protocol (SNMP)
Session	MIL-STD-1780 RFC 959	MIL-STD-1781 RFC 821	MIL-STD-1782 RFC 854	RFC 1098
Transport	Transmission Control Protocol (TCP) MIL-STD-1778 RFC 793		User Datagram Protocol (UDP) RFC 768	
Network	Address Resolution ARP RFC 826 RARP RFC 903	Internet Protocol (IP) MIL-STD-1777 RFC 791		Internet Control Message Protocol (ICMP) RFC 792
Data Link	Network Interface Cards: Ethernet, StarLAN, Token Ring, ARCNET RFC 894, RFC 1042, RFC 1051			
Physical	Transmission Media: Twisted Pair, Coax, or Fiber Optics			

Figure 6-5. DoD Protocol Implementations

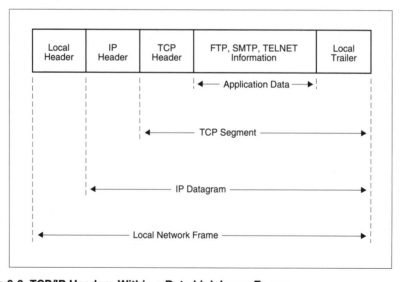

Figure 6-6. TCP/IP Headers Within a Data Link Layer Frame

6.3   DoD Data Link Layer Alternatives

Because of the diverse number of LAN and WAN implementations, the DoD architecture does not specify a particular Data Link Layer protocol to be used. DoD standards exist, however, to support Ethernet (RFC 894), IEEE 802 (RFC 1042), and ARCNET (RFC 1051) LANs, and Public Data Networks by means of the X.25 protocols (RFC 877). As shown in Figure 6-6, the host process (e.g. FTP, SMTP, TELNET) data is passed to the TCP Layer, then the IP Layer, and finally the Network Access Layer, which then completes the Data Link Layer frame header and trailer for transmission on the internet. We'll look at the three LAN implementations separately.

6.3.1   Ethernet

Ethernet (the DEC, Intel and Xerox Blue Book version) was developed around the same time (1970s) as the DoD protocols, and as a result, has been used extensively for TCP/IP implementations. RFC 894 (reference [6-14]) specifies a type (or Ethertype) of 0800H for IP datagrams. Other Ethertypes used for DoD protocols include 0806H (ARP) and 8035H (RARP). (We'll discuss these protocols further in Section 6.4.) Also noted in RFC 894 is the fact that IP must control the Ethernet Data field size (46-1500 octets) shown in Figure 6-7. For frames with less than 46 octets of data, the Data field is padded with zeros. At the upper limit, gateways (IP routers) must be able to accept and fragment maximum length (1500 octet) frames that exceed the typical 576-octet IP datagram limit.

A mapping between 32-bit Internet addresses and the 48-bit Ethernet addresses can be accomplished with either static tables within the host, or dynamically using two specific protocols. The Address Resolution Protocol (ARP), described in RFC 826 (reference [6-15]) converts the IP addresses to Ethernet addresses. A second protocol, the Reverse Address Resolution Protocol (RARP), described in RFC 903 (reference [6-16]) converts Ethernet addresses to IP addresses.

6.3.2   IEEE 802

IP datagrams can be encapsulated within 802.3, 802.4, or 802.5 frames, and the techniques are described in detail in RFC 1042 (reference [6-17]). Most significant is an extension to the IEEE 802.2 Logical Link Control (LLC) header known as the Sub-Network Access Protocol (SNAP). From Figure 6-8, note that the 802.X Medium Access Control (MAC) header is transmitted first. Transmitted next are the 802.2 LLC header fields containing the Destination and Source Service Access Point (DSAP and SSAP) addresses, set to AAH. The 802.2 Control Field is set to 03H (for Unnumbered Information). The SNAP Header consists of a 3-octet Protocol ID or Organizational Code, followed by a 2-octet Ethertype (0600H for IP). RFC 1042 may be consulted for further details.

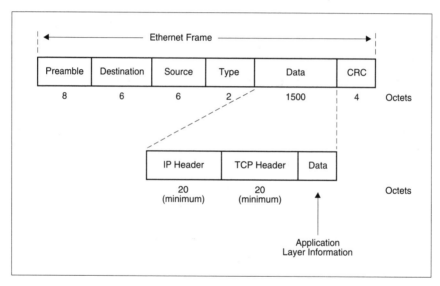

Figure 6-7. TCP/IP Headers Within an Ethernet Frame

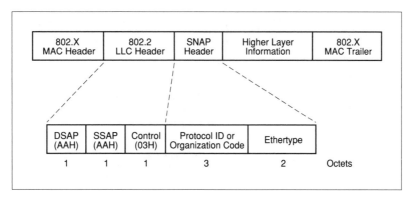

Figure 6-8. Sub-Network Access Protocol (SNAP) Header Encapsulated Within an IEEE 802.X Frame

6.3.3 ARCNET

Both IP and ARP datagrams can be encapsulated within an ARCNET frame, as shown in Figure 6-9. Several unique points, elaborated in RFC 1051 (reference [6-18]) are noted here.

First, Internet addresses (32 bits) can be mapped to ARCNET addresses (8 bits) using the Address Resolution Protocol (ARP) discussed in Section 6.3.1. Second, the System Code field, assigned by Datapoint Corporation, is the first octet within the ARCNET data field. The value for IP is 240 decimal (F0H), and for ARP is 241 decimal (F1H). The maximum ARCNET frame of 508 octets is less than the maximum IP datagram length of 576 octets, thus requiring fragmentation and reassembly at the IP level. More details on the fragmentation/reassembly function follow in Section 6.4.

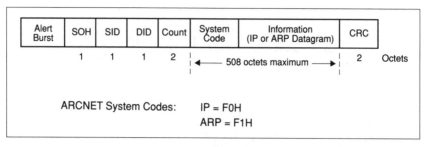

Figure 6-9. TCP/IP Headers Within an ARCNET Frame

6.4   The DoD Network Layer

The Network Layer functions include routing and switching of the datagram through the communications subnetwork or subnet. The Internet Protocol (IP) provides this fundamental function, forwarding the datagram based upon the network address contained within the IP header (reference [6-19]). Each datagram is an independent entity, not related to any other datagram. In addition, delivery of that datagram is not guaranteed by IP; therefore, the service provided by that protocol is considered an unreliable service. The next highest layer, TCP, provides the reliability that IP lacks. A secondary IP function is the fragmentation and reassembly of the datagram to match the frame size specified by the Data Link Layer protocol (e.g. Ethernet, IEEE 802.5, etc.) in use.

Notice that two addresses are involved up to this point: the hardware address specified within the Data Link Layer header (e.g. the 48-bit Ethernet address); and a 32-bit IP address that defines the network and the datagram's host destination within that network. (We'll study the addressing scheme in more detail in Section 6.4.3.) To begin our study of the internal functions' IP, let's look at the operation of an IP router.

232

6.4.1 IP Router Operation

Reviewing Figure 6-3, recall that an IP router (often called a gateway) connects either locally or remotely attached networks, and routes datagrams between them.

User data originating at one of the upper layer protocols (ULPs), e.g. FTP, is passed to the IP Layer for transmission. The host's IP process examines the network (i.e. IP) address of that datagram and determines if the destination node resides on the local network or a remote network. If the processing host and destination host are on the same network, the datagram is directly forwarded to the destination host. If not, the datagram is forwarded to the locally attached IP router. The router, in a similar fashion, examines the IP address and relays the datagram to either another IP router or network, as appropriate. Each datagram is thus routed individually, based upon a table lookup within each router.

In order for these routing tables to be established and maintained, the various IP routers exchange information with each other detailing the current network topology. Another protocol, known as the Internetwork Control Message Protocol (ICMP), is used for this purpose. RFC 792 (reference [6-20]) is devoted to ICMP. Reference [6-21] discusses IP router operation in some detail.

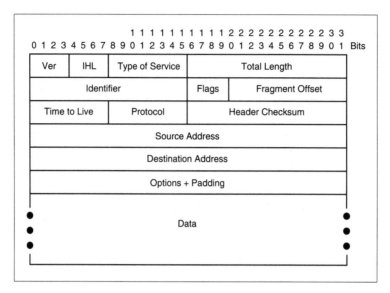

Figure 6-10. The IP Header

6.4.2 The Internet Protocol (IP) Header

Again reviewing Figure 6-6, note that the IP header is the first subfield within the local network (Ethernet 802.X, ARCNET, etc.) Information field. The minimum length of the IP header is 20 octets (assuming no options or padding) and its Data field will contain the TCP header and ULP data. Note also that the structure of the DoD protocol fields are based upon a 32-bit word, the width of the original ARPANET processors. Referring to Figure 6-10, let's examine the IP header fields in more detail.

- Version (4 bits): the IP version number (currently 4).

- Internet header length (4 bits): the length of the header in 32 bit words (minimum of 5 words or 20 octets).

- Type of service (8 bits): flags to specify reliability, precedence, delay and throughput parameters.

- Total length (16 bits): total length of the IP datagram, given in octets, including the IP header.

- Identification (16 bits): provides a unique identifier for this datagram.

- Flags (3 bits): options that indicate if fragmentation is permitted and/or used.

- Fragment offset (13 bits): indicates where in the entire datagram this fragment belongs; measured in 64-bit units from the beginning of the datagram.

- Time to live (8 bits): measured in gateway hops and/or seconds.

- Protocol (8 bits): identifies the next protocol that follows the IP header, e.g. TCP.

- Header checksum (16 bits): a checksum on the IP header that may be recomputed at each gateway.

- Source address (32 bits): the internet address of the originating host.

- Destination address (32 bits): the internet address of the destination host.

- Options (variable): options from the sender, e.g. a route specification.

- Padding (variable): provided so that the IP header ends on a 32 bit boundary.

- Data (variable): a multiple of 8 bits, not to exceed 65,535 octets for IP header plus data (TCP header, TCP data, etc.).

Note that the limits on the IP datagram are 576 octets minimum and 65,535 octets maximum.

6.4.3 IP Network Addresses

When a network joins a TCP/IP internet, the network administrative agency assigns an IP network number. The DDN Internet is administered by the DDN Network Information Center (reference [6-9]); networks joining other internets (e.g. CSNET, BITNET, NSFNET) should contact those respective agencies (reference [6-5]).

The internet address consists of two parts: a Network address, assigned by the administrative agency; and a Host address, assigned by the local administrator. These 32 bit addresses are typically displayed as four decimal integers, separated by a period (e.g. 95.0.0.1). Each of these fields represents 8 bits of the 32 bit address and can have a value from 0 to 255. There are five classes (A, B, C, D, and E) of IP addresses (see Figure 6-11).

Class A networks are used for very large networks, and begin with bit 0 = 0. Examples would be the ARPANET (now extinct), where the network address = 10, and MILNET, where the network address = 26. Class B networks are medium-size networks—such as campuses—that have the first octet begin with a 10, and network addresses that range between 128 and 191 (decimal). Class C networks are used for small networks, and have a very large Network ID field (24 bits) and a small Host ID field (8 bits). The first octet begins with a 110, and the network addresses would range from 192 to 254. Class D addresses begin with a 1110, and are used for IP multicasting, as defined in RFC 988. Class E addresses begin with 1111 and are reserved for experimental use. For all classes, addresses 0 and 255 are reserved, with 0 representing the originating entity—"this network" or "this host"—and 255 used for broadcast messages.

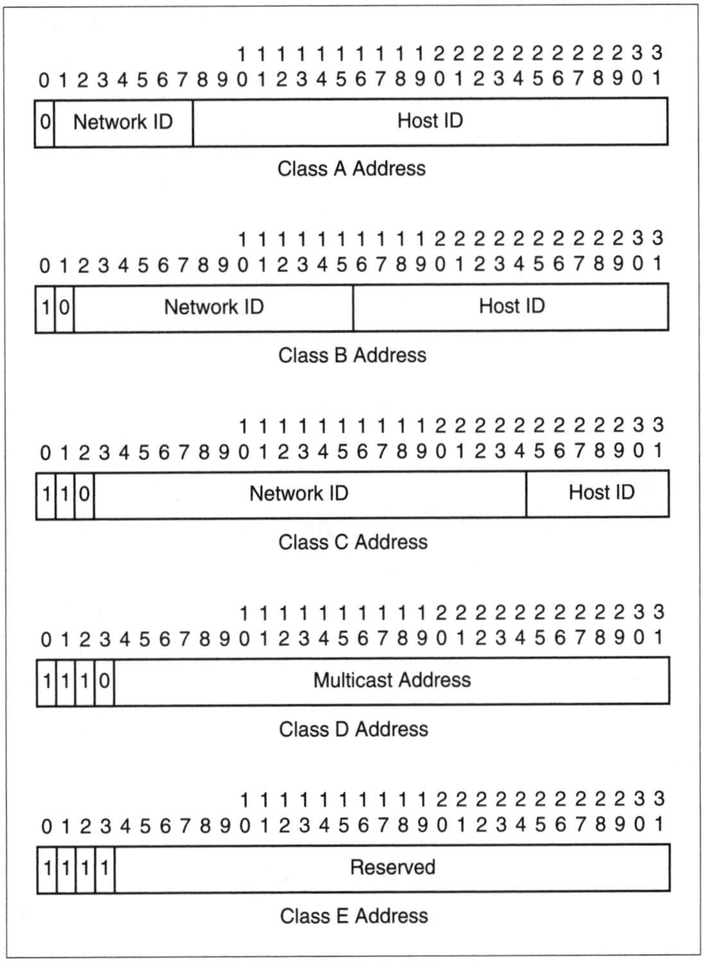

```
                        1 1 1 1 1 1 1 1 1 1 2 2 2 2 2 2 2 2 2 2 3 3
      0 1 2 3 4 5 6 7 8 9 0 1 2 3 4 5 6 7 8 9 0 1 2 3 4 5 6 7 8 9 0 1
```
| 0 | Network ID | Host ID |

Class A Address

```
                        1 1 1 1 1 1 1 1 1 1 2 2 2 2 2 2 2 2 2 2 3 3
      0 1 2 3 4 5 6 7 8 9 0 1 2 3 4 5 6 7 8 9 0 1 2 3 4 5 6 7 8 9 0 1
```
| 1 | 0 | Network ID | Host ID |

Class B Address

```
                        1 1 1 1 1 1 1 1 1 1 2 2 2 2 2 2 2 2 2 2 3 3
      0 1 2 3 4 5 6 7 8 9 0 1 2 3 4 5 6 7 8 9 0 1 2 3 4 5 6 7 8 9 0 1
```
| 1 | 1 | 0 | Network ID | Host ID |

Class C Address

```
                        1 1 1 1 1 1 1 1 1 1 2 2 2 2 2 2 2 2 2 2 3 3
      0 1 2 3 4 5 6 7 8 9 0 1 2 3 4 5 6 7 8 9 0 1 2 3 4 5 6 7 8 9 0 1
```
| 1 | 1 | 1 | 0 | Multicast Address |

Class D Address

```
                        1 1 1 1 1 1 1 1 1 1 2 2 2 2 2 2 2 2 2 2 3 3
      0 1 2 3 4 5 6 7 8 9 0 1 2 3 4 5 6 7 8 9 0 1 2 3 4 5 6 7 8 9 0 1
```
| 1 | 1 | 1 | 1 | Reserved |

Class E Address

Figure 6-11. IP Address Fields

6.4.4   IP Routing Protocols

As we have seen, routers receive the IP header information, look at the destination network address, and make a routing decision for that particular datagram, based upon a real-time table lookup. The question is, then, how do these tables get established and maintained? The answer lies in the IP routing protocols, which are a dynamic process providing a mechanism for the routers to exchange status information regarding the various transmission paths between them. Two different protocols are commonly used for this purpose. The first, Routing Information Protocol (RFC 1058), was originally designed by Xerox in its Xerox Network Systems (XNS) implementation (see Section 7.5.1). It was then modified for TCP/IP and incorporated into the Berkeley UNIX systems. The routing metric is the hop count, which is limited to 16 hops (a hop being a transmission through an intermediate router). The hop count is not always efficient, as it cannot consider the cost factor of the path, only the number of hops.

The second emerging standard—designed for greater internetwork efficiency—is called Open Shortest Path First (OSPF), defined in RFC 1131. OSPF is an improvement on RIP, because it allows the path to be selected based upon cost or delay factors—a process known as least-cost routing. Other capabilities include multi-path routing for load balancing, and network management functions. Instead of a routing metric based solely upon hops, the OSPF metric is a 16-bit user-configurable field. The network manager defines the factors that are most applicable (e.g. delay, transmission cost, bandwidth) and the router then makes the path choice based upon that metric (reference [6-22]). Look for support for OSPF when you are shopping for routers.

6.4.5 Internet Control Message Protocol (ICMP)

ICMP is also a Network Layer protocol, and is used for communication between the various IP entities. ICMP messages are the result of a Network Layer problem such as network congestion or an unreachable port. This protocol uses IP services; an ICMP message is sent using IP, with the ICMP message occupying the IP Data field (see Figure 6-12). The ICMP Header is 8 octets in length, and contains the following fields:

- Type (8 bits): indicates the type of ICMP message. Currently defined are destination unreachable, time exceeded, parameter problem, source quench, redirect, echo, echo reply, timestamp and timestamp reply.

- Code (8 bits): specifies parameters of the message that can be briefly encoded.

- Checksum (16 bits): checksum of the ICMP message.

- Data (variable): additional information that is related to the message.

RFC 792 (reference [6-20]) describes the operation of ICMP in greater detail.

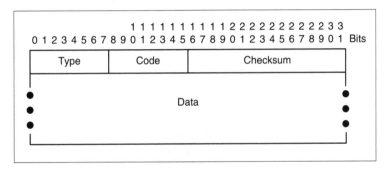

Figure 6-12. ICMP Header

6.4.6   DoD Network Layer Summary

Reviewing Figure 6-5, notice that ARP, RARP, and ICMP are slightly offset from the fundamental DoD Network Layer protocol, IP. ARP and RARP are providing services to IP, and as such are shown at a slightly lower architectural level. ICMP is a user of IP services, and is therefore shown at a slightly higher architectural level. We will next discuss how the DoD Transport Layer uses these three different Network Layer protocols.

6.5   DoD Transport Layer Protocols

Two protocols are defined at the DoD Transport Layer: Transmission Control Protocol (TCP) (reference [6-23]) and User Datagram Protocol (UDP) (reference [6-24]). Both protocols have unique applications: TCP provides reliability with high overhead, while UDP provides unreliable service with much less overhead. We'll look at each of the protocols separately.

6.5.1   Transmission Control Protocol

TCP provides a virtual circuit service between end-user applications—reliable data transfer—that was lacking in the datagram-oriented IP. Additional functions are also present in TCP that supports the end-to-end connection between host processes. First, the ULP process must be identified to TCP by a port address, sometimes known as a socket. Examples of port numbers (in decimal) would be FTP (21), TELNET (23), or SMTP (25). The Upper Layer Protocol connection is thus completely identified by this port address (16 bits) plus the IP address (32 bits). Second, error control must detect any missing, out-of-sequence, or duplicate information. Third, flow control must assure that a fast sender does not overwhelm a slower receiver with more data than it can handle. Finally, connection control must provide for end-to-end connection establishment, termination and interruption.

TCP treats the higher-layer information (from SMTP, FTP, etc.) as a continuous stream of data. This stream is divided into segments of up to 65K octets in length. Each octet of the segment is assigned a sequence number to provide the required error control and flow control functions. Each segment is then passed to the IP Layer, which creates and passes the datagrams to the Data Link Layer in use. At that layer, the local access protocol (e.g. IEEE 802.3, X.25) adds the local network header and trailer, and sends the bits over the transmission medium. At the remote host, a similar, but opposite, process occurs.

To support the reliability functions defined for TCP, a header with a minimum length of 20 octets is required (see Figure 6-13). These fields are described below:

- Source port (16 bits): the number of the calling port.

- Destination port (16 bits): the number of the called port.

- Sequence number (32 bits): a sequence number assuring the correct arrival and sequentiality of the data. This number indicates the byte sequence number of the first octet in this TCP data block, and is incremented according to the number of octets transmitted in each TCP segment.

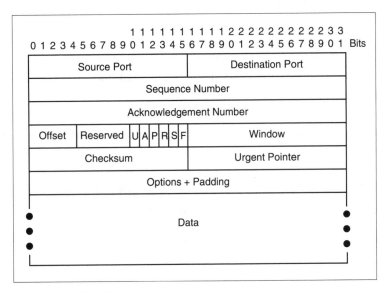

Figure 6-13. The TCP Header

- Acknowledgment number (32 bits): a piggyback acknowledgment of the next expected TCP octet.

- Data offset (4 bits): the number of 32 bit words in the TCP header.

- Reserved (6 bits): set to zero.

- Flags (6 bits): control functions such as the setup and termination of a session, expedited or urgent data flow, reset of a connection, or indication of the end of the data.

  URG: urgent pointer field significant
  ACK: acknowledgment field significant
  PHS: push function
  RST: reset connection
  SYN: synchronize sequence numbers
  FIN: no more data from sender

- Window (16 bits): the receive window size, indicating the number of octets—beginning with the one in the acknowledgment field—that the sender is willing to accept.

- Checksum (16 bits): a checksum based upon the IP address fields plus the TCP header and its length.

- Urgent pointer (16 bits): points to the first octet that follows the urgent data, and allows the receiver to determine how much urgent data is coming.

- Options (variable): one option (maximum TCP segment size) is currently defined.

TCP provides reliable delivery, but does it at an expense of higher overhead. A TCP/IP connection protocol (known as SLIP (Serial Line IP), reference [6-25]) to support serial lines has also been defined. For situations where reliability is not as critical, another Transport Layer protocol is available.

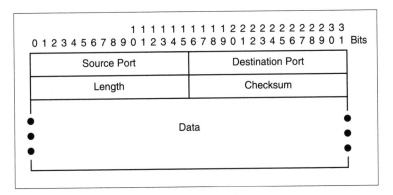

Figure 6-14. The UDP Header

6.5.2 User Datagram Protocol (UDP)

Some applications do not require the extensive error control functions provided by TCP. One example would be the Simple Network Management Protocol (SNMP) that is used to communicate status updates and parameter values between a remote device and a network management workstation. For such applications, absolute reliability is not a requirement, thus the lower overhead User Datagram Protocol (UDP) can be used. The UDP header, shown in Figure 6-14, has four fields:

- Source port (16 bits): the number of the calling port.

- Destination port (16 bits): the number of the called port.

- Length (16 bits): length of the UDP datagram.

- Checksum (16 bits): checksum for the UDP header.

Note the absence of the reliability-related fields such as the Sequence and Acknowledgment numbers. Since guaranteed delivery is not a UDP requirement, the header is shortened accordingly.

6.5.3 DoD Transport Layer Summary

Both the TCP and UDP headers begin with 16-bit Source and Destination port addresses. Values between 0-255 are reserved and designated Well-Known ports. The other port numbers, known as Ephemeral Ports, are available. See reference [6-26] for a listing of the reserved port numbers. Software developers may be interested in the TCP/IP implementation of the NetBIOS Application Program Interface (API). Reference [6-27] contains those details.

6.6 DoD Higher Layer Protocols

Extensive literature exists on the Application protocols used within the Internet (references [6-13] and [6-28] through [6-31]). A brief summary is presented here.

Simple Mail Transfer Protocol (SMTP) is an electronic messaging utility. SMTP is only concerned with the destination of the message, not its contents, and as such requires local host processing for message editing. See RFC 821 (reference [6-28]) for further details. TELNET is a protocol for virtual terminal operation, providing a facility to log-in to remote hosts. Once logged-in, the user appears to be connected locally. RFC 854 (reference [6-29]) details the TELNET protocol.

File Transfer Protocol (FTP), as its name implies, specifies how users can transfer files from a remote host without regard to the hardware or operating system involved. Both text and binary files are supported. Provisions also exist to restrict access by use of passwords. Further details are found in RFC 959 (reference [6-30]).

Simple Network Management Protocol (SNMP) is used to manage remote internetwork devices. It uses datagram transport (UDP) to provide communications between a network management station, and a network management agent in the managed object. A number of vendors are accepting SNMP as the network management protocol of choice, and incorporating it into their products. See RFC 1098 (reference [6-31]) for further information.

6.7   TCP/IP Internetworking Examples

As mentioned previously, a very large number of vendors support the TCP/IP protocols for PCs, LANs, minis, and mainframes. Reference [6-32] is a large compilation of the hardware and software products available. Following are three examples of LAN internetwork products that utilize the TCP/IP protocols.

6.7.1   Wollongong Pathway

The Wollongong Group, Inc. of Palo Alto, California provides a variety of products to connect PCs, minis, mainframes, supercomputers, and LANs. The first product group is known as WINS (Wollongong Integrated Networking Solutions). This family provides TCP/IP, NFS and OSI protocol support for DOS, VMS, and UNIX based platforms. The second group of software is Wollongong's PathWay family which is a client/server system for workstation access to minicomputers and LAN servers. Protocols supported include TCP/IP, OSI, NFS, NetBIOS and SMB. PathWay products are available to support a wide variety of hardware platforms including DOS, OS/2, Macintosh, UNIX, VAX/VMS and VAX/ULTRIX operating systems.

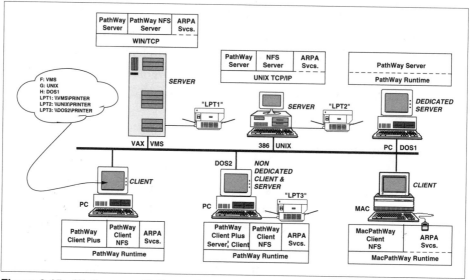

Figure 6-15a. Wollongong Pathway Connectivity Options
(Courtesy The Wollongong Group, Inc.)

A number of PathWay software products are available (see Figure 6-15a). PathWay Client PLUS for DOS is based upon the SMB protocols, and allows users access to files, print and mail services, and databases on any SMB-based server. The software also supports the NetBIOS interface. The PathWay Server for DOS allows a PC to be a high-performance server to the SMB-based Clients. PathWay Client/NFS for DOS supports access to servers with the NFS protocols. Both of the PathWay client products are available with an option supporting FTP, TELNET and SMTP protocols. 3Com, Tiara, and Western Digital Ethernet Network Interface Cards (NICs) can be used, and concurrent operation with Novell NetWare is possible. Support for Microsoft's NDIS (Network Driver Interface Standard) allows many other NICs to be used as well.

For UNIX systems, PathWay Server for UNIX allows non-dedicated file server operation. Supported versions are UNIX System V release 3, and UNIX 4.3 BSD. Supported hardware platforms include DEC, SUN, AT&T, NCR, and 80386 workstations with Interactive 386/ix. DOS and UNIX files can be shared and stored. DOS files on the UNIX server can be sent to any of the UNIX printers.

Another member of the software family, PathWay Server for VMS, provides support for VAX/VMS systems. Like the other products, the VMS version uses SMB, NFS and TCP/IP protocols. The DOS Client is given the impression that the VAX files appear to be directly connected to the PC.

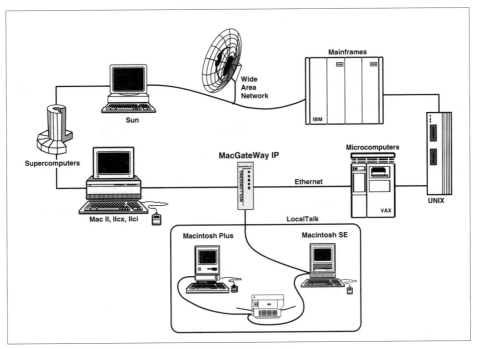

Figure 6-15b. Wollongong MacPathWay Configuration
(Courtesy The Wollongong Group, Inc.)

The final member of the PathWay series is named MacPathWay Access. It allows Apple Macintosh computers to connect to TCP/IP hosts. Installed as a HyperCard application, MacPathWay is fully compatible with the other PathWay products. Macintosh users are thus provided with FTP and TELNET support, as well as a variety of terminal emulations. A separate product, MacGateWay, provides gateway service between Ethernet and LocalTalk networks (see Figure 6-15b).

6.7.2 Novell's LAN WorkPlace

Novell, Inc. of San Jose, California (formerly Excelan), long known for its TCP/IP connectivity solutions, offers some unique hardware/software connectivity products known as the LAN WorkPlace. The LAN WorkPlace supports DOS, OS/2, Macintosh, XENIX, and UNIX operating systems. Communication is thus possible among a variety of dissimilar hosts, including Apple Macintosh, DEC VAX minicomputers, IBM mainframes and UNIX workstations. The connectivity is provided without a dedicated gateway by incorporating the TCP/IP protocols into the host's operating system and hardware platform.

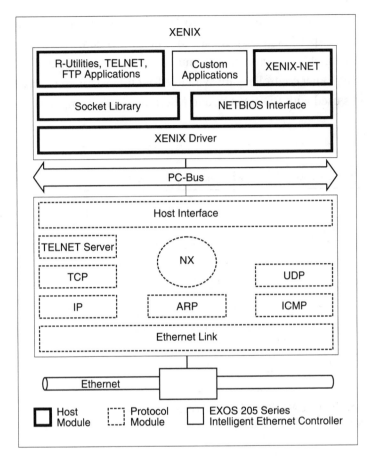

Figure 6-16a. Novell EXOS Controller Architecture
(Courtesy Novell, Inc. © 1988 Novell, Inc. All rights reserved.)

EXOS (for Excelan Open System) hardware is an intelligent Ethernet board (see Figure 6-16a) that acts as an intelligent front-end processor to the LAN. Each controller contains an Intel 80186 communications processor, an 82586 LAN coprocessor and 256 Kbytes of RAM. The on-board RAM is used to execute the TCP/IP software, thus relieving the host's CPU of that task. A multi-tasking operating system known as the Network Executive (NX) resides in EPROM and controls the protocol processing on the intelligent boards. By offloading many of the protocol processing tasks from the Host CPU and memory to the controller, LAN communication speed is greatly enhanced. The EXOS hardware supports PC, AT and MicroChannel architectures, and contains interfaces for thin and thick Ethernet and LattisNet. Other controllers are available for DEC's Bi-bus, Q-bus, and Unibus architectures used with PDP, VAX, and MicroVAX minicomputers.

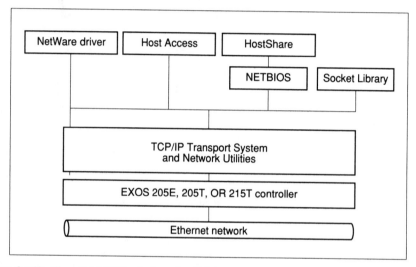

Figure 6-16b. Novell LAN Workplace for DOS Architecture
(Courtesy Novell, Inc. © 1988 Novell, Inc. All rights reserved.)

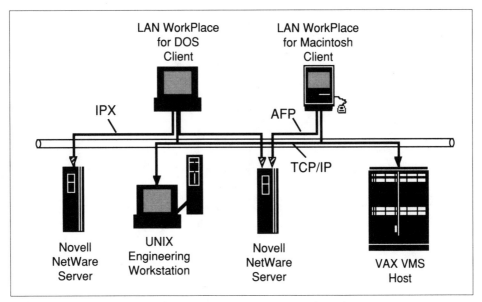

Figure 6-16c. Concurrent Access to NetWare and TCP/IP Environments
(Courtesy Novell, Inc. © 1988 Novell, Inc. All rights reserved.)

The LAN WorkPlace for DOS is a software package that builds upon the EXOS hardware, providing a number of user applications (see Figure 6-16b). The DOS, Xenix, and UNIX versions require EXOS adapters. The OS/2 product is built on top of Microsoft's NDIS and therefore does not require a front-end EXOS intelligent adapter. The Mac product also supports a variety of network adapters. The TCP/IP Transport System and NetWork Utilities provides the driver for the EXOS controller, utilities for administering the Ethernet network, plus the TCP/IP software. The future direction for the DOS product is to support a variety of network adapters.

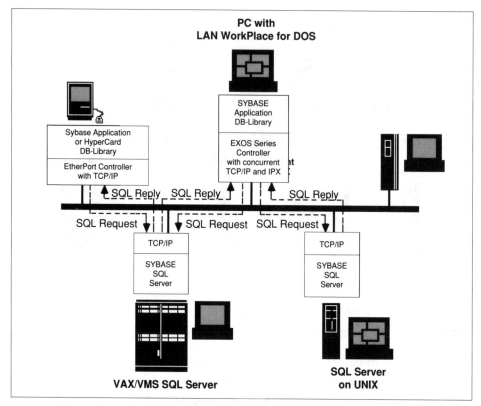

Figure 6-16d. Sybase Open Client/Server Architecture
(Courtesy Novell, Inc. © 1988 Novell, Inc. All rights reserved.)

Five different user applications are available. Host Access provides utilities and terminal emulation for accessing hosts on Ethernets. Utilities include FTP, TFTP (Trivial File Transfer Protocol), TELNET, and the R-Utilities to execute remote commands. HostShare implements Microsoft Networks and SMB (Server Message Block) protocols. The NetBIOS API (INT 5CH) is also supported, and is compliant with RFCs 1001 and 1002. NetWare drivers support workstations, servers, and internetwork bridges. Concurrent connections between NetWare servers and other TCP/IP hosts is thus possible. Finally, a Socket Library (in C) allows programmers to run custom applications on top of TCP/IP. A number of host servers are thus supported with the LAN WorkPlace for DOS, including NetWare, SMB and LAN Manager. Let's look at two applications of the LAN WorkPlace software.

Many Ethernet networks connect hosts running dissimilar software platforms such as UNIX, NetWare or DEC's VMS. Different file systems and transport protocols may be used as well. NetWare uses a distributed file system and the IPX protocol for file transport. Many TCP/IP-based hosts use FTP or TELNET for file transfer and terminal emulation, respectively. The LAN WorkPlace software allows these multiple protocol stacks to coexist on the same workstation hardware (see Figure 6-16c) The concurrent access implies that the NetWare file systems are always mounted, and also maintain the ability to execute any TCP/IP application such as FTP or TELNET. This is achieved by a unique design of direct and concurrent protocol architecture at the desktop, and unlike most other solutions, there is no gateway required. Thus, the DOS machine could map drives A:, B:, and C: locally; drives G: and H: to NetWare; and drives D:, E:, and F: to the Xenix (via PC-LAN/XenixNet) or SUN or VAX/VMS (via PC-LAN/SMB server). This design creates a user-transparent file system with all the protocol conversion handled at the desktop, transparent to the user. In addition, files can be copied between a TCP/IP host and a NetWare server. A Macintosh user would have similar abilities provided by the comparable LAN WorkPlace for Macintosh software, and would be able to access either TCP/IP applications or the NetWare Server using the AppleTalk Filing Protocol (AFP).

A second LAN WorkPlace application is the Sybase Open Client Architecture. This SQL database architecture is based upon two independent applications: a client portion that runs on a DOS or Macintosh workstation and a server that runs on an OS/2, VAX/VMS Stratus/VOS, or UNIX platform. The TCP/IP protocols are used to tie the complete architecture together (see Figure 6-16d). Clients use the LAN WorkPlace for DOS or Macintosh, and issue SQL requests. Servers run under their native operating system with TCP/IP transport, and issue SQL replies. Database users are thus provided the best of both worlds: a familiar user interface and a high-powered server. The glue connecting all of these dissimilar hosts is our familiar TCP/IP.

To summarize, the LAN WorkPlace family of products from Novell is a very strong, very stable state-of-the-art technology. The LAN WorkPlace provides TCP/IP connectivity in several ways. The EXOS intelligent Ethernet controllers optimize the protocol overhead and speed network throughput. The software supports DOS, OS/2, Macintosh, UNIX, and XENIX operating systems, thus facilitating interoperability in the host's native operating system. It provides heterogeneous and multi-vendor TCP/IP and NetWare support.

6.7.3   FTP Software PC/TCP

FTP Software, Inc. of Wakefield, Massachusetts was founded in 1886 by two of the developers of PC/IP, the first PC-based TCP/IP. They have continually updated the software and the current product, PC/TCP, is a complete implementation of the TCP/IP suite for PCs. The package is available for over 60 Ethernet, StarLAN, Token Ring, and X.25 Interfaces. SLIP and NDIS drivers are also supported. Other LANs—notably Novell, Banyan VINES, DECNet (via PCSA), and 3Com 3+Open—can be run on a single network interface card at the same time as PC/TCP.

PC/TCP includes many applications and utilities, such as file transfer provided by ftp, tftp, and rcp. An ftp server is added, so PCs equipped with PC/TCP can transfer files between themselves, as well as to and from servers. TELNET, rlogin, and supdup can be used for remote host log-in. The PC/TCP telnet allows up to 10 simultaneous connections, and offers DEC VT52, VT100, VT220, and IBM 3270 emulators. Third-party emulators are supported via DOS INT 14. Mail services are provided by SMTP-based mail programs. Many programs for resource sharing are included: network printers can be accessed with Lpr and iprint; tar and rmt provide remote backup of the PC files on Berkeley-derived UNIX systems (such as SUNOS); remote command execution on such systems is supported with rexec and rsh. PC/TCP also includes a bootp client, so systems managers with a bootp server can remotely configure PCs.

There is also a range of programs for getting information from the network. "Ping" and "inet" yield network debugging statistics; "finger" and "who is" give information about users; and "host" and "nicname" provide information about hosts.

Options for the PC/TCP software include:

- InterDrive and NFS client implementation, which provide transparent access to virtual drives on any NFS server.

- A NetBIOS add-on package, available for PC/TCP and PC/TCP Plus, supports NetBIOS applications over TCP/IP, in accordance with RFCs 1001 and 1002.

- A Development Kit is available for people who want to build their own applications.

To summarize, PC/TCP Plus provides the widest range of TCP/IP applications in a fast, reliable, hardware-independent solution.

To conclude our discussion of the TCP/IP protocols, note three characteristics that summarize their strength. First, the protocols were designed to internetwork dissimilar hosts—certainly a requirement in today's multi-vendor networks. Second, TCP/IP's roots were in military applications, necessitating reliability—also a requirement today. Finally, the wide vendor support for the protocol suite includes all major computer and LAN manufacturers worldwide. References [6-33] and [6-34] are recent articles that support TCP/IP use in LAN environments. We will look at how the Network Operating Systems support TCP/IP in Chapter 8.

6.8   References

[6-1] Schultz, Brad. "The Evolution of ARPANET." *Datamation* (August 1, 1988): 71–74.

[6-2] Padlipsky, M. A. "A Perspective on the ARPANET Reference Model." IEEE Infocom 83 Proceedings: 39-253

[6-3] The Wollongong Group, Inc. *Internetworking: An Introduction.* June 1988.

[6-4] Comer, Douglas. *Internetworking with TCP/IP Principles, Protocols and Architecture.* 2nd ed. Prentice-Hall, 1991.

[6-5] Telephone numbers for further information on internet-connected networks are:

NSFNET:	(617) 873-3400
CSNET:	(617) 873-1777
BITNET:	(202) 872-4200

[6-6] Cerf, Vinton and R. Kahn. "A Protocol for Packet Network Interconnection." *IEEE Transactions on Communications*, May 1974.

[6-7] Retz, David. "TCP/IP: DoD Suite Marches into the Business World." *Data Communications* (November 1987): 209–225.

[6-8] Cerf, Vinton G. and Edward Cain. "The DoD Internet Architecture Model." *Computer Network* Vol. 7, no. 5 (October 1983): 307–318.

[6-9] Request for Comments (RFC) documents may be obtained from: DDN Network Information Center SRI International, Room EJ291, 333 Ravenswood Avenue, Menlo Park, CA 94025, 800-235-3155/415-859-3695 NIC, @ SRI-NIC.ARPA

[6-10] DDN Network Information Center. *Tools for Monitoring and Debugging TCP/IP Internets and Interconnected Devices*. RFC 1147, April 1990.

[6-11] Mogul, Jeffrey C. *The Experimental Literature of the Internet: An Annotated Bibliography*. Digital Equipment Corp. WRL Research Report 88/3, August 1988.

[6-12] Hedrick, Charles L. "Introduction to the Internet Protocols." Rutgers the State University of New Jersey, September 1988.

[6-13] Stallings, William. *Handbook of Computer-Communications Standards*. Vol. 3, Howard W. Sams, 1987.

[6-14] DDN Network Information Center. *A Standard for the Transmission of IP Datagrams over Ethernet Networks*. RFC 894 April 1984.

[6-15] DDN Network Information Center. *An Ethernet Address Resolution Protocol*. RFC 826, November 1982.

[6-16] DDN Network Information Center. *A Reverse Address Resolution Protocol*. RFC 903, June 1984.

[6-17] DDN Network Information Center. *A Standard for the Transmission of IP Datagrams Over IEEE 802 Networks*. RFC 1042. February 1988.

[6-18] DDN Network Information Center. *A Standard for the Transmission of IP Datagrams and ARP Packets over ARCNET Networks*. RFC 1051, March 1988.

[6-19] DDN Network Information Center. *Internet Protocol*. RFC 791, September 1981.

[6-20] DDN Network Information Center. *Internet Control Message Protocol*. RFC 792, September 1981.

[6-21] Davidson, John. *An Introduction to TCP/IP*. New York: Springer-Verlag, 1988.

[6-22] Moy, John. "OSPF: Next Generation Routing Comes to TCP/IP Networks." *LAN Technology* (April 1990): 71–79.

[6-23] DDN Network Information Center. *Transmission Control Protocol*. RFC 93, September 1981.

[6-24] DDN Network Information Center. *User Datagram Protocol*. RFC 768, August 1980.

[6-25] DDN Network Information Center. *Compressing TCP/IP Headers for Low-Speed Serial Links*. RFC 1144, February 1990.

[6-26] DDN Network Information Center. *Assigned Numbers*. RFC 1060, March 1990.

[6-27] DDN Network Information Center. *Protocol Standard for a NetBIOS Service on a TCP/UDP Transport: Concepts and Methods*. RFC 1001. Detailed Specifications. RFC 1002, March 1987.

[6-28] DDN Network Information Center. *Simple Mail Transfer Protocol (SMTP)*. RFC 821.

[6-29] DDN Network Information Center. *TELNET Protocol Specification*. RFC 854.

[6-30] DDN Network Information Center. *File Transfer Protocol (FTP)*. RFC 959.

[6-31] DDN Network Information Center. *Simple Network Management Protocol*. RFC 1098, April 1989.

[6-32] DDN Network Information Center. *DDN Protocol Implementations and Vendors Guide*. February, 1989.

[6-33] Sharkey, Scott, et. al. "TCP/IP Provides Passage to Foreign LANs." *LAN Technology* (April 1989): 23–28.

[6-34] Stallings, William." The Glue for Internetworking." *Byte* (September 1989): 221–224.

CHAPTER 7

XNS Protocols

Unlike TCP/IP, the Xerox Network Systems (XNS) protocols may not be an internetworking protocol suite that comes immediately to mind. XNS has, however, made a very significant—albeit quiet—impact on the architecture of many LAN operating systems. XNS was developed at Xerox Corporation's Palo Alto Research Center during the late 1970s in conjunction with research into Ethernet. (Recall that DEC, Intel and Xerox collaborated on the Ethernet development, which was announced in 1973.) With interest in Ethernet networks growing in the late 1970s, the need for many more internetworking supports—such as network address formats—evolved, and research extended toward developing a mechanism to internetwork multiple LANs. The culmination of the effort was the Xerox Network Systems architecture and protocols, first published in 1980.

XNS was initiated as an open architecture, and was designed with multi-vendor internetworking in mind. As a result, major networking software vendors, including Novell, 3Com, and Banyan, have implemented the XNS protocols within their respective architectures. We will investigate these XNS derivatives in Section 7.7. First, however, let's study the architecture of an XNS internetwork.

7.1 XNS Internetwork Architecture

The XNS architecture makes two basic assumptions about its users: the internetwork's underlying LAN technology is Ethernet, and multiple Ethernets exist. These Ethernets are connected by various communication channels, such as dial-up or leased lines (see Figure 7-1), and the intelligence to communicate between them resides in an internetwork router. The unit of information transferred via the internetwork is known as an internet packet, which must necessarily contain additional addressing to assure proper delivery of the packet to the desired destination network and host. This packet is delivered on a datagram (not virtual circuit)

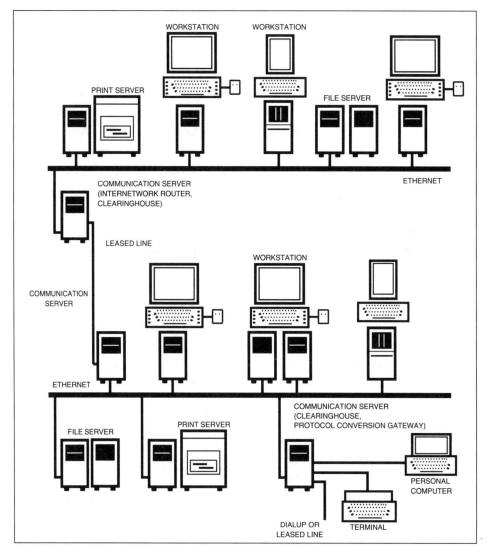

Figure 7-1. An Internetwork of Ethernet LANs
(Courtesy Xerox Corporation)

basis, in which neither delivery nor sequentiality is guaranteed. To provide for those situations requiring reliable transfer, a number of Transport Layer protocols (which we will study in Section 7.5) are used.

The XNS Architecture defines five different layers (zero through four), and corresponds closely to the OSI model (see Figure 7-2)—so closely, in fact, that XNS is credited, in part, as being the inspiration behind the OSI layered structure.

XNS Level 0 defines the transmission media protocols that provide the physical mechanism for packet transport. This level corresponds to the OSI Physical and Data Link Layers, and includes internetworking options such as Ethernet (naturally!), X.25, leased and dial-up lines. Typical interfaces such as RS-232-C, RS-449, and X.21 are supported.

XNS Levels 1 and 2 are collectively known as the Transport protocols. XNS Level 1 defines the destination of the datagram (or packet), and how it will get there. The Internetwork Datagram Protocol (IDP) is defined, as well as an addressing scheme to designate the various networks, hosts and sockets through which that packet will originate, traverse, or terminate. (We'll look at the addressing and routing schemes in Section 7.2. XNS Level 1 corresponds to the OSI Network Layer.)

XNS Level 2 provides structures for the stream of datagrams. This level deals with the multitude of issues such as sequencing, flow control and retransmissions that are required of the OSI Transport Layer. Five different protocols are defined at this level in order to satisfy varying user requirements: Routing Information Protocol (RIP); Error Protocol (Error); Echo Protocol (Echo); Sequenced Packet Protocol (SPP); and Packet Exchange Protocol (PEP).

XNS Level 3 provides structures for the actual data that was transmitted, and also controls various processes. As such, Level 3 covers the OSI Session and Presentation Layers, and is designated the Control Protocols.

XNS Level 4 deals with the various Application Protocols, similar to the OSI model. We will briefly discuss the XNS Control and Application protocols in Section 7.6.

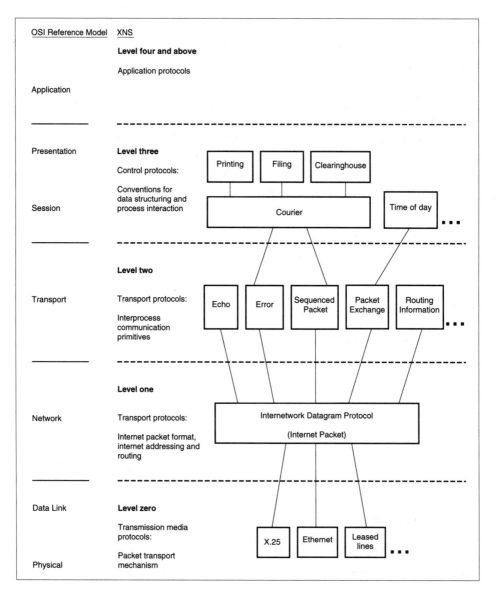

Figure 7-2. XNS Protocol Architecture
(Courtesy Xerox Corp.)

Xerox offers two excellent references on Ethernet ([7-1]) and the XNS development ([7-2]). A third, [7-3], written by a Novell software architect, provides some interesting XNS history. To begin our study, we'll look at the addressing schemes that facilitate router operation.

7.2   Datagram Addressing and Routing Within XNS

The XNS packet (or datagram) must be delivered to the correct destination to assure meaningful communication. Since the source and destination may be on different networks, additional addressing is required.

The Internet packet includes three specific address fields. The Host address is a 48-bit number that identifies any system that is connected to a network. The host address numbering is a flat scheme (not hierarchical) and uniquely identifies each hardware element. By implementing a flat Host address (which can be burned into a ROM), Xerox allowed for that host to be moved from one network to another without requiring the revision of its address. The 48-bit field can address up to 281,474,977 different hosts (reference [7-4]).

A Network address identifies a specific network (e.g. LAN) within an internet. This number is required for internetwork routing and is a 32-bit field. All networks within an internet have a unique Network address; a host may be connected to multiple networks, each of which would have a unique identity.

A Socket address locates a specific host process that can send and receive packets. Of the 65,536 possible socket numbers, the first 3000 are reserved for well-known sockets that are defined within the internet. All other socket numbers can be re-used.

To illustrate the process of packet addressing and routing within an XNS internet, consider Figure 7-3, taken from reference [7- 5]. The Source host (#s) exists on an Ethernet (Network A), and needs to communicate with the Destination host

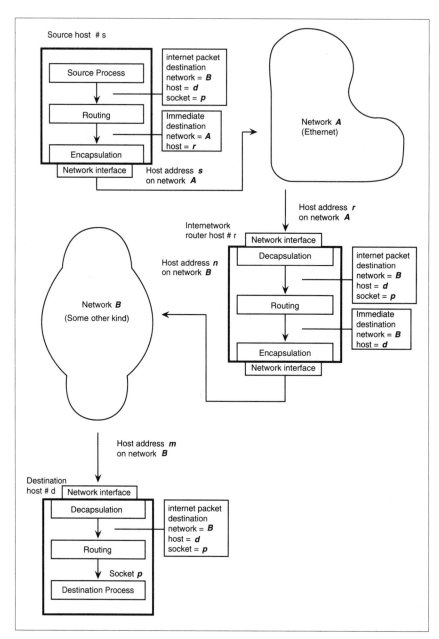

Figure 7-3. XNS Internetwork Packet Delivery
(Courtesy Xerox Corp.)

(#d), which exists on some other type of network (B). The Destination socket (p) is also specified by the source process. The routing table within the Source host determines that the Destination host is not known on its network (A), and encapsulates the packet for transmission on network A to the internetwork router (#r). At the router, the packet is decapsulated, and the full destination address (Network B, host #d, Socket p) is read. Router (#r) performs another table lookup and determines that the desired host (#d) exists on network B. Another encapsulation of the packet occurs (for transmission on network B, to network-specific host # m) and the packet then reaches the desired host (#d). Additional routing within that host provides packet delivery to the appropriate socket (p).

With this introduction to the XNS architecture and addressing scheme, let's now look at the protocols in detail.

7.3   XNS Level 0: Transmission Media Protocols

Referring again to Figure 7-2, note that several options, including Ethernet, X.25, and leased line connections are available for the XNS Level 0 protocols. The function of these protocols is to move the data across the transmission medium, which may be a coaxial cable (in the case of Ethernet), or twisted pair used with either analog or digital private lines. Since the transmission (or Data Link Layer) frame format may differ in length from the internet packet, provisions must also be made to fragment the packet prior to encapsulation within that frame. The specific frame header and trailer must also be added as required by the transmission media protocol of choice. Ethernet is the most obvious choice for XNS LAN implementations, and thus a brief description of the Ethernet frame and its addressing scheme is in order.

As discussed in Section 7.2, a 48-bit flat address is used for both Destination and Source addresses (see Figure 7-4). These 48 bits are divided into six octets—A, B, C, D, E, and F—transmitted in that order with the least significant bit (LSB) of each

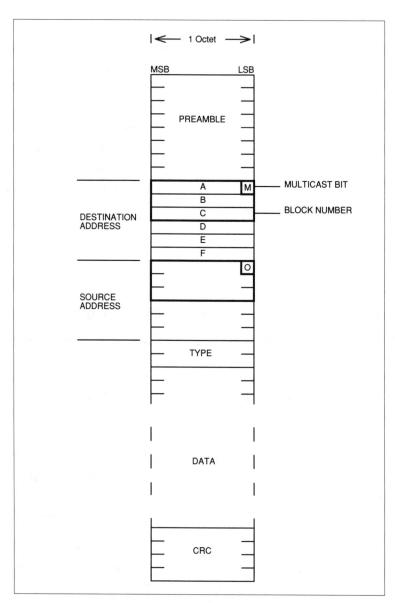

Figure 7-4. Ethernet Frame Format
(Courtesy Xerox Corp.)

octet being transmitted first. Octets A, B, and C are considered a block number, with blocks assigned to individual manufacturers. Each of the 8,388,608 (2 to the 23rd power) blocks contains 16,777,216 (2 to the 24th power) Host address numbers (octets D, E, and F). The LSB of octet A is reserved for the multicast bit, indicating that the address is destined for more than one host. Multicasts to all hosts (known as broadcasts) are indicated with all 48 bits of the Destination address set to 1. Note that the multicast bit is set to zero within the Source address, since a multicast transmission is meaningless.

A Type field (sometimes called an Ethertype) follows the Source address, and this two-octet field indicates the type of higher-layer protocol encapsulated within the Data field. The value 0600H is assigned to the XNS protocols. From 46 to 1500 octets of data may be transmitted with each frame; values outside of these ranges are considered invalid and rejected by the intended receiver. A 32-bit Cyclic Redundancy Check (CRC) completes the frame (reference [7-4]).

An encapsulated packet within an Ethernet frame is illustrated in Figure 7-5. In the next section we'll look in detail at the packet format.

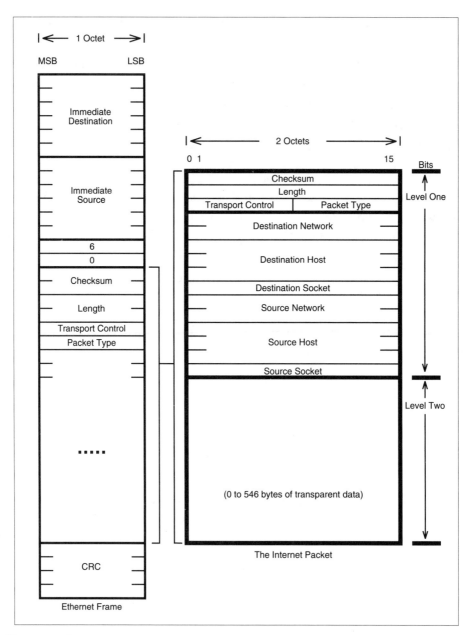

Figure 7-5. The Internet Packet Within an Ethernet Frame
(Courtesy Xerox Corp.)

7.4 XNS Level 1: Transport Protocols—Internet

Only one protocol, the Internet Datagram Protocol (IDP), is defined by XNS Level 1. IDP's function is to address, route, and deliver internet packets on a best-effort basis. Recall that this type of service is termed an unreliable datagram. The term "unreliable" is used because delivery of that data is not guaranteed. The term "datagram" is used because each packet is routed independently of all other packets within the data stream.

Figure 7-6 shows the format of the XNS Internet Packet. The individual fields are described below:

- Checksum (2 octets) is a software checksum of the 16-bit words within the internet packet (excluding the checksum field). Since the Data Link Layer also provides a checksum (CRC), many vendor software implementations will replace this field with FFFFH indicating that the internet packet is unchecksummed (although the frame is).

- Length (2 octets) is the length of the internet packet measured in octets. This length is nominally 576 octets: 30 octets of header, 12 octets of Sequenced Packet Protocol (SPP) header, 512 octets of data (a typical disk page), plus 12 octets for Level 3 protocol use. A garbage byte (octet) may be added to fill the data to an integral number of 16-bit words, but is not included in the length count.

- Transport Control (1 octet) is used by the internetwork routers, and is initialized to zero by the Source process. As the routers modify this field, they also recompute the Checksum. The Hop Count (bits 4-7) is incremented as the packet traverses each router. A packet requiring a hop count of sixteen would be discarded. Bits 0-7 are reserved and set to zero.

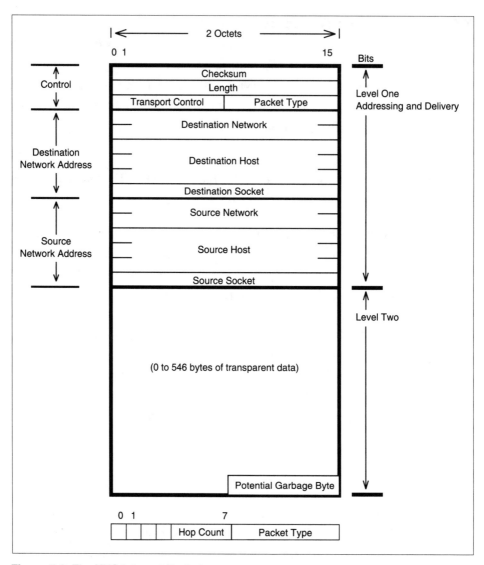

Figure 7-6. The XNS Internet Packet
(Courtesy Xerox Corp.)

- Packet Type (1 octet) identifies the format of the Data field, similar to the Ethertype. Defined types include:

Protocol	Packet Type (hexadecimal)
Unknown	00
Routing Information	01
Echo	02
Error	03
Packet Exchange	04
Sequenced Packet	05
Experimental	10-1F

- Destination and Source addresses (12 octets each) define the internet addresses, and specify the Network (4 octets), Host (6 octets), and Socket (2 octets). Socket numbers may also be assigned, and two are reserved: zero (unknown) and all ones (all). Other well-known sockets are:

Function	Well-Known Socket (hexadecimal)
Routing Information	01
Echo	02
Router Error	03
Experimental	20-3F

- Data (0-546 octets) information from the higher layers.

- Garbage byte (optional 1 octet) allows the data to occupy an integral number of 16-bit words.

Note that the various internetwork routers may modify the Destination and Source network numbers via table lookups as the packet moves through the internetwork (we saw an example of this in Figure 7-3). Our next topic of study will be the various Level 2 protocols that fill the Data field of the internet packet. Reference [7-6] gives a summary of these protocols, and [7-7] provides extensive details.

7.5   XNS Level 2: Transport Protocols—Interprocess

From Figure 7-2 we saw that five different protocols are implemented at the Interprocess level. We'll study each of these separately.

7.5.1   Routing Information Protocol

Each router contains a table that performs a lookup to determine the correct route for each internet packet. This table is maintained with information transmitted or received at the well-known Routing Information socket, as the various routers inform each other of the changes in the internetwork topology. The Routing Information Protocol (RIP) is used for this purpose.

The RIP packet is specified by the Packet Type field of the IDP header (see Figure 7-7). The first field (two octets) of the RIP packet indicates the Operation— either a request for routing information (Operation = 1), or a response containing routing information (Operation = 2). The Contents portion of the RIP packet contains one or more tuples (six octets each). Each tuple consists of a 32-bit Object Network number, and a 16-bit Internetwork Delay, measured in hops. For a request, the Object Network defines the network of interest, and the Internetwork Delay is set to 16 hops (defined as infinity). Requested information regarding all Object Networks would use the "all" address and set the Internetwork Delay to infinity (16 hops).

Response packets indicate the number of hops required to reach any host on that network via the responding router. The delay to reach a router on a directly connected network is defined as zero hops.

7.5.2 Error Protocol

The Error Protocol (see Figure 7-8) is used for diagnostic purposes, and is sent from the well-known router error socket to the source socket that caused the error. The Error Number (two octets) indicates the kind of error:

Error Number (octal notation)	Description
0	An unspecified error is detected at destination.
1	The checksum is incorrect, or the packet has some other serious inconsistency detected at destination.
2	The specified socket does not exist at the specified destination host.
3	The destination cannot accept the packet due to resource limitations.
1000	An unspecified error occurred before reaching destination.
1001	The checksum is incorrect, or the packet has experienced some other serious inconsistency before reaching destination.
1002	The destination host cannot be reached from here.
1003	The packet has passed through 15 internet routers without reaching its destination.
1004	The packet is too large to be forwarded through some intermediate network. The Error Parameter field contains the length of the largest packet that can be accommodated.

Certain kinds of errors are elaborated upon within the Error Parameter field (2 octets). The Error packet contents contain a copy of the first portion (IDP header plus higher-layer headers) of the offending packet.

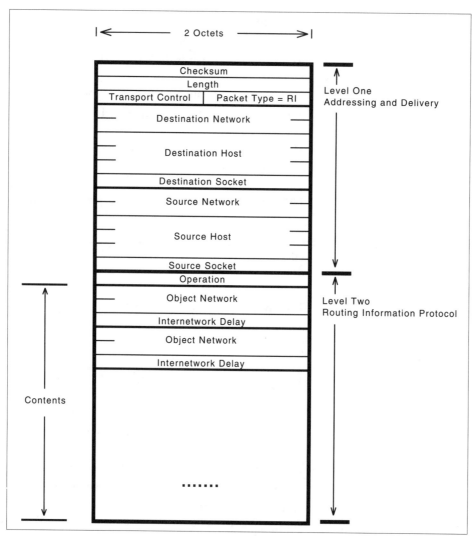

Figure 7-7. XNS Routing Information Protocol Packet
(Courtesy Xerox Corp.)

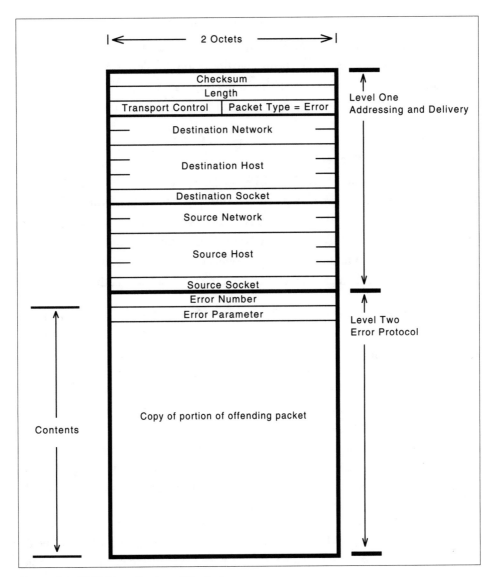

Figure 7-8. XNS Error Protocol Packet
(Courtesy Xerox Corp.)

7.5.3   Echo Protocol

The Echo Protocol is a simple protocol used to verify the existence of, and transmission path to, a designated host. Two operations are defined (see Figure 7-9): Echo Request (Operation = 1) and Echo Reply (Operation = 2). The data portion of the Echo Protocol packet will contain the data of the arriving packet.

7.5.4   Sequenced Packet Protocol

The Sequenced Packet Protocol (SPP) is the workhorse of the XNS Transport Layer (Levels 1 and 2), providing reliable transmission of data from the various higher-layer processes. All transmissions include sending and receiving sequence numbers for message reassembly, flow control, and error control. The basis of the process-to-process communication is a connection that is opened between two sockets. Packets are then exchanged between the two sockets via that connection.

The SPP header (see Figure 7-10) is a 12-octet field that is transmitted immediately after the IDP header. Up to 534 octets of data may complete the datagram. Fields in the SPP header include:

- Connection Control (1 octet) includes four subfields plus four reserved bits (set to zero). System Packet determines if that packet contains system (control) information or client process data. Send Acknowledgment is a request from sender to receiver requesting an acknowledgment. Attention provides a signal to the client process that this packet has arrived. End-of-Message indicates that this packet terminates one message and that the subsequent packet will begin another message.

- Datastream Type (1 octet) is used by the higher-layer protocols to define the type of information contained within that packet's data field. Examples would be data, interrupt, or end-of-data types.

- Source and Destination Connection ID (2 octets each) are specified at each end of the connection at the time of connection establishment. All subsequent transmissions will reference these same ID numbers.

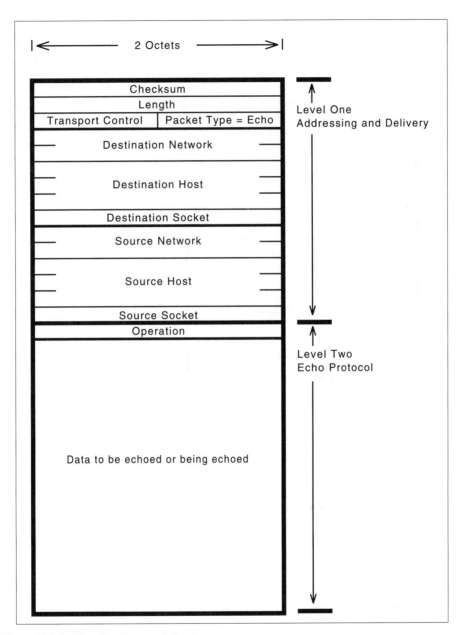

Figure 7-9. XNS Echo Protocol Packet
(Courtesy Xerox Corp.)

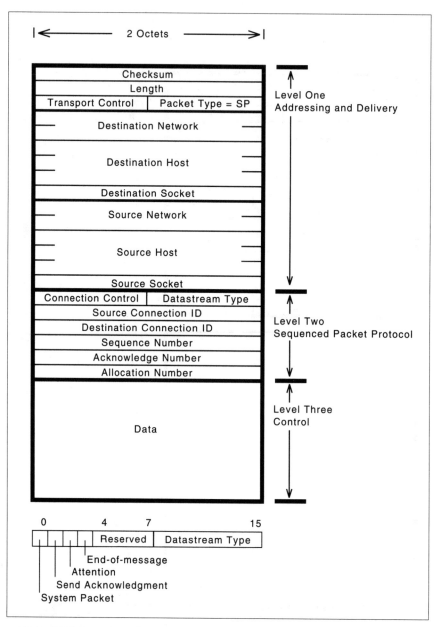

Figure 7-10. XNS Sequenced Packet Protocol Packet
(Courtesy Xerox Corp.)

- Sequence Number (2 octets) is the send sequence number that provides the receiver packet with sequencing, duplicate suppression, and flow control. Packet sequencing always begins at zero, and extends to a maximum of 65,536.

- Acknowledge Number (2 octets) indicates the sequence number of the next expected packet from the other end of the link.

- Allocation Number (2 octets) indicates the maximum packet sequence number that will be accepted from the other end of the link.

The Data field of the SPP packet (0 to 534 octets) is the higher-layer information. Note that Data packets must not have the System Packet bit set. Packets with the Attention bit set will have only one octet of data.

7.5.5   Packet Exchange Protocol

The Packet Exchange Protocol (PEP) is used to transmit packets with reliability greater than that of independent packets, but without the overhead associated with SPP. Its purpose is somewhat analogous to the DoD User Datagram Protocol (UDP) that we studied in Section 6.5.2. (Recall that UDP provides some Transport Layer reliability without the extensive header overhead required by TCP.) PEP is similar, and operates on a single packet basis, using any socket as source and destination locations.

Two fields are included in the PEP header (see Figure 7-11). The ID field is a 32-bit number that identifies the transaction (a pair of packets) between sender and receiver. The Client Type field defines the higher-layer client protocol.

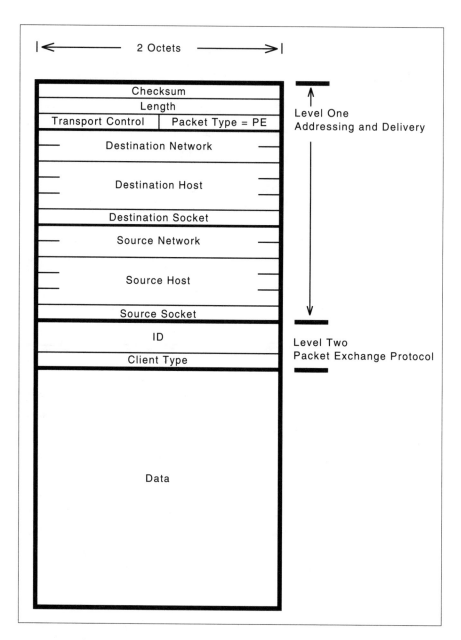

Figure 7-11. XNS Packet Exchange Protocol Packet
(Courtesy Xerox Corp.)

7.6   XNS Levels 3 and 4

Reviewing Figure 7-2, note that XNS Level 3, the Control Protocols, perform OSI Session and Presentation Layer functions, and that XNS Level 4 contains the Application Layer procedures. (Since these higher layers are somewhat implementation-specific, we won't go into great detail.) One protocol, the XNS Courier, has been used extensively in LAN operating systems such as Banyan VINES and will be studied here.

7.6.1   XNS Courier Protocol

The Courier protocol, which is subtitled the Remote Procedure Call (RPC) protocol, defines a mechanism for transmission between various entities. The underlying assumption in Courier is that two types of elements exist within the network (see Figure 7-12). The Active System Element issues the Call requests with the necessary arguments that request an action. The other element, called the Passive System Element, is a provider of the requested service. The Remote Program responds with the Return results or an error statement in the event that the requested function could not be completed.

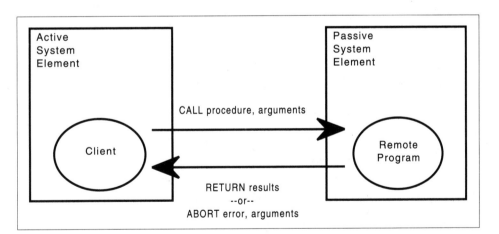

Figure 7-12. XNS Courier Remote Procedure Call Model
(Courtesy Xerox Corp.)

Most importantly, it is assumed that the Active System Element (or Client) and the Passive System Element (or Remote Program) may not be located on the same physical network. As a result, the Courier protocols rely upon the underlying Internetwork Transport protocols (XNS Levels 1 and 2) to facilitate the required communication between Client and Remote Program.

The Courier protocol interfaces with the Sequenced Packet Protocol (SPP) at XNS Level 2 to move the request or response to the appropriate network destination (review Figure 7-2). Courier also interfaces with the higher-level Control and Application protocols to translate the specific service request into call messages and the resulting Return or Abort messages. To facilitate the Application Layer interface, the Courier protocol has its own language—described further in reference [7-8].

7.6.2 Clearinghouse Protocol

As we saw, the Courier protocol provides Remote Procedure Call functions so that services on a remote host can be requested and obtained. A mechanism must be established, however, to identify the location of that remote host containing the desired information. The Clearinghouse protocol provides this directory service. Clearinghouse is a database of objects, with each entry including various properties associated with that object. The naming of those objects follows a three-level hierarchy—Local Name: Domain: Organization. An example would be John Doe:Accounting:Denver. The database can also be distributed throughout several locations, and for larger networks many Clearinghouse servers would exist.

A Clearinghouse request example is shown in Figure 7-13, taken from reference [7-2]. The user needs to locate a particular resource, such as a printer, and issues a request for the Clearinghouse address. The Courier and Internet protocols are invoked in turn, and result in an Ethernet broadcast message. The Clearinghouse server responds and identifies itself. The user then interrogates the Clearinghouse database to determine the specific address of the printer in question. See reference [7-9] for further details on the Clearinghouse protocols.

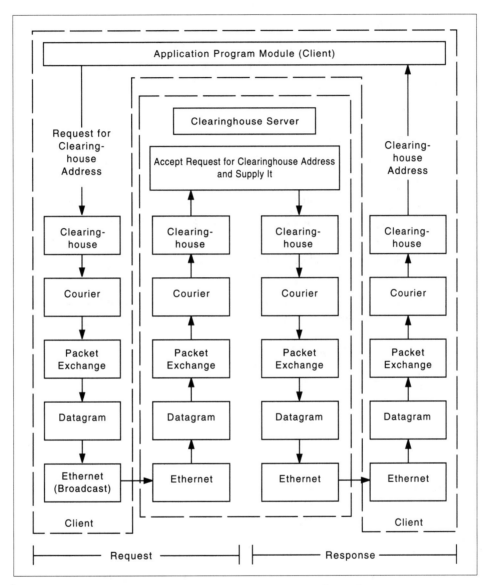

Figure 7-13. XNS Clearinghouse Request and Response Operation
(Courtesy Xerox Corp.)

285

7.7   XNS Implementations

As described earlier and in reference [7-3], the XNS protocols have been implemented extensively in various networking software architectures in addition to Xerox's. We'll briefly describe three of these implementations.

7.7.1   Novell's NetWare

NetWare, one of the most popular LAN operating systems, has made extensive use of the XNS protocols in both the Network and Transport Layer implementations. NetWare's Network Layer protocol, the Internetwork Packet Exchange (IPX), is identical to the XNS IDP packet format. Reviewing Figure 7-6, the Transport Control field is used by the NetWare internetwork routers. Defined Packet Types are 0 (Unknown Packet), 4 (Packet Exchange), 5 (Sequenced Packet Protocol), or 17 (NetWare Core Protocol). The Destination/Source Network numbers are assigned by the network administrator, and the Destination/Source Host numbers are assigned by the specific node hardware (either within a ROM or by DIP switches).

Xerox has assigned five sockets for NetWare use:

0451H   File Service Packet

0452H   Service Advertising Packet

0453H   Routing Information Packet

0455H   NetBIOS Packet

0456H   Diagnostic Packet

File servers identify themselves using the Service Advertising Protocol (SAP), socket 0452H. File service requests are addressed to socket 0451H.

The Data field is not always limited to 546 octets. For throughput optimization, Novell extends this field based upon the local network hardware (Ethernet, Token Ring, etc.) in use.

NetWare's Transport Layer, the Sequenced Packet Exchange (SPX) protocol, is based upon XNS SPP and uses IDP Packet Type 5. The SPX header also uses the various SPP fields that were discussed in Section 7.5.4. Another higher-layer option is the NetWare Core Protocol (NCP), which uses IPX Packet Type 17. NCP is Novell's proprietary protocol, used for file access, printer sharing, and application program communication. Reference [7-10] is a good source for further details on NetWare's XNS implementation.

7.7.2   3Com 3+ and 3+Open

3Com Corporation utilizes the XNS protocols in both the DOS-based 3+ and the OS/2 LAN Manager-based 3+Open network operating systems. The 3Com Network Layer is based upon XNS IDP, and supports four of the five XNS Transport Layer protocols (the Error Protocol is not used). The XNS IDP header, as well as the RIP, Echo, PEP, and SPP header formats are identical to their XNS counterparts. Like Novell, 3Com also extends the maximum length of the IDP packet to accommodate the Data Link Layer hardware in use. See Appendix B of reference [7-11] for further details.

7.7.3   Banyan VINES

Banyan Systems' VINES (Virtual Networking System) also has strong roots in XNS. At the Network Layer, VINES defines four protocols. One of these, the VINES Internet Protocol (IP), is structured similarly to XNS IDP (reference [7-12]). The Checksum (set to FFFFH), Length, Transport Control and Protocol Type fields are similar to their XNS IDP counterparts. The Addressing fields differ, with XNS IDP using 12 octets each for Destination and Source, and VINES IP using 6 octets each. As a result, the VINES IP header requires 18 octets, not the 30 octets specified by XNS IDP.

The VINES Transport Layer also has a number of protocols defined for specific functions. Two of these, the Interprocess Communications Protocol (IPC) and the Sequenced Packet Protocol (SPP) are similar, but not identical, to the XNS SPP. In view of the network addressing scheme differences discussed above, the VINES IPC and SPP headers (16 octets in length) include Source/Destination port addresses, similar to the XNS SPP socket addresses. For VINES IP, IPC, and SPP protocols, the VINES headers thus occupy a total of 34 octets, instead of the 42 octets defined by XNS. All differences aside, however, it is clear to see the influence that the XNS protocols had on the VINES architecture. See reference [7-13], Chapter 6 for further VINES details.

Xerox has thus had a dramatic influence on the shape of today's LANs and internetworks. Both the Ethernet network and the XNS protocol suite developments have made significant contributions to distributed computing.

7.8 References

[7-1] DEC, Intel and Xerox. *The Ethernet, A Local Area Network-Data Link Layer and Physical Layer Specification, Version 2.0.* DEC document no. AA-K759B-TK, November 1982.

[7-2] Xerox Corp. *Xerox Network Systems Architecture General Information Manual.* Document no. XNSG 068505, April 1985.

[7-3] Neibaur, Dale. "Understanding XNS: The Prototypical Internetwork Protocol." *Data Communications* (December 21, 1989): 43 – 51.

[7-4] Dalal Y.K. and R. S. Printis. "48-bit Absolute Internet and Ethernet Host Numbers." Reprinted in *Office Systems Technology*, Xerox document OSD-R8203A, January 1984, pp. 161-166.

[7-5] Y. K. Dalal, "Use for Multiple Networks in the Xerox Network System." Reprinted in *Office Systems Technology,* Xerox document no.OSD-R8203A (January 1984): 150-160.

[7-6] White, J. and Y. K. Dalal. "Higher-level Protocols Enhance Ethernet." Reprinted in *Office Systems Technology,* Xerox document no. OSD-RS203A (January 1984): 167-175.

[7-7] Xerox Corp. *Internet Transport Protocols.* Document no. XNSS 028112, December 1981.

[7-8] Xerox Corp. *Courier: The Remote Procedure Call Protocol.* Document XNSS 038112, December 1981.

[7-9] Xerox Corp. *Clearinghouse Protocol.* Document no. XSIS 078404, April 1984.

[7-10] Novell, Inc. *NetWare System Interface Technical Overview.* Document no. 100-00569-001, 1989.

[7-11] 3Com Corp. *NetProbe Network Utility Guide*. Document no. 3914-00, September 1988.

[7-12] Banyan Systems, Inc. *VINES Protocol Definition*. Document no. DA254-00, December 1989.

[7-13] Miller, Mark A. *LAN Protocol Handbook*. Redwood City, CA: M&T Books, 1990.

CHAPTER 8

Networking Software, Internetworking, and Interoperability

Recall your first Network Operating System (NOS). If yours was like mine, it was probably a basic file-sharing system that required any network printer to physically reside on a single server. Communication with the outside world was limited to a proprietary electronic mail application which was built into the system and handled only a small amount of data transfer, such as one line (80 characters). You probably wished that the network's limited communications capabilities could be expanded. Perhaps you needed to access a mini-computer at your facility or a remote host via the TCP/IP protocols. Earlier NOSs lacked these capabilities, but as users (like us) demanded greater performance, vendors rose to the challenge.

That challenge to expand NOS capabilities has been addressed in three ways. First, hardware platforms and peripherals have been advanced to the point where 32-bit computing and megabytes of storage capacity are commonplace. Second, support for standard internetworking protocols—such as X.25 and TCP/IP—is being added to the core systems of most NOSs. And, with the advent of internetworking and standardized protocols comes a third, ever-evolving internetworking solution—interoperability.

Interoperability is the antithesis of incompatibility. Let's define the term by example. Users need the flexibility to employ whatever hardware platform (PC, Macintosh, Sun workstation) or operating system (DOS, OS/2, NetWare, LAN

291

Manager) best suits their requirements. Further, a constraint exists at the Application Layers: users require seamless (i.e. transparent) access between applications. For example, an electronic mail program for a Macintosh should be able to send and receive a message from another package running on a UNIX-based minicomputer. (If we throw the WAN variable into the equation, the Macintosh and UNIX-minicomputer would be across the country from each other.)

In this chapter, we will discuss the internetworking and interoperability of the key networking software implementations: Apple Computer AppleTalk; Sitka Corporation TOPS; Banyan Systems VINES; Novell NetWare 386; Microsoft Corporation OS/2 LAN Manager; 3Com Corporation 3+Open; AT&T StarGROUP LAN Manager Server; and IBM OS/2 LAN Server. In Chapter 9, we'll discuss the interoperability issue further by exploring various gateway products. An excellent summary of interoperability issues between various protocol suites is given in reference [8-1]. Let's begin with AppleTalk.

8.1   Apple Computer AppleTalk

In 1985, Apple Computer, Inc. of Cupertino, California developed the AppleTalk architecture (reference [8-2]) which became known as AppleTalk Phase 1. An extension of this architecture, known as AppleTalk Phase 2, was released in 1989 (reference [8-3]). An excellent article about the Phase 1 to Phase 2 enhancements is reference [8-4]. The AppleTalk protocol suite (Figure 8-1) was examined in detail in a companion volume (reference [8-5]); we'll briefly summarize it here.

8.1.1   AppleTalk Protocols

The AppleTalk Physical and Data Link Layers support a variety of hardware connections. Phase 1 networks support Ethernet and LocalTalk (the 230 Kbps Macintosh-based network). Phase 2 added IEEE 802.2, 802.3, and 802.5 support. Links to IBM's SNA and DEC's DECnet architectures are also available; we'll explore those later.

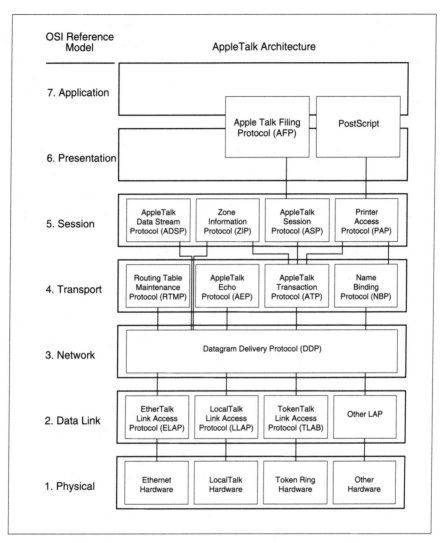

Figure 8-1. Comparing the AppleTalk Architecture with OSI
(*Courtesy Apple Computer, Inc.*)

The Network Layer is implemented with the Datagram Delivery Protocol (DDP), the core protocol operating within the internet routers. The channel between the routers can be a dial-up or leased telephone line (like the Hayes Interbridge, discussed in section 4.3.2); a LAN backbone (such as Ethernet or Token Ring); or some other network (such as DECnet).

The AppleTalk Transport Layer implements a number of protocols, including RTMP (Routing Table Maintenance Protocol); AEP (AppleTalk Echo Protocol); ATP (AppleTalk Transaction Protocol); and NBP (Name Binding Protocol). Closely tied to these are the Session Layer protocols. Together, these two layers perform the functions of establishing and assuring reliable communications over the network.

The Session Layer protocols include ADSP (AppleTalk Data Stream Protocol); ZIP (Zone Information Protocol); ASP (AppleTalk Session Protocol); and PAP (Printer Access Protocol).

The OSI Presentation and Application Layers are implemented in AFP (AppleTalk Filing Protocol) and Postscript—a page description protocol used with the LaserWriter printers.

8.1.1.2 AppleTalk Network Architecture

The heart of the AppleTalk network is the internetwork router, which can exist in three different configurations (see Figure 8-2). A Local Router (Configuration A) connects networks that are in close proximity—for example, within the same building. Two Half Routers (Configuration B) can be used with a WAN facility to connect two remote locations. A Backbone Router (Configuration C) connects a LocalTalk network to an Ethernet or Token Ring backbone. The internetwork that results from these router connections can be quite large, and as such, may contain a number of third-party components (see Figure 8-3).

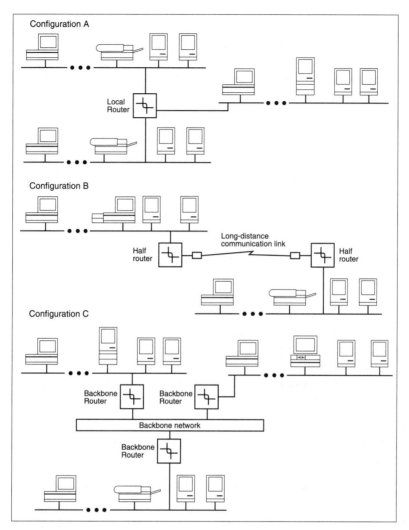

Figure 8-2. AppleTalk Router Configurations
(Courtesy Apple Computer, Inc.)

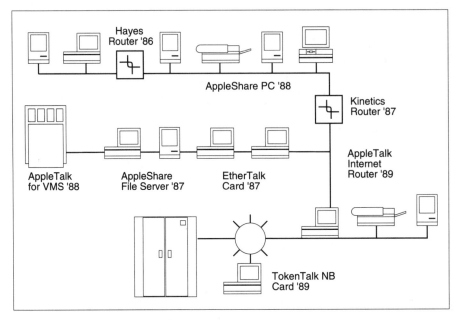

Figure 8-3. AppleTalk Network Components
(Courtesy Apple Computer, Inc.)

An AppleTalk node (e.g. Macintosh or router) is identified by a 2-octet Network number and a 1-octet Node number, both of which are carried within the DDP packet. In Phase 1, nodes that existed on a single cable could communicate using only the 8-bit Node number. Two of these addresses (0 and 255) were reserved (for unknown and broadcast addresses, respectively), thus allowing up to 254 nodes per cable. In AppleTalk Phase 2, a node is always identified by its Network number and Node number in what is known as extended addressing. As a result, over 16 million nodes can be uniquely identified on an extended network. Because of the extended addressing (and associated protocol changes described in Chapter 7 of reference [8-5]), AppleTalk Phase 1 routers must be upgraded to support the Phase 2 protocols.

The complete Phase 2 internet can thus support 1024 networks and over 16 million nodes (reference [8-6]). When all of the different connectivity options operate within one internetwork, a number of devices—including DEC minis and IBM mainframes—can communicate. Let's explore these two options separately.

8.1.1.3 AppleTalk/DEC Connectivity

The Apple-DEC alliance dates back to January 1988, when a joint development agreement for a common network architecture was announced. The result was a product known as DEC LanWORKS for Macintosh (reference [8-7]).

The common hardware architecture requires several connectivity options, all based upon an Ethernet backbone (see Figure 8-4a). Either a VAX minicomputer or Macintoshes can be directly attached to the Ethernet with the appropriate Network Interface Card. (Reference [8-8] is an excellent review of Ethernet NICs for the Macintosh family.) Macs can also be attached via serial lines to the VAX or to a terminal server. As a third option, the Ethernet backbone and a LocalTalk network can be connected via an internet router.

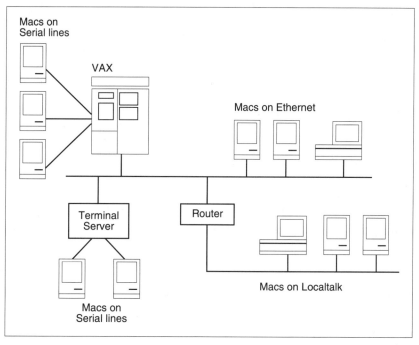

Figure 8-4a. Macintosh and VAX Physical Connections
(Courtesy Apple Computer, Inc.)

Four different protocol suites serve the common architecture development: AppleTalk, DECnet, TCP/IP, and LAT (DEC's Local Area Transport protocol for terminals). Six different products support networking functions within the LanWORKS architecture. The Macintosh Communication Toolbox provides support for protocols (e.g. AppleTalk, DECnet, TCP/IP, and LAT); terminal emulation (VT102 and VT320); and file transfer applications via ASCII or XMODEM. AppleTalk for VMS 3.0 places the AppleTalk Phase 2 protocols and internet router functions within a VAX minicomputer (Figure 8-4b).

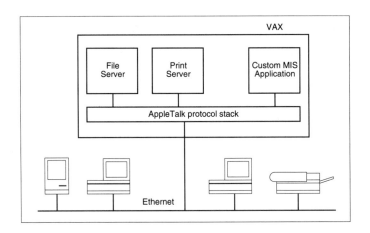

Figure 8-4b. AppleTalk for VMS 3.0 Architecture
(Courtesy Apple Computer, Inc.)

The AppleTalk/DECnet Transport Gateway (Figure 8-4c) provides connections between DECnet and AppleTalk networks. The gateway software resides within the VAX. TCP/IP for the Macintosh (MacTCP) supports the TCP/IP protocols on the Macintosh. Support for these multiple protocols between a Macintosh and a VAX is shown in Figure 8-4d. Note that the TCP/IP connection is integrating the two dissimilar operating systems: TCP/IP Tool on the Macintosh and TCP/IP (Ultrix Connection) on the VAX.

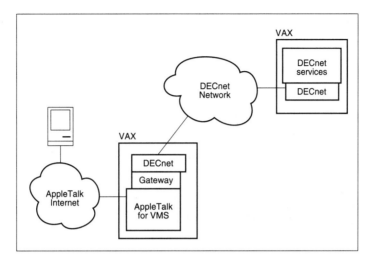

Figure 8-4c. AppleTalk/DECnet Gateway
(Courtesy Apple Computer, Inc.)

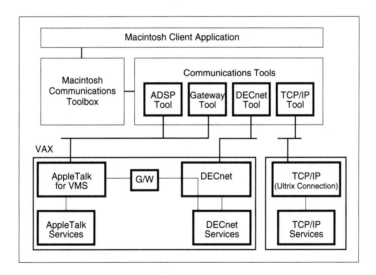

Figure 8-4d. AppleTalk/DECnet Multi Protocol Support
(Courtesy Apple Computer, Inc.)

This joint development has united two major hardware platforms, Apple Macintosh and DEC VAX. The native architectures (AppleTalk and DECnet) and industry-wide (TCP/IP) protocols are used to provide this internetworking.

8.1.1.4 Appletalk/IBM Connectivity

Unlike the connectivity developments that resulted from a formal alliance between Apple and DEC, the Apple/IBM connections have been formed by a number of third parties, including Novell, 3Com, Microsoft, IDEAssociates (Billerica, Massachusetts), DCA (Roswell, Georgia), and Avatar (Hopkinton, Massachusetts). Connectivity options are focused in two areas: IBM host connections, and LANs (reference [8-9]).

Host connectivity is facilitated by two hardware products that were introduced by Apple at the time of the release of AppleTalk Phase 2 (June 1989). The Apple Coax/Twinax Card provides access to 3270 protocol services. Also included is the MacDFT software which supports single-session CUT (Control Unit Terminal) emulation, or up to five-session DFT (Distributed Function Terminal) emulation. File transfer between the Mac and a host is supported via IBM's IND$FILE format on mainframes running the VM/CMS or MVS/TSO operating systems. Twinax connections to IBM mid-range processors with 5250 terminal services are also supported by the Coax/Twinax card (see Figure 8-5).

A second hardware product, the Apple Serial NB Card, is a four-port serial communications board for the Macintosh II family. This board supports RS-232, RS-422, X.21 or V.35 interfaces. A companion software product is called MacAPPC, which supports IBM's SDLC (Synchronous Data Link Control) protocols. Typical host applications that are used with these Apple packages include file transfer, electronic mail, and database access.

For network applications, Apple provides the TokenTalk NB Card, an IEEE 802.5-compliant product operating at 4 Mbps. The card is designed for the Macintosh II bus, and supports AppleTalk, 3270, LU6.2 and SMB (Server Message Block) protocols. This board supports two software packages: MacDFT for host access; and the Macintosh SMB File Transfer Utility for connections to servers running IBM's PC LAN program. The coexistence of IBM hosts, PCs, and Macintoshes on the same token ring is thus possible (see Figure 8-5).

The companion software has flexible applications as well. MacDFT can run over the coax/twinax card, the serial NB card, or the Token Talk NB card. MacAPPC runs over the Serial NB card or the Token Talk NB card.

A number of innovative connectivity enhancements have come with AppleTalk Phase 2. The Macintosh is no longer just a fine computer known for its graphics capabilities but is now a full-fledged participant in both DEC and IBM environments.

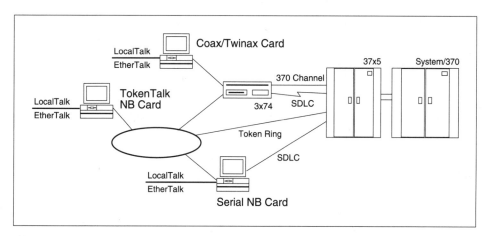

Figure 8-5. Integrated LAN Services and Host Access
(Courtesy Apple Computer, Inc.)

301

8.2   Sitka Corporation TOPS

No discussion of networking software implementations would be complete without considering the TOPS network, an extremely elegant and easy to install LAN operating system for connecting DOS, Macintosh, and UNIX workstations. Before we look at the TOPS operating system, let's have a brief history lesson.

Sitka Corporation of Alameda, California (a wholly-owned subsidiary of Sun Microsystems, Inc.) was formerly known as TOPS, Inc. which stands for Transcendental Operating System. In 1990, TOPS, Inc. changed its name to Sitka, after a remote fishing village in Alaska. This fishing village is populated by three diverse cultures: Tlingit Indians, descendants of Russian settlers, and the adventuresome who have moved from the lower 48 states. Unique to Sitka, according to some visitors, is the manner in which these three diverse cultures coexist. Sitka Corporation operates on the theme that dissimilar computer cultures should be able to coexist as well: the original idea behind TOPS was to find a mechanism for Apple Macintosh and PC-compatibles to communicate via the AppleTalk network. The basis for the TOPS architecture is the TOPS Filing Protocol (TFP) which runs on AppleTalk.

The first TOPS products, known as TOPS/DOS, TOPS/Mac, and TOPS/Sun are software packages for file sharing. These products transparently transfer files between DOS, Macintosh, and Sun operating systems. The TOPS software claims an installed base of over 750,000 users, and is built upon an Apple LocalTalk cabling scheme (see Figure 8-6). The TOPS software may also run over a variety of cabling schemes, including Ethernet and Token Ring. Macintosh workstations connect directly to the AppleTalk network via the LocalTalk interface built into every workstation. PC and Micro Channel-compatible workstations require an additional add-in card, known as a FlashCard. This card allows a PC, XT, AT, PS/2, or compatible to communicate on a LocalTalk network. Sun workstations connect to the AppleTalk through one of two methods: an Ethernet to AppleTalk router (such as the Shiva FastPath), or the addition of an AppleTalk interface card into the workstation. TOPS is a peer-to-peer, distributed server network, which allows PC and Macintosh workstations to address each other's disk drives on a virtual connection basis.

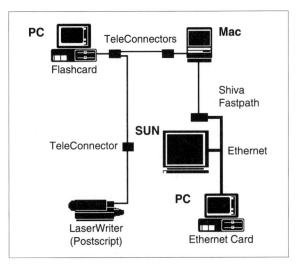

Figure 8-6. TOPS Network Configuration
(Courtesy Sitka)

TOPS/Sun enables a Sun workstation to act as a non-dedicated TOPS file server. In addition, the Sun workstation may serve as a TOPS-to-NFS gateway, allowing Macintosh computers and PCs on the TOPS network to access an NFS file server. Printer sharing is also included, allowing workstations access to PC-compatible serial or parallel printers, or Apple LaserWriter or other PostScript-compatible printers.

The latest additions to the TOPS product line are Network Bundle for DOS, Network Bundle for Macintosh, InBox 3.0 and InBox Plus. Sitka Network Bundles provide three essential network services: file sharing, print sharing, and electronic mail between the three types of workstations. The DOS Bundle takes advantage of extended memory, leaving more conventional memory for applications. The Macintosh Bundle works with AFP-compatible multiuser applications, including FoxBase+, FileMaker II, and 4th Dimension. One of the most useful features is the incorporation of the MacLink Plus/TOPS translators, developed by DataViz, Inc. of

Trumbull, Connecticut. These translators convert the file formats of both PC and Macintosh application programs to and from each other. Many popular formats—including word processor, graphic, spread sheet, and data base—are available.

InBox 3.0 is an entry-level electronic mail system that can operate on networks consisting of PCs, Macintoshes, or a combination of both. Work groups of up to 20 users are supported. The Message Center can reside on a PC, Macintosh, or other computer on the network such as a DEC VAX or UNIX-based minicomputer. InBox Plus is a powerful, enterprise-wide electronic mail system which supports gateways for connectivity to other electronic mail systems, such as IBM Profs, DEC VMS Mail, and UNIX Mail. This flexible system runs over a number of network operating systems, including NetWare, VINES, and 3+. FAX server capabilities are also supported, with a capacity of up to 250 users per message center.

TOPS is one of the most interesting internetworking and interoperability products available for networks combining dissimilar hardware platforms. (An excellent reference is [8-10], co-authored by a Sitka executive).

8.3   Banyan VINES

Banyan Systems, Inc. of Westboro, Massachusetts is the developer of VINES, an operating system that strongly supports both LAN and WAN connections. (As we investigate the architecture, we'll discover why.)

The company name and logo provide some insight into the characteristics of VINES capabilities. The Banyan tree, native to India, consists of a main trunk and broad foliage. As the tree grows, slender vines form from the branches and extend to the ground. These then root and develop another trunk system. After a few years, a single Banyan tree proliferates to become a small forest. The VINES (Virtual Networking System) software is similar, having a number of "branches" that communicate with dissimilar systems and protocols. For example, VINES servers can communicate using block asynchronous, HDLC, X.25, TCP/IP, or IEEE 802.2 protocols. We'll begin by looking at the VINES protocols.

8.3.1 VINES Protocols

The VINES operating system is based upon UNIX System V, and consists of both workstation and server modules (see Figures 8-7a and b). (Chapter 6 of reference [8-5] covers these protocols in detail.) Physical and Data Link Layers (as we will see) allow for almost all protocol possibilities, including asynchronous, HDLC, IEEE 802.X and X.25. Device drivers are used to communicate with the various Network Interface Cards. The VINES Network Layer supports the DoD IP, ARP, and ICMP protocols, plus four proprietary VINES protocols: IP (Internet Protocol), RTP (Routing Update Protocol), ARP (Address Resolution Program), and ICP (Internet Control Protocol). The Transport Layer implements the DoD, TCP, and UDP protocols plus the VINES proprietary IPC (Interprocess Communications Protocol) and SPP (Sequenced Packet Protocol). Higher (Session, Presentation, and Application)-layer support includes a variety of VINES and third-party applications. The Microsoft SMB (Server Message Block) protocol is also available. Extensive details on the VINES architecture and protocols are available in reference [8-11].

A higher-level architectural view of VINES is shown in Figure 8-7c. A device driver communicates with the hardware. A socket interface, the UNIX Transport Layer Interface (TLI), or Named Pipes connect to the higher layers. A variety of protocol stacks, including TCP/IP, VINES, AppleTalk, ISO (future), and others are planned. VINES version 3.10 supports the Network Layer of the AppleTalk stack (the Datagram Delivery Protocol) over Ethernet, and offers a socket interface to this layer. Future versions of VINES should support the entire AppleTalk suite. The UNIX kernel is at the core of the VINES system.

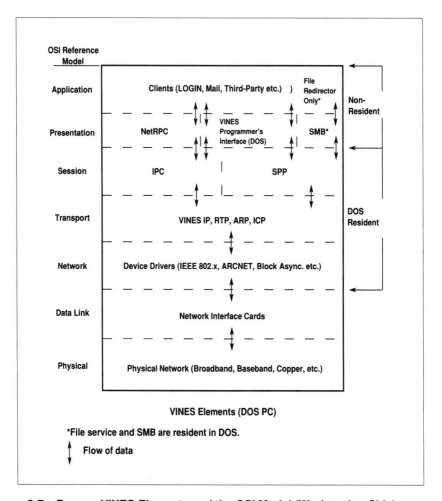

Figure 8-7a. Banyan VINES Elements and the OSI Model (Workstation Side)
(Courtesy Banyan Systems, Inc.)

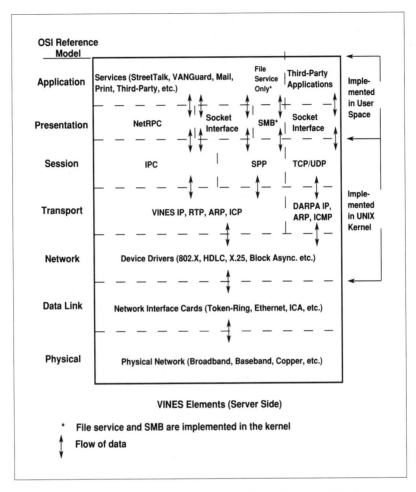

Figure 8-7b. Banyan VINES Elements and the OSI Model (Server Side)
(Courtesy Banyan Systems, Inc.)

8.3.2 VINES Serial Communications

VINES contains a number of WAN connection alternatives. This strength becomes evident when the architecture of the ICA (Intelligent Communications Adapter) Card is considered. The ICA is a six-port high-performance serial communications card that is available for the PC-AT and Micro Channel hardware platforms. Two of the ports operate at up to 64 Kbps and the other four operate at up to 19.2 Kbps. When installed in a VINES server, the ICA card can support a mixture of protocols including asynchronous, HDLC, SDLC, BSC (Bisynchronous), and X.25 (see Figure 8-8). VINES Communication software for the specific application is also required. With a single ICA card, the VINES server can simultaneously maintain one IBM SNA connection, an X.25 connection, two connections to a DEC VAX, and two dial-in connections. An aggregate of 400 Kbps data throughput is allowed.

The X.25 option allows server-to-server or server-to-host connections via Public Data Networks (PDNs). Both Permanent Virtual Circuits (PVCs) or Switched Virtual Circuits (SVCs) are supported. The EiconCard (discussed in section 5.8.3) is an alternative to Banyan's ICA Card. The IBM 3270/SNA server support allows host connectivity from any workstation on the VINES network. Each server can support 16, 32, 64, or 96 concurrent sessions with up to 4 concurrent host sessions and one DOS session per PC. The communication channel between server and host is a synchronous line into an SDLC interface on the IBM front end processor.

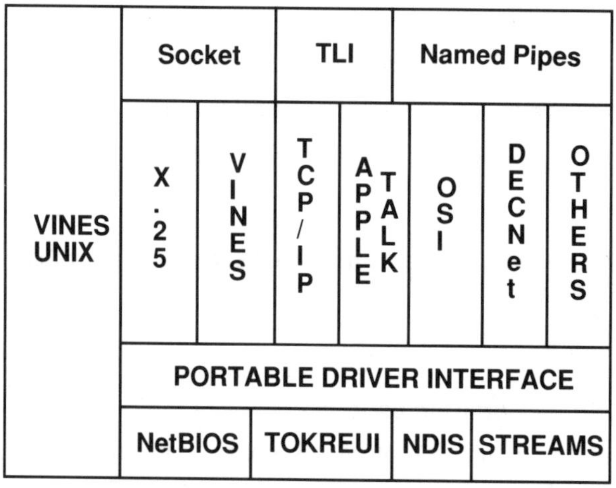

VINES UNIX	Socket		TLI		Named Pipes		
	X.25	VINES	TCP/IP	APPLE TALK	OSI	DECNet	OTHERS
	PORTABLE DRIVER INTERFACE						
	NetBIOS		TOKREUI		NDIS	STREAMS	

Figure 8-7c. VINES Integrated Protocol Architecture
(Courtesy Banyan Systems, Inc.)

308

The flexible connections into VINES support the claim for a both a WAN and LAN operating system. The wide range of speed and protocol options makes for a very powerful communications server.

8.3.3 VINES TCP/IP Support

A number of the DoD protocols have been included in the VINES architecture (Figures 8-7a and b). As a result, five separate internetwork communications options are available (see Figure 8-9). The TCP/IP Routing Option lets the VINES server act as an IP router. When communication between servers is required, the VINES software encapsulates the TCP/IP message within a VINES packet. The SMTP Mail Gateway options integrates the VINES mail system with the DoD SMTP standard.

The PC/TCP option uses FTP Software's PC/TCP package on VINES client workstations (see section 6.7.3). PC/TCP is tightly integrated with VINES to provide access from data links—such as ARCNET or dial-up connections—that are not typically associated with TCP/IP. In addition, the VINES client does not have to be directly connected to the VINES server running the VINES Routing Option. Instead, the client can be physically located on another VINES network, with the two VINES servers providing the communications path. The PC/TCP package allows the client to perform a number of TCP/IP applications, including FTP file transfer, TELNET terminal emulation, and SMTP electronic mail. The TCP/IP Server-to-Server option permits VINES servers to be connected by means of existing TCP/IP networks. At the sender's end, VINES data is encapsulated within TCP/IP packets and forwarded to a foreign TCP/IP gateway. The receiver strips the TCP/IP header and places the packet on the remote VINES network. Lastly, the TCP/UDP API (Applications Programming Interface) allows developers to combine TCP/IP host applications and VINES services.

In summary, VINES incorporates the popular TCP/IP protocol suite into its operating system to provide the maximum flexibility in server-to-server and server-to-gateway applications.

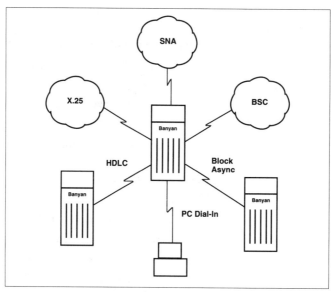

Figure 8-8. VINES Communications Options
(Courtesy Banyan Systems, Inc.)

8.3.4   VINES-OS/2 LAN Server Interoperability

In a final look at VINES, consider the requirement to integrate this UNIX-based operating system with an OS/2-based operating system, IBM's OS/2 LAN Server. In Figure 8-10, a Token Ring (IEEE 802.5) network supporting the IEEE 802.2 LLC protocol contains an IBM OS/2 LAN Server and other clients. One of these clients is also a VINES client, running client software from both operating systems, and containing two Network Interface Cards (Token Ring plus Ethernet). The Banyan CNS (Corporate Network Server) is resident on the Ethernet side. Banyan's OS/2 integration allows the dual client (VINES and LAN Server) to access either network. The VINES-OS/2 Architecture (Figure 8-11) describes the process. The VINES

310

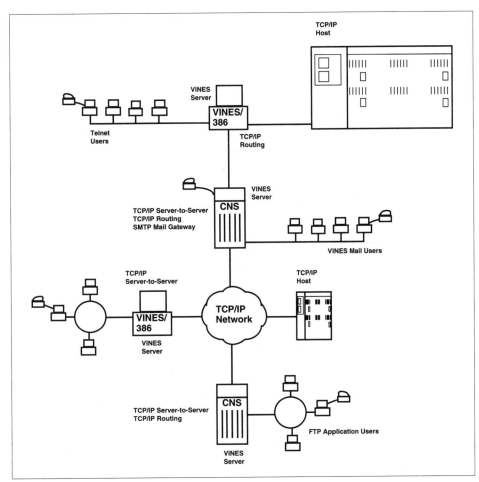

Figure 8-9. VINES TCP/IP Options
(Courtesy Banyan Systems, Inc.)

Dynamic Link Libraries (DLL) for OS/2 allow OS/2 applications (such as OS/2 LAN Server) to interface with other VINES clients operating on OS/2, DOS, Macintosh, or UNIX platforms. The key to the process is the VINES Redirector, which links the OS/2 kernel to the VINES socket driver. Communication with any VINES LAN or WAN facility is then available, and interoperability is maintained.

Banyan VINES is an operating system with strengths in three areas: LANs (Ethernet, IEEE 802.5, and ARCNET); WANs (asynchronous, HDLC, SDLC, BSC, X.25 and TCP/IP); and interoperability with OS/2 workstations (now) and Macintosh workstations (future).

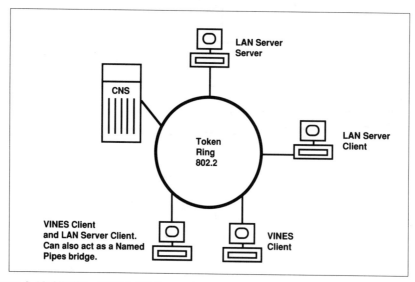

Figure 8-10. VINES - OS/2 LAN Server Interoperability
(Courtesy Banyan Systems, Inc.)

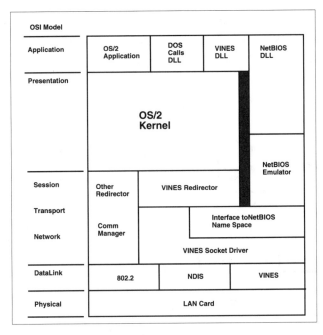

Figure 8-11. VINES OS/2 Process Architecture
(Courtesy Banyan Systems, Inc.)

8.4 Novell NetWare 386

Volumes could be (and have been) written about the NetWare operating system from Novell, Inc. of Provo, Utah. NetWare is rather unique among the networking software products in that it is available for several different server platforms, including 80386-based computers, DEC VAX/VMS minicomputers, and UNIX-based hosts (see Figure 8-12). NetWare supports a number of workstation platforms as well, including DOS, Macintosh, UNIX, and OS/2 Standard and Extended Editions (SE and EE) (reference [8-12]). Novell's latest release is NetWare 386, which began shipping in September 1989. This operating system is designed to integrate dissimilar hardware platforms and communications protocols. A set of NetWare Loadable Modules (NLMs), known as Communications Services (which can be purchased separately) provides some key internetworking functions. Before looking at Communications Services, let's consider some of the other NetWare products for internetwork communications. Those readers wishing further technical information on NetWare 386 architecture may find references [8-13] and [8-14] useful. Reference [8-5], Chapter 3, contains details on the NetWare protocols.

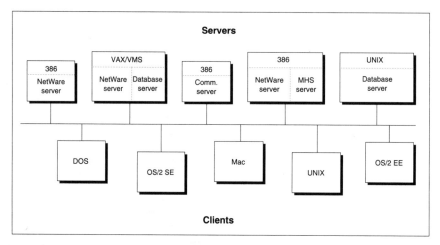

Figure 8-12. NetWare Multiprotocol Support
(Courtesy Novell, Inc.)

8.4.1   Novell Communication Products

A number of communication products are available as functional adjuncts to various versions of the NetWare operating system (see Figure 8-13). Reference [8-12] describes these functions in detail; we'll provide a summary here for those readers who might be shopping for a particular internetwork solution.

NetWare Asynchronous Remote Bridge is a software product that is installed in a NetWare workstation, an external bridge, or a file server. This option permits dial-up connections at speeds of up to 9.6 Kbps. Asynchronous modems are also required to complete the connection.

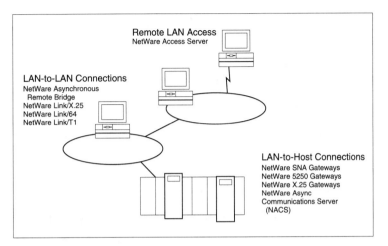

Figure 8-13. Novell Communication Products
(Courtesy Novell, Inc.)

NetWare Link/X.25 provides a single synchronous link to a Public Data Network (PDN) using the X.25 protocol. This product functions as an external router, and can link one LAN with up to eleven remote LANs. NetWare Link/X.25 supports the 1980 and 1984 CCITT X.25 recommendations, with a maximum link speed of 64Kbps.

NetWare Link/64 is used to connect remote LANs by means of synchronous communication lines. The software runs in a NetWare file server or in an external router. The connection also requires a synchronous WAN adapter for the V.35, RS-232, or RS-422 interface, and permits transmission speeds from 9.6 to 64 Kbps.

NetWare Link/T1 is the product that supports high-speed LAN-to-LAN connections. Similar in installation to the Link/64 product, it also requires the synchronous WAN adapter, but operates at speeds of up to 2.048 Mbps.

NetWare Access Server permits up to 15 remote users to get on the NetWare LAN and access all applications, services, and files. The remote workstation can be a PC-compatible, Macintosh, or ASCII terminal. The server is installed in a dedicated 80386-based PC, and designed for heavy traffic.

The NetWare Asynchronous Communications Server (NACS) allows network workstations to dial out to remote asynchronous hosts such as a DEC VAX. The NACS software runs on a PC-compatible, and requires a Wide Area Network Interface Module Plus (WNIM+) adapter to provide the multiple asynchronous ports. The software supports up to 16 simultaneous connections at speeds of up to 19.2 Kbps per port.

NetWare SNA Gateway is used for connections to IBM mainframe and mid-range computers. Four different host connection options are available: a coaxial connection to 3x74 cluster controllers; a CoaxMux connection to a 3299 multiplexer port on a 3x74 cluster controller; a remote connection to a 37xx front-end processor via synchronous modems operating at speeds of up to 64 Kbps; or a Token Ring connection to any Token-Ring compatible device. The SNA Gateway operates in a dedicated PC or PS/2 compatible. (Reference [8-15] explores the SNA gateways in great detail.)

The NetWare 5250 Gateway is used for connections between the NetWare LAN and an IBM System/3X. The gateway operates in a PC or PS/2 Model 25- or 30- compatible workstation, and communicates to the System/3X via a synchronous SDLC line. A similar product, the NetWare 5250 Twinax Gateway, connects to an IBM S/3X or AS/400 host by means of a local twinaxial cable connection. Up to seven (via Twinax Gateway) or nine (via 5250 Gateway) host sessions are distributed to users on the LAN.

While the above communications functions were designed as adjuncts to NetWare, the NetWare Communications Services has been designed as an integrated solution. We'll explore this architecture next.

8.4.2 NetWare Communications Services

As we learned in the last section, Novell has three adjunct product lines for internetworking support. The NetWare Link family is for LAN-to-LAN connectivity; the NetWare Access Server allows remote access; and the NetWare SNA Gateway supports connections to IBM mainframe and mid-range systems. NetWare 386 integrates all of these functions into the NetWare Communications Services.

The modular design of NetWare 386 (see Figure 8-14a) allows various components of the operating system to be loaded and unloaded according to specific network requirements. The NetWare 386 System Executive is the master scheduler of the operating system, allocating memory, controlling access to the network file system, and scheduling tasks for the NetWare Loadable Module (NLM) bus. The Communication Services (see Figure 8-14b) are NLMs that may access that bus. All NLMs can be loaded or unloaded at any time, without rebooting the network server.

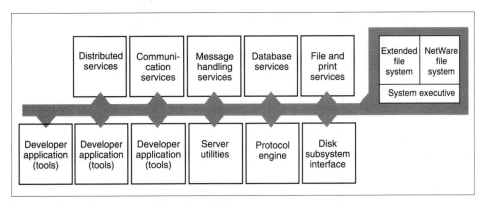

Figure 8-14a. NetWare 386 Modular Design
(Courtesy Novell, Inc.)

What is significant about this modular architecture is the concept that these communications services operate simultaneously with the other file access, printer support, and database services. LAN-to-LAN, LAN-to-Host, and remote services can thus be accessed from DOS, Windows, OS/2, Macintosh, or UNIX clients on the network.

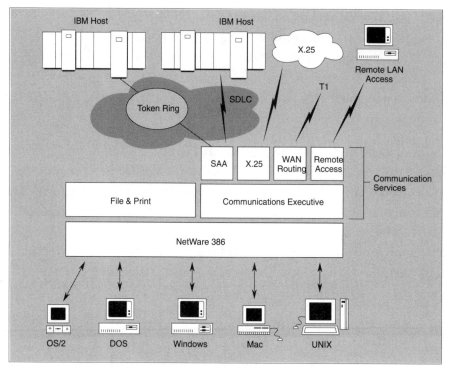

Figure 8-14b. NetWare Communication Services
(Courtesy Novell, Inc.)

The architecture of the Communications Executive uses the NetWare 386 kernel as a base (reference [8-16]). Within that kernel is the Open Data Link Interface (ODI) as well as support for a variety of protocols, including Novell's Internetwork Packet Exchange/Sequenced Packet Exchange (IPX/SPX), based upon the XNS protocol suite, TCP/IP, AppleTalk, and OSI. The Logical Link between the kernel and the Communications Executive is NetWare Streams. Let's investigate ODI first, and then look at the other interfaces.

8.4.3 NetWare Open Data Link Interface

In previous versions of NetWare, a very close tie existed between the LAN hardware (e.g. IEEE 802.3, Token Ring, and ARCNET) and the lowest layer of the IPX operating system. The LAN Driver that was a component of both the workstation and server software provided that logical link. Unfortunately, a close tie existed between the hardware and protocol (e.g. ARCNET and IPX). This required a unique driver (e.g. NetWare's IPX.COM) for each type of hardware used. As more protocol stacks—such as AppleTalk and TCP/IP—were added to the architecture, additional drivers would also be required.

Novell and Apple Computer developed a way around this hardware/protocol constraint with the Open Data Link Interface (ODI), shown in Figure 8-15 (reference [8-17]). The ODI permits multiple protocol stacks to simultaneously share a single NIC. The first layer of ODI is the Multiple Link Interface Driver (MLID) that communicates with the hardware. The MLID is added to the AUTOEXEC.BAT file for DOS workstations, or CONFIG.SYS file for OS/2 workstations. A MLID can service one or more LAN adapters. The second layer, the Link Support Layer (LSL), directs incoming data packets to the appropriate protocol stack. A table within the workstation identifies the protocols that are available. The various protocol stacks (e.g. SPX/IPX, AppleTalk, or TCP/IP) are the next layer, communicating with the various NetWare services for file access, printing, and communications.

The ODI has thus enhanced the internetworking capabilities of NetWare 386 by decoupling the hardware and protocols, allowing independence at both ends of the architecture. References [8-18], [8-19], and Chapter 10 of [8-13] provide further details for those readers who are interested.

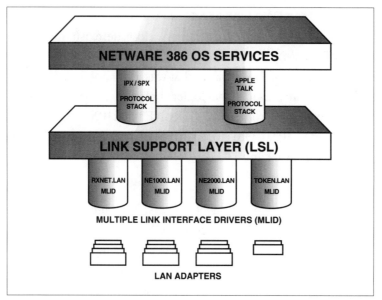

Figure 8-15. Open Data Link Interface
(Courtesy Novell, Inc.)

8.4.4   NetWare Transport Level Interface and Streams

Two additional key components of the NetWare 386 kernel are the Transport Level Interface (TLI) and the Streams protocols (review Figure 8-16). The TLI is a protocol-independent interface between the higher-layer NetWare services (such as NCP, the NetWare Core Protocols) and the lower-layer protocols. NetWare Streams allows the NetWare 386 services to operate independently of the underlying protocols. Notice, in Figure 8-16, that an interface exists between TLI and Streams, as the TLI is the preferred Streams API (see references [8-20] and [8-21]).

NetWare 386 has thus dramatically enhanced the internetworking and interoperability features of Novell's product line. By incorporating support for similar hardware and software platforms into the already rich NetWare Communications Services, Novell has provided a migration path for both Novell and third-party applications. NetWare users will clearly reap the benefits.

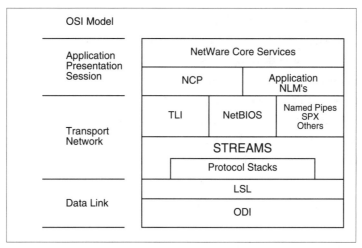

Figure 8-16. NetWare 386 TLI and STREAMS
(Courtesy Novell, Inc.)

8.5   OS/2 LAN Manager Implementations

Microsoft Corporation of Redmond, Washington, has played a significant role in the history of networked computing. In the DOS world, the Microsoft Networks program, including the Redirector and Server Message Block (SMB) protocol, was adopted by a number of vendors—including IBM, AT&T, and 3Com—for incorporation into their DOS-based operating systems. Microsoft made a mark with the OS/2 LAN Manager program as well, providing networked computing for OS/2-based servers and DOS or OS/2 workstations. As of this writing, over 30 vendors have licensed the OS/2 LAN Manager, porting it to other platforms, such as UNIX, or integrating other functions, such as support for Macintosh workstations.

In this section, we will study the Microsoft product and three other implementations: 3Com's 3+Open LAN Manager version 2.0, IBM's LAN Server version 1.3, and AT&T's StarGROUP Server for Macintosh Clients. For a good summary of the differences between the Microsoft, 3Com, and IBM versions, see reference [8-22].

8.5.1 Microsoft OS/2 LAN Manager Version 2.0

OS/2 LAN Manager (LM), released by Microsoft Corporation of Redmond, Washington in 1988, was developed as a client-server operating system (reference [8-23]). In addition to the native file and print services of LAN Manager, Microsoft also provides two other servers for SQL database and SNA communications. The Microsoft SQL Server is a Structured Query Language (SQL)-based relational database (reference [8-24]). The DCA/Microsoft Communications Server (reference [8-25]) provides enterprise-wide connectivity (see Figure 8-17a).

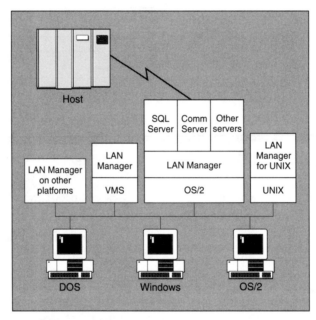

Figure 8-17a. Microsoft Systems Platform
(Courtesy Microsoft Corporation)

A number of LAN Manager implementations have been developed for other hardware/software platforms (see Figure 8-17b). Examples include an IBM mainframe version (for MVS operating systems from Micro Tempus (Montreal, Quebec); DEC VAX minicomputers running VMS; and UNIX platforms from AT&T,

Hewlett-Packard, and Santa Cruz Operation (Santa Cruz, California). For example, LAN Manager is part of DEC's PCSA (Personal Computing Systems Architecture). LAN Manager for UNIX (formerly LM/X), has been licensed by AT&T, NCR, and Data General. Microsoft's intention is to provide users with transparent access to enterprise-wide network resources, regardless of the platform on which they reside.

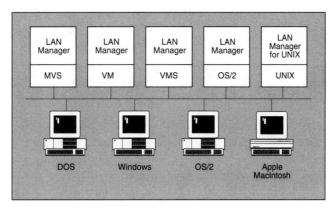

Figure 8-17b. LAN Manager Enterprise Service Architecture
(Courtesy Microsoft Corporation)

For IBM SNA communications requirements, the Communications Server—jointly developed by DCA (Roswell, Georgia) and Microsoft—provides a client-server solution. Two elements make up the system (see Figure 8-17c). The Communications Server software runs on an OS/2 server (which may also be running the SQL server), and assumes the heaviest load of host communications. Client workstations can run under DOS or OS/2. The Communications Workstation allows OS/2 workstations to access SNA networks. Up to 32 simultaneous connections are allowed, by means of multiple hardware links. Options include coaxial connections to 3x74 Cluster Controllers; X.25/QLLC (Qualified Logical Link Control) access to Public Data Networks; SDLC connections by means of dial-up or leased lines; and Token Ring connections (supporting IEEE 802.2) to 37xx Front-End Processors or 3x74 Cluster Controllers.

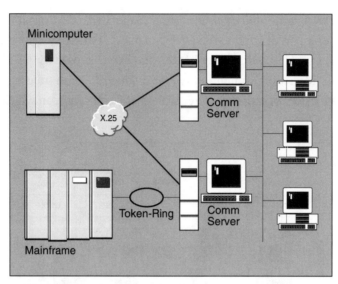

Figure 8-17c. DCA/Microsoft Communications Server Architecture
(Courtesy Microsoft Corporation)

The Communications Server has some unique features. First, multiple servers can be installed on a LAN, and will load-balance automatically. In other words, users are dynamically (and transparently) routed through the server best able to accommodate the extra demand. Should one server fail, another one is standing by as a hot backup. Links exist between IBM's NetView network management architecture and the Communications Server. APC can thus participate in the host's central network management scheme. Users and administrators can view each 3270 session's response time with NetView.

The Communications Server is an added value to Microsoft's OS/2 LAN Manager release. Other vendors' (such as AT&T and NCR) implementations also add some unique features. Interoperability between these different versions is a current topic in trade literature; see reference [8-26] for details on Microsoft and IBM software integration.

8.5.2   3Com 3+Open

3Com Corporation's implementation of OS/2 LAN Manager is known as 3+Open, and it very effectively uses another feature, Demand Protocol Architecture (DPA), for interoperability. DPA contains three principal components: a Primary Protocol, Secondary Protocol(s), and a Protocol Manager, shown in Figure 8-18a (also see references [8-27], [8-28], and [8-29]).

The primary client-server protocol is known as NBP (NetBIOS Protocol) and facilitates communication between network servers and workstations. (Chapter 4 of reference [8-5] examines NBP in depth.) Secondary protocols, such as TCP, XNS, or Novell's IPX, are loaded on demand as specific communication requirements dictate. (The TCP or XNS protocols are also available as primary protocols). The third principal element is the Resident Protocol Manager, which links and unlinks the secondary protocols as required.

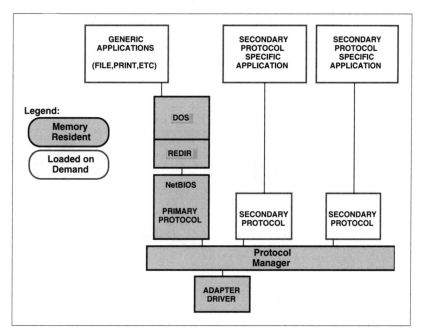

Figure 8-18a. Demand Protocol Architecture
(Courtesy 3Com Corporation)

An auxiliary element to DPA is the Network Driver Interface Standard (NDIS) developed by Microsoft and 3Com. Similar in purpose to Novell's ODI (Open Data Link Interface), the NDIS provides a standard interface between network hardware and the higher-layer protocols (see reference [8-19]). This NDIS driver is shown as the Adapter Driver in Figure 8-18a.

An example of DPA in use is the interoperability it provides between 3+Open and Novell's NetWare. For a single DOS (not OS/2) client, the 3+Open connection for NetWare allows simultaneous connectivity to a NetWare 286 or 386 server and a 3+Open LAN Manager Server (see Figure 8-18b). Other workstations, such as a Macintosh, can also coexist—but not interoperate—with the 3+Open workstation. 3+Open allows AFP (AppleTalk Filing Protocol) connectivity to a 3+Open server via 3+Open Mac. This is accomplished with an OS/2 AFP implementation on the 3+Open server. The obvious advantage to the client workstation is the ability to integrate the strengths of NetWare 286 or 386 and OS/2 LAN Manager servers on the same network without a reloading of the workstation software. In addition, the network operations are completely transparent to the users; they need not know where files are stored once the network drivers are redirected.

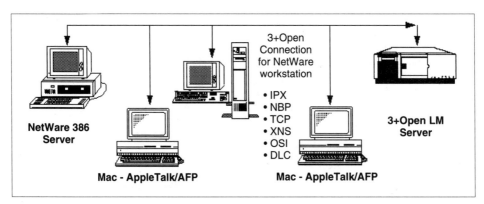

Figure 8-18b. 3+Open Connection for NetWare
(Courtesy 3Com Corporation)

A block diagram detailing the software interaction described above is shown in Figure 8-18c. Applications requiring NetWare are intercepted by the Shell (Net3) and pass through the IPX, NWNDIS, and NDIS layers to the Protocol Manager. 3+Open Applications pass through the DOS and Redirector to MINSES (a minimum Session Layer), NBP, and finally the Protocol Manager. The user logs into the servers (ATTACH for NetWare, NET LOGON for 3+Open), and the Protocol Manager of DPA makes it all transparent.

Other DPA modules include TCP and XNS, adding to 3+Open's interoperability menu. Other functions are summarized in reference [8-30]; users can expect this product to remain a strong presence in the marketplace.

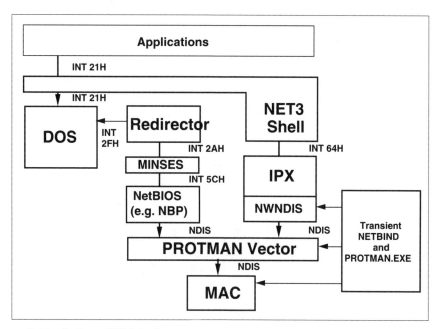

Figure 8-18c. 3+Open IPX Interfaces
(Courtesy 3Com Corporation)

8.5.3 IBM OS/2 LAN Server

IBM's OS/2 LAN Server Version 1.3 is only part of the total IBM interconnectivity strategy (reference [8-31]). In Figure 8-19a the OS/2 LAN Server connects to a Token Ring network that is only part of the internetwork shown. (Concurrent connectivity from a DOS workstation to NetWare and OS/2 LAN Server is a demonstrated technology, rather than an IBM product offering.) The Token Ring also connects to a 3172 Interconnect Controller, which links into 802.3 and other networks. The 3172 also connects to the IBM mainframe channel.

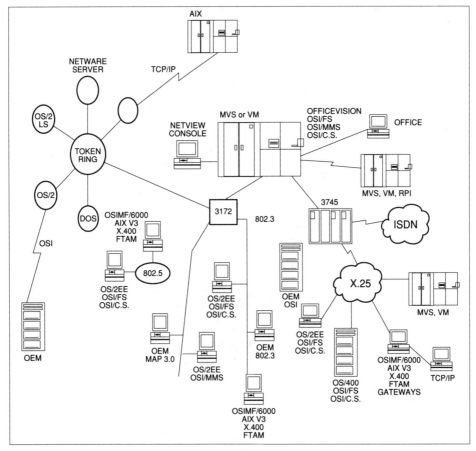

Figure 8-19a. IBM Interconnectivity

(Reprinted by permission. International Business Machines Corporation.)

The OS/2 LAN Server is a component of IBM's OS/2 LAN communication support environment, shown in Figure 8-19b. (Protocol details of the OS/2 LAN Server are given in Chapter 5 of reference [8-5]). Two elements make up the LAN components: the OS/2 LAN Requester, client side (included in OS/2 EE 1.3); and the OS/2 LAN Server, server side (available as a separate product.) A third product (shown in Figure 8-19c) is the DOS LAN Requester for DOS clients, included in the OS/2 LAN Server. All of these components are built upon the NetBIOS interface. Other components of the OS/2 LAN communications support environment include terminal emulation (3270 and 5250), Remote Data Services (RDS), and the Structured Query Language LAN-only Option (SQLLOO).

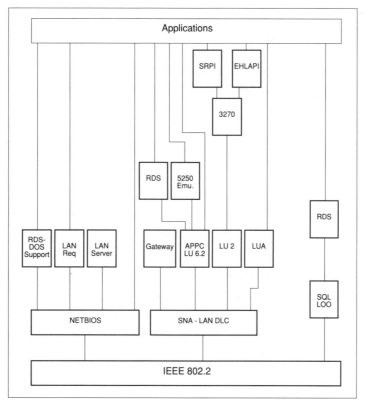

Figure 8-19b. IBM OS/2 LAN Communications Support Environment
(Reprinted by permission. International Business Machines Corporation.)

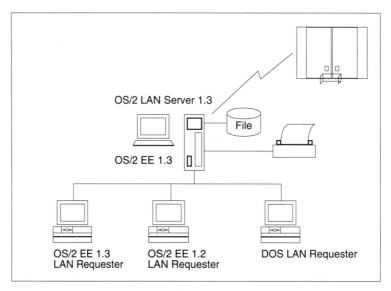

Figure 8-19c. IBM LAN Server/Requester Architecture
(Reprinted by permission. International Business Machines Corporation.)

An extension of the OS/2 EE LAN communications support environment supports IEEE 802.2, which provides Ethernet and 802.3 connectivity (see Figure 8-19d and reference [8-32]). This extension also provides a number of gateway functions (shown as Gateway in Figure 8-19b and illustrated in Figure 8-19d). X.25, SDLC, and Token Ring protocols can be supported through these gateway functions.

Both OS/2 EE and OS/2 LAN Server were recently enhanced to Version 1.3. OS/2 EE Version 1.3 provides increased performance in memory-constrained environments by reducing the minimum memory requirement from 3.5 to 3.0 MB. ACDI (Asynchronous Communication Device Interface) calls can now be redirected across a LAN to the ACS (Asynchronous Communication Server) Version 2.0. The ACS provides modem pooling for asynchronous connections. In addition, the Database Manager DOS Database Requester supports Ethernet DIX (DEC, Intel and Xerox) Version 2.0, as well as IEEE 802.3.

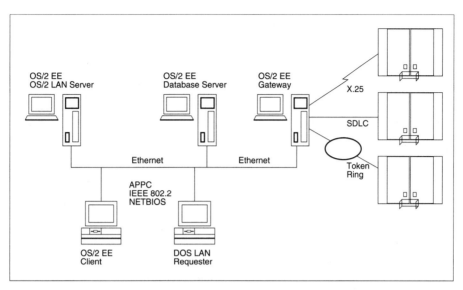

Figure 8-19d. IBM OS/2 LAN Server Version 1.3 Ethernet Capabilities
(Reprinted by permission. International Business Machines Corporation.)

Enhancements to Version 1.3 of OS/2 LAN Server include the improved program load facility of OS/2 EE 1.3—which provides performance enhancements when loading multiple OS/2 applications from Servers to Requesters. DOS LAN Requester support for Microsoft Windows 3.0, and Ethernet support via LAN Support Program Version 1.2 are also included with the software.

IBM considers the OS/2 LAN Server and OS/2 Extended Edition to be vital components of Systems Application Architecture (SAA) and Systems Network Architecture (SNA). (A good reference on current SNA topics is [8-33]). For LAN or WAN connectivity in the SNA environment, IBM's implementation of the OS/2 LAN Manager product is the clear choice.

8.5.4 AT&T StarGROUP Server for Macintosh

AT&T Computer Systems of Morristown, New Jersey, traditionally strong in UNIX system environments, has based their OS/2 LAN Manager on a UNIX server platform. Client workstations can be DOS, OS/2, UNIX System V, or Macintosh-based. As described in reference [8-34], integrating DOS, OS/2, and UNIX into one cohesive network is a challenging task. Figure 8-20a illustrates a DOS program using the Microsoft Redirector and SMB protocols for communication with the server. When the server is UNIX-based, it must also implement the SMB protocols; however, differences in the file systems—such as the maximum number of open files, naming conventions, and file/record locking—make the integration more difficult.

With these challenges solved, however, comes a server architecture with the high performance of the UNIX operating system. This architecture allows for file and print resourcing, as well as client access to multiple computing environments from the same server. These environments include: TCP/IP through a TCP/IP Access Program; SNA Host connectivity with a full LU6.2 implementation; Asynchronous Gateway; and Remote PC Gateway.

One example of AT&T's server software offering is the StarGROUP Server for Macintosh, shown in Figure 8-20b. This server solves a number of interoperability problems. First, Macintosh files can be shared between DOS clients, OS/2 clients, and UNIX workstations. Secondly, PostScript printer services are made available to DOS, OS/2, Macintosh, and UNIX users. Finally, with support for the AppleTalk protocols, remote access via AppleTalk Phase 2 routers is possible.

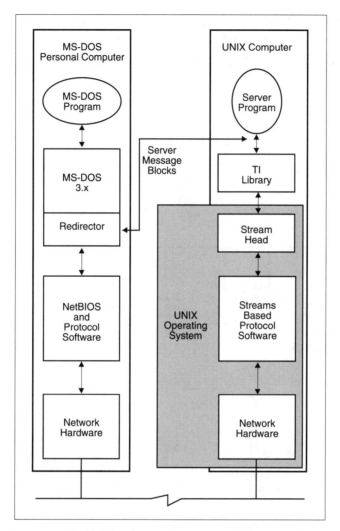

Figure 8-20a. DOS/UNIX Interaction
(Reproduced with permission of AT&T)

In addition to the Macintosh client solution, AT&T Computer Systems has also announced a NetBEUI (NetBIOS Extended User Interface) stack to allow IBM PC LAN and OS/2 LAN Server clients to share print and file services.

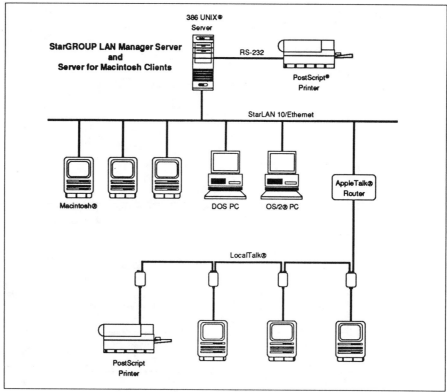

Figure 8-20b. AT&T StarGROUP Server for Macintosh clients
(Reproduced with permission of AT&T)

In summary, AT&T has risen to the challenge of providing interoperability between DOS, OS/2, Macintosh, and UNIX clients, and provided a UNIX System V-based OS/2 LAN manager product which can serve 2 (or 200) clients from vastly differing operating system platforms.

In this chapter, we have seen how the industry's key software vendors support internetworking and interoperability. In the next chapter, we will explore a situation where a "built-in" solution is not available, and thus requires use of an Application Layer gateway.

8.6   References

[8-1] Hurwicz, Mike. "Scaling the Heights—The Arduous Climb Up the Interoperability Mountain." *LAN Magazine* (October 1990): 40 – 43.

[8-2] Apple Computer, Inc. "Inside AppleTalk." Addison-Wesley Publishing Co., Inc., 1989.

[8-3] Apple Computer Inc. "AppleTalk Phase 2 Protocol Specification, an Addendum to Inside AppleTalk." Document no. ADPA #CO144LL/A, 1989.

[8-4] Sanz, Steve. "AppleTalk Grows Up," *LAN Technology* (April 1990): 63 – 68.

[8-5] Miller, Mark A. *LAN Protocol Handbook.* Redwood City, CA: M&T Books, 1990.

[8-6] Harrison, Dana. "AppleTalk Networking and Communications." Interop 90 Conference Proceedings, October 1990.

[8-7] Leclercq, Pierre, and Dave Glasson. "Apple/Digital Joint Development Agreement: DEC LanWORKS for Macintosh." Interop 90 Conference Proceedings, October 1990.

[8-8] Kosiur, Dave. "On the Ethernet Highway." *Macworld* (March 1990):133 –137.

[8-9] Nagy, David. "Integrating Macintosh into IBM Environments." Interop 90 Conference Proceedings, October 1990.

[8-10] Rogers, Mike, and Virginia Bare. *Hands-On AppleTalk.* Simon and Schuster, Inc., 1989.

[8-11] Banyan Systems, Inc. *VINES Protocol Definition*. Document no. DA254-00, 1989.

[8-12] Novell, Inc. *NetWare Buyers' Guide.* Document no. 482-000020-003, July 1990.

[8-13] Novell, Inc. *NetWare 386 Theory of Operations*. Document 479-000042-001, August 1989.

[8-14] Novell, Inc. *NetWare 386 Technical Overview.* Document no. 471-000011-002, July 1989.

[8-15] Novell, Inc. *Accessing IBM Mainframe Computers.* Document no. 481-000019-001, January 1990.

[8-16] Olsen, Carl. "Communication Services APIs." Novell Developers' Conference, 1990.

[8-17] Lemon, Scott, and Deni Connor. "A New Driver Choice." *LAN Times* (July 1989): 123 – 125.

[8-18] Dixon, Drex. "Open Data Link Interface Presentation." Novell Developers' Conference, 1990.

[8-19] Richer, Mark. "Who Needs Universal Network Interface Standards." *Data Communications* (September 21, 1990): 71 – 72.

[8-20] Richey, Jonathan. "Transport Level Interface." Novell Developers' Conference, 1990.

[8-21] Richey, Jonathan. "Streams." Novell Developers' Conference, 1990.

[8-22] Morrissey, Jane. "Microsoft Dips In To Blend OS/2 LAN Manager Flavors." *PC Week* (September 10, 1990): S/6 – S/23.

[8-23] Microsoft Corp. *Microsoft LAN Manager*. Part no. 098-12266, September 1990.

[8-24] Microsoft Corp. *Microsoft SQL Server*. Part no. 098-14054, September 1990.

[8-25] Microsoft Corp. *DCA/Microsoft Communications Server*. Part no. 098-14832, September 1990.

[8-26] Microsoft Corp. "Using Microsoft LAN Manager with IBM LAN Requester and IBM LAN Server." Technical Note no. 098-15659, September 1990.

[8-27] 3Com Corp. *3+Open LAN Manager Technical Reference*. Document no. 3C2633, November 1989.

[8-28] 3Com Corp. 3+Open *LAN Manager 1.1 with Demand Protocol Architecture*. October 1989.

[8-29] 3Com Corp. *3+Open: LAN Manager and Beyond*. 1990.

[8-30] Brenner, Aaron. "3+Open—At Last an OS/2 Operating System Delivers." *LAN Magazine* (February 1989): 127 – 134.

[8-31] Soyring, John. "IBM Interconnectivity." *LAN Manager in a Growing Multivendor Internetted Environment Session*. Interop 90 Conference Proceedings, October 1990.

[8-32] IBM. LAN Operating System Software. 1990 Networking Forum Notes, February 1990.

[8-33] Panza, Robert. "Open SNA." *LAN Magazine* (Fall 1990): 25 – 31.

[8-34] Faulkner, Deborah T. "The AT&T StarGROUP Software LAN Manager Server: A Technical Review." *LAN Dispatch* (Summer 1990): 20 – 27.

CHAPTER 9

Gateways

The last stop on our tour of internetworking devices is at the highest level of the OSI Reference Model—the Application Layer. Recall from Figure 1-9 that gateways operate at all layers of the OSI Model and that protocol conversions may be required at each of these layers.

In practice, however, it would be more appropriate to consider the interconnectivity architecture as two "half gateways." This is because two dissimilar systems are being linked, and one half of the gateway is required to communicate with each. At some level within the gateway (most likely the Application Layer), the protocols of each half are equivalent. The other layers communicate with their peer protocols on either "one-half" of the gateways.

While this theory may be interesting to academics, most readers are responsible for making two or more dissimilar systems communicate, and are therefore more interested in gateway application. Many gateway products are available for specific purposes and a listing of representative vendors is given in Appendix B. In this chapter we will study twelve products for linking dissimilar systems. This is by no means an exhaustive study. Instead, it is intended as a survey of representative products that can be used for linking dissimilar LANs, such as Novell's NetWare and Banyan Systems' VINES; or a LAN and a minicomputer, such as a NetWare network and a Hewlett-Packard HP3000. Each of these examples is relatively independent; pick and choose those that apply to your internetwork.

9.1   Communications Research Group BLAST

Communications Research Group of Baton Rouge, Louisiana has successfully marketed their software through ten revisions. BLAST, which stands for Blocked Asynchronous Transmission, began as a program to transfer files between dissimilar hosts. Let's suppose that you wanted to transfer an ASCII file from an IBM mainframe to a DEC VAX minicomputer. You would need two different BLAST packages, BLAST 3270 and BLAST VAX. Each package would run under the native operating system (i.e. VM/MVS and VMS, respectively). The common denominator linking the two systems became the proprietary BLAST protocol.

The program was named for its transmission format, which uses a proprietary sliding window protocol. The protocol specifies a full-duplex transmission format, with data blocks of up to 4096 characters in length (see Figure 9-1a). Each block is provided with a Cyclic Redundancy Check (CRC) for error detection, plus a sliding window for additional accuracy. The sliding window performs two key functions: it provides a sequence number for each data block, and it assures that one computer with a fast transmitter will not overwhelm a slower computer with too much data. Each end of the transmission link maintains a "window" indicating how many more data blocks can be sent or received. Acknowledgments from the opposite end of the link move the near-end's transmit window, thus permitting an additional block (or blocks) to be transmitted. Should a problem occur mid-transmission (such as a noise hit on the transmission line or a total interruption), the sliding window protocol also serves to mark the file at the point of interruption and resume the transfer after communication is re-established. Other file transfer protocols, such as Kermit and XMODEM, operate in a half-duplex mode (see Figure 9-1b). These protocols operate in a less efficient manner since each block of data must be acknowledged (ACK'd) before the transmitter forges ahead.

As noted above, the software was initially released in 1980 and is currently available for over thirty different operating platforms, including MS-DOS, UNIX, Xenix, Macintosh, and VMS (see Figure 9-1c). Along the way, a number of other features were added to the software. These are especially relevant for LAN-to-host support, and are key features of the BLAST PC Plus LAN product. They include terminal emulation, remote control, and a script language. BLAST PC Plus LAN operates with any NetBIOS-compatible LAN, and interfaces with communication server software that supports NACS (Novell Asynchronous Communication Server), ACS (IBM Asynchronous Connection Server) and AGS (AT&T Asynchronous Gateway Server). (Since BLAST is a software interface, it does not care about the physical topology and is equally comfortable with Ethernet, StarLAN, or Token Ring networks). The physical communication channel between LAN and host could be a dial-up line or access to a PDN via the X.25 protocol.

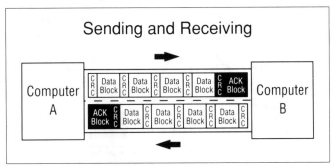

Figure 9-1a. BLAST Full Duplex Protocol
(Courtesy Communications Research Group)

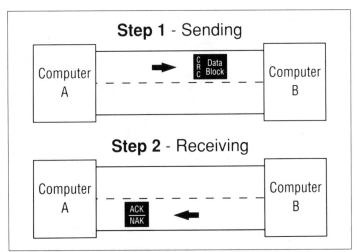

Figure 9-1b. Kermit and XMODEM Half Duplex ACK/NAK Protocol
(Courtesy Communications Research Group)

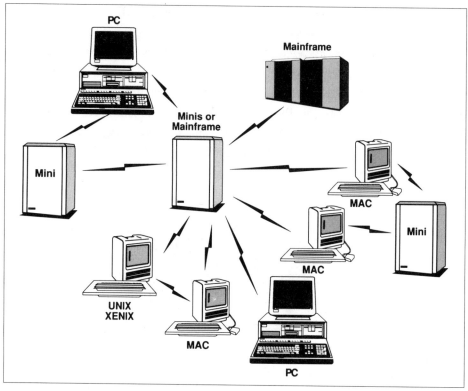

Figure 9-1c. BLAST Platform Options
(Courtesy Communications Research Group)

The terminal emulation feature permits access to local or remote host computers and allows terminal emulation and file transfer. Keyboard remapping is also available, allowing the PC's keys to be remapped for any specific terminal function. Emulators supported include DEC VT52/100/220/320, Wyse 50 series, IBM 3103, Data General D200/410/411/461, Televideo 920, and Hewlett-Packard 2392.

Remote Control permits total screen and keyboard control of LAN workstations from a remote site, or a LAN-attached workstation to control a remote workstation via dial-up lines. For example, if a network problem occurs when the administrator is off-site, he or she can access the network console remotely and initiate troubleshooting procedures immediately.

A powerful script language (which is identical for all BLAST versions—e.g., PC, Macintosh, VAX, and UNIX) allows automated logins, remote access, and file transfers. An application could be a large file transfer or backup from the LAN to a host overnight (in order to take advantage of lower dial-up telephone line charges). The BLAST script language provides for these unattended transfers and provides sample scripts for login to Value Added Networks such as CompuServe.

A most impressive feature of the BLAST software is the vast number of workstations, minicomputers, mainframes, and LANs that are supported by the software. For file transfer, terminal emulation, and remote access functions, it's safe to assume that a BLAST product exists to connect your LAN to almost any other platform. Reference [9-1] explores these host connectivity issues in greater detail.

9.2   Atlantix CocoNet and Axcess

Atlantix Corporation of Boca Raton, Florida has developed three software products that permit interoperability between Xenix, UNIX, Novell, OS/2 LAN Manager, TCP/IP, or NetBIOS-based operating systems on the same network. Two of these products—CocoNet and Axcess—are server-based, and the other, WindowView, is a workstation utility. Let's look at these three utilities individually.

CocoNet is based upon Santa Cruz Operation's (SCO) Xenix-Net. (Xenix was developed by SCO and Microsoft, and Xenix-Net is a Xenix-based version of Microsoft Networks [MS-Net] which provided the DOS Redirector and Server Message Block [SMB] protocols). CocoNet consists of server software that runs on an 80386-based PC. This server must also be running SCO Xenix 386 Version 2.2.3 or higher, with 2 MB (minimum) of RAM. Other workstations on the network must be connected with Ethernet, StarLAN, or ARCNET hardware, and may include DOS, OS/2, or Xenix workstations, or a Novell NetWare fileserver. Usually DOS and OS/2 workstations can access either the NetWare server or the Xenix server, and Xenix workstations can access the Xenix server, but not the NetWare server. What makes CocoNet unique is its ability to integrate Xenix, DOS, OS/2, and their respective platforms within one network. CocoNet does all this by providing a proprietary software gateway within the Xenix server that provides protocol translations between the Xenix-Net, SMB protocol, and Novell's IPX. NetBIOS applications are supported as well. A small (2 KB) driver in each workstation differentiates requests and directs them to each server. The driver, NetBIOS, and redirector require a total of 70 KB in each workstation. Novell users require 58 KB additional memory over normal networks, with the option of high memory (allowing zero memory impact).

Several user applications are facilitated with CocoNet. Files can be shared between two Xenix servers, or between a Xenix server and a NetWare server. Printers can also be shared between the dissimilar servers. Probably the most useful application is the ability of a DOS workstation to simultaneously login to both Xenix and NetWare servers. The CocoNet software maps different logical drives to each server, thus allowing the user seamless access to each (see Figure 9-2a). A virtual terminal program, known as vtp and xnterm, provides these functions at the workstations (reference [9-2]).

The second Atlantix product, Atlantix Axcess, is based upon the Microsoft OS/2 LAN Manager (not Microsoft Networks) operating system. Axcess is a superset of CocoNet, providing a UNIX-based LAN Manager server that supports UNIX, Xenix, DOS, OS/2, and Macintosh workstations. While CocoNet uses a Xenix server to integrate Xenix, NetWare, and NetBIOS applications, Axcess is UNIX-based, and can integrate OS/2 LAN Manager, NetBIOS, NetWare, and TCP/IP-NFS-based networks. Release 1.0 of Axcess runs under SCO UNIX Version 3.2.2. Support for TCP/IP-NFS (Sun Microsystem's Network File System protocols over TCP/IP) can also be integrated within the network. In addition, Token Ring and StarLAN hardware support has been added. Up to 255 concurrent users per server are possible. The product provides transparent bridging of files and applications between multiple operating systems and networks. Axcess offers a UNIX-based platform for the development of client-server applications that draw on data and experience from existing systems and networks.

Atlantix has plans to support 3Com and Banyan XNS implementation and offer UNIX-support for the NetWare Core Protocols (NCP) in release 2.0 (see Figure 9-2b). Integration of TCP/IP networks with Sun NFS networks is possible with the common Logical Link Control interface to the hardware. NetBIOS, Novell, or OS/2 LAN Manager workstations can be integrated into SUN, NeXT, or DEC networks.

344

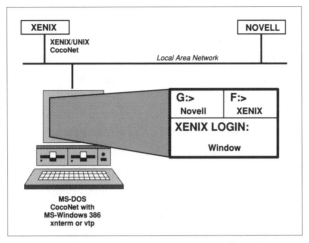

Figure 9-2a. Simultaneous NetWare and Xenix Access with CocoNet
(Courtesy Atlantix Corporation)

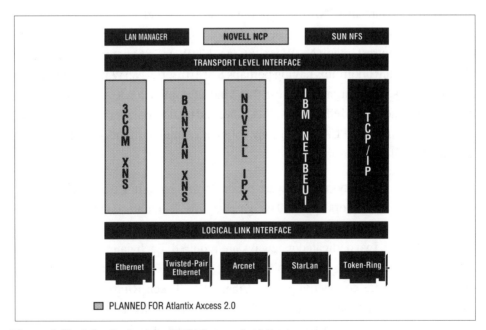

Figure 9-2b. Atlantix Axcess UNIX Server Architecture
(Courtesy Atlantix Corporation)

The third Atlantix product, which can be used with both CocoNet and Axcess, is known as WindowView. This product is a Microsoft Windows-based terminal emulator which permits DOS users simultaneous access to multiple DOS or UNIX sessions. Information transfer by means of cut-and-paste functions are also available.

With CocoNet, Axcess, and WindowView, Atlantix has provided transparent interoperability between a variety of dissimilar operating system platforms. The ability to mix UNIX, Xenix, NetWare, OS/2, and DOS on a single network is an answer to a lot of network managers' design and integration dilemmas.

9.3   Trellis Banyan/Novell Gateway

Trellis Software, Inc. of Hopkinton, Massachusetts has solved a problem with which many LAN, WAN, and internetwork managers have struggled. As we studied in Section 8.2, Banyan VINES incorporates both LAN and WAN internetworking functions and, as a result, VINES networks are typically large and geographically dispersed. In contrast, many NetWare 286 (not NetWare 386) networks are used by clusters of small workgroups having perhaps 8 or 10 users. (NetWare's Entry-Level System [ELS] was designed for just this kind of application.) A problem arose, however, whenever a VINES-based WAN needed to incorporate files or services of smaller NetWare-based LANs. No easy solution existed until the advent of Trellis Banyan/Novell Gateways.

The Trellis Gateways are software products which run in a dedicated PC, AT, or 80386-compatible workstation. Two gateways are available: one for NetWare to VINES, and a second for VINES to NetWare (see Figure 9-3). If bi-directional file access is desired, two dedicated gateways are required. Each gateway requires two Network Interface Cards for Physical Layer access to both networks, although dissimilar hardware connectivity (e.g. Ethernet to Token Ring) is allowed. The gateway server must have both VINES and NetWare shells loaded as well as an additional 256 KB of available memory for the gateway server software. All workstations require 14 KB beyond the network driver or shell. All gateways and servers must have DOS 3.0 or greater, VINES 3.0 or greater, and/or NetWare 2.1 or greater. NetBIOS is not required.

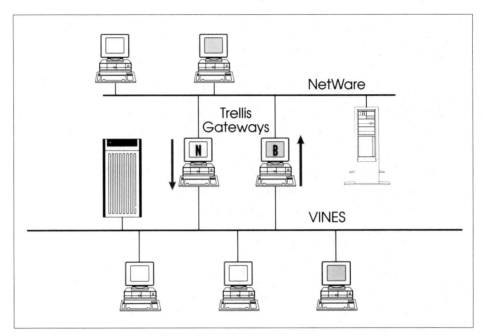

Figure 9-3. Trellis Banyan/Novell Gateways
(Courtesy Trellis Software)

One application of bi-directional gateway use would be file access. Users logged into the VINES server can read and write files on the NetWare server. Similarly, users on the NetWare side can read and write files on the VINES server. Applications can also be run on the opposite side, providing they are DOS-based (i.e. not NetWare IPX/SPX- or VINES IP-specific applications). A second application would be an electronic mail package, such as cc:Mail (from cc:Mail, Inc. of Mountain View, California), which can operate under NetWare but not VINES. Users on the VINES network can access cc:Mail residing on the NetWare Server (via the Trellis gateway), even though VINES is not currently supported.

Trellis has indeed provided an extremely useful product with these Banyan/ Novell Gateways. Future releases are planned for 3Com and OS/2-based networks as well. The simplicity of these products makes you wonder why Banyan and Novell don't integrate the Trellis software directly into their NOS, eliminating the external gateway workstation. It will be interesting to wait and see what new gateway products come from Trellis in the future.

9.4   Shiva FastPath 4 Ethernet to AppleTalk Gateway

Shiva Corporation of Cambridge, Massachusetts is a developer of peripherals that enhance the connectivity of AppleTalk networks. Shiva has a number of devices in its product line. The EtherGate is an EtherTalk/LocalTalk/Serial gateway (actually an AppleTalk router) that allows EtherTalk (AppleTalk over Ethernet or IEEE 802.3), LocalTalk (AppleTalk over unshielded twisted pair cable), Serial AppleTalk (AppleTalk over asynchronous or synchronous serial lines), and serial devices such as printers, plotters, or modems to be combined into a single internetwork. The TeleBridge provides an AppleTalk to Serial (RS-232) interface for asynchronous modems at speeds of up to 57,600 bps. The EtherGate and TeleBridge can be combined to provide both local and remote access between EtherTalk and LocalTalk networks (see Figure 9-4a). Other products include modems and bridges specifically for the AppleTalk market.

Perhaps the best known Shiva product is the FastPath 4, an AppleTalk to Ethernet gateway (this product is truly a gateway) that supports a number of higher-layer protocols. The FastPath 4 has an interesting history. The product was originally developed by Kinetics, Inc. of Walnut Creek, California in 1985. Kinetics was merged with Excelan, Inc., which was then acquired by Novell, Inc. In June 1990, Novell sold the FastPath product to Shiva, where it became a natural extension to Shiva's AppleTalk product line. It looks like the FastPath has found the right home.

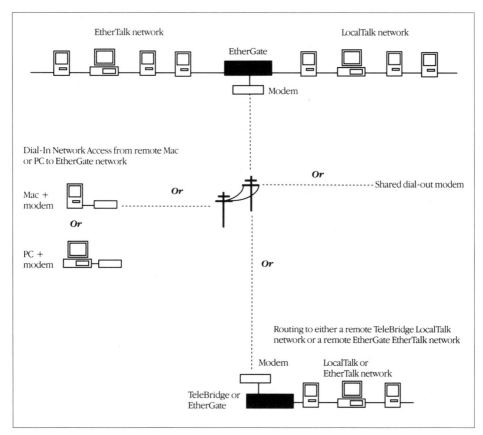

Figure 9-4a. EtherGate Configuration
(Courtesy Shiva Corporation)

The FastPath 4 is a hardware gateway that allows connection to one thick or thin coaxial IEEE 802.3 network, and one LocalTalk network (see Figure 9-4b). Installation is accomplished using an installation disk (provided) and a customer-supplied Macintosh Plus, SE, or II computer. The installation disk includes proprietary software, known as K- Star, that supports a number of protocols, including AppleTalk Phase 1 and 2, TCP/IP, DECnet, and SNMP (Simple Network Management Protocol). Most applications require that Macintosh workstations be connected to a UNIX or VAX ULTRIX-based minicomputer. For TCP/IP-based Ethernets, the FastPath 4 accepts the AppleTalk packets from the LocalTalk network, encapsulates

349

them within a UDP (User Datagram Protocol) message, and re-transmits them on the Ethernet. Access to TELNET and FTP services from the LocalTalk side are thus possible. The K-Star software also supports DECnet Level 1 routing, allowing Macintoshes running a DECnet implementation such as the one provided by Alisa Systems, Inc. (Pasadena, California), known as TSSnet. TSSnet allows a Macintosh to communicate with DECnet networks as a DECnet Phase IV end node. Access to DECnet services such as VMS mail, Network Terminal Emulation, and Remote File Access are then possible. The SNMP protocol for network management is also available. In addition, since TCP/IP and DECnet are WANs, the Macintosh user has access to distributed resources anywhere on the internet—not just the locally-connected Ethernet.

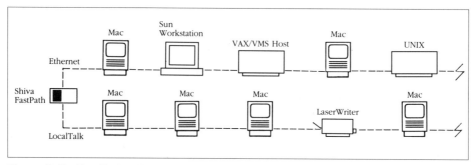

Figure 9-4b. FastPath 4 Configuration
(Courtesy Shiva Corporation)

A recent announcement profiled compatibility between the Wollongong Group's PathWay Client NFS for Macintosh (see Section 6.7.1) and FastPath 4. This combination allows a Macintosh workstation running the Client NFS software to access a UNIX host on the Ethernet running NFS. (NFS [or Network File System] is a file sharing system developed by Sun Microsystems, Inc. [Mountain View, California], and widely used on TCP/IP-based internets.)

Shiva Corporation has a number of interesting AppleTalk connectivity products. With the software-configurable FastPath 4 gateway, users are provided with a platform to connect their Macintosh networks with a number of other Ethernet-based minicomputers.

9.5 Andrew KMW NetAxcess AppleTalk to AS/400 Gateway

Integrating the Macintosh into IBM midrange and mainframe systems is a technology that is somewhat limited in the number of vendor choices available. For shoppers, Macintosh 5250 terminal emulation products are reviewed in reference [9-3]; references [9-4] and [9-5] address Macintosh gateways to larger IBM systems.

One solution, however, for integrating AppleTalk to AS/400 and System/3X minicomputers is available from Andrew KMW Systems of Austin, Texas. Known as NetAxcess, this gateway is both a hardware and software solution. The hardware consists of the NetAxcess card which may be installed in any Macintosh II, SE-30 or LC. The physical connection is via twinaxial cable to the AS/400 and via LocalTalk-compatible unshielded twisted pair cable to the Macintosh network. Existing EtherTalk (IEEE 802.3) and TokenTalk (IEEE 802.5) cabling can be used as well. The hardware interfaces with all AppleTalk Phase 2 devices, and may also be integrated with remote access devices such as Shiva's EtherGate. Each NetAxcess card supports up to seven minicomputer connections (see Figure 9-5), and up to five cards can be installed per gateway Macintosh. The installation of additional cards permits access to multiple minicomputers.

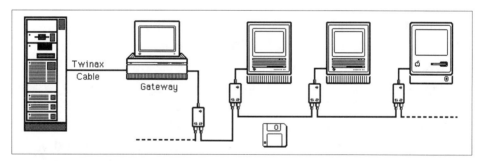

Figure 9-5. AppleTalk to AS/400 Gateway
(Courtesy Andrew KMW Systems)

The software portion of the gateway offers several user functions. A terminal emulation program (TwinAxcess) provides IBM 5250 terminal emulation functions for the Macintosh. IBM 5224/5225/5256 printers are also emulated, allowing use of an Apple LaserWriter as an IBM AS/400 or S/3X printer. A file transfer utility (ETU, or Emulator Transfer Utility/400) emulates IBM's PC Support Program, and is a host-based utility, supporting all the security features of the host. An Apple HyperCard API is also available.

The Macintosh to AS/400 might not be the most common gateway product in use, but it is good to know that the functional need is being met. The NetAxcess product meets this need with a user interface that will make the Macintosh user feel very comfortable.

9.6   Miramar MACLAN

As you will recall from our study of the AppleTalk internetworking architecture, there was one standard missing—NetBIOS (the Network Basic Input/Output System), an IBM standard Applications Programming Interface (API—widely implemented on other LAN operating systems, including Banyan Systems' VINES, Novell's NetWare, and 3Com's 3+Open) is not built into the AppleTalk architecture. According to one user's research (reference [9-6]), little hope is given for an AppleTalk to NetBIOS interface in the near future.

A third party, Miramar Systems, Inc. of Santa Barbara, California, offers an interface solution with their MACLAN product family. MACLAN Connect is a Macintosh-to-PC gateway, allowing Macintosh computers to be integrated into a PC network. The package will work with a number of network operating systems, including VINES, OS/2 LAN Server, DCA 10/Net, and all versions of NetWare. MACLAN operates by sitting in-between DOS and AFP (the AppleTalk Filing Protocol, from Section 8.1). As long as the PC workstation presents a logical, virtual, or physical DOS prompt, then this "drive" is passed to the interconnected Macintosh as an AppleShare volume.

On the PC side of the internetwork, all topologies—including Ethernet, Token Ring, and ARCNET —are supported. On the Macintosh side, AppleTalk Phase 2 topologies—which include LocalTalk, EtherTalk, and TokenTalk—are supported.

Two different software products are available. The MACLAN Connect permits any PC-compatible to function as an AppleShare server. For this configuration, the PC/AT/386 server must have both an AppleTalk and a network (Ethernet or Token Ring) interface card and necessary workstation software installed (see Figure 9-6a). The physical interface is the cabling system native to that architecture, such as unshielded twisted pair for LocalTalk or Token Ring, or RG58A/U coax for thin Ethernet. The PC server thus becomes a dedicated AppleShare server while the MACLAN connect software provides an implementation of the AppleTalk Filing Protocol (AFP) for DOS. Transparent sharing of volumes, folders, and files between the AppleTalk and DOS environments thus becomes possible.

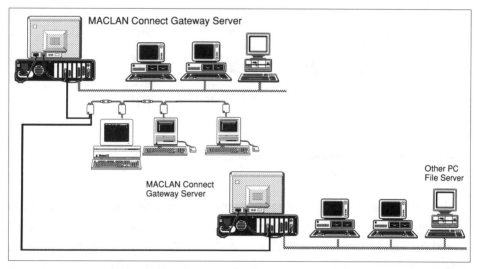

Figure 9-6a. MACLAN Connect Gateway Server
(Courtesy Miramar Systems)

A second gateway product is known as MACLAN Print, which allows PCs and Macintoshes simultaneous access to PostScript printers (see Figure 9-6b). The print server software requires a dedicated PC/AT/386/486 workstation that is also configured as a LAN workstation. It is, however, possible for a MACLAN Connect gateway to be configured for both printer and file-sharing functions; however, with this configuration, two MB of RAM are required on the gateway. Physical connection between printer and print server may be established through the PC network, AppleTalk cabling, or serial/parallel interface.

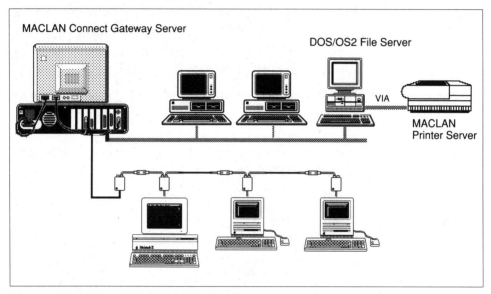

Figure 9-6b. MACLAN PostScript Printer Support
(Courtesy Miramar Systems)

In addition to supporting file and printer sharing, the MACLAN gateway offers a third application—electronic mail interoperability. MACLAN supports several popular E-mail packages, including cc:Mail (cc:Mail, Inc., Mountain View, California) and Network Courier (Consumer Software Inc., Vancouver, BC). With MACLAN's support, other applications are sure to be identified. For those users wishing Macintosh-to-PC LAN integration, this product is certainly worthy of consideration.

9.7 Hewlett-Packard OfficeShare-NetWare Gateway

Hewlett-Packard Company of Irving, Texas has developed a gateway linking their HP3000 minicomputers with Novell NetWare networks. The core of the gateway is the HP OfficeShare software. Components of this software run on the client PC, the gateway, and the HP3000 minicomputer. The OfficeShare software allows an HP3000 to be used as a server for a Novell PC-based network, and provides logon access to the HP3000 from the Novell client. Let's study the operation of the gateway by first comparing the HP OfficeShare and Novell NetWare protocol stacks.

HP OfficeShare (see Figure 9-7a) is a LAN operating system that runs on both a DOS and MPE (HP's MultiProgramming Executive) platform. It supports protocols such as IEEE 802.3, Ethernet, TCP, and IP. The Session Layer protocol is known as NetIPC (Network InterProcess Communication). OfficeShare uses a Virtual Terminal (VT) program at the Presentation Layer and HP AdvanceLink terminal emulation software at the Application Layer.

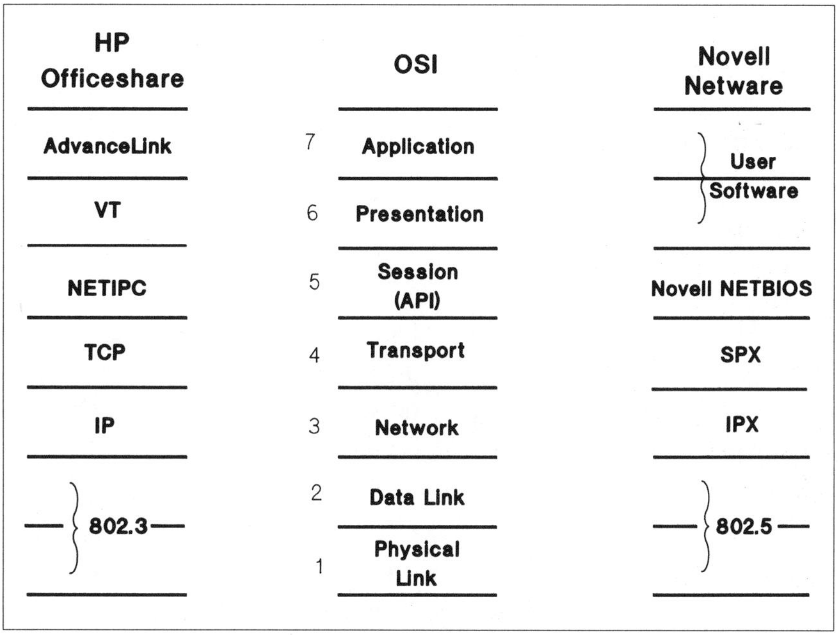

HP Officeshare		OSI	Novell Netware
AdvanceLink	7	Application	User Software
VT	6	Presentation	
NETIPC	5	Session (API)	Novell NETBIOS
TCP	4	Transport	SPX
IP	3	Network	IPX
802.3	2	Data Link	802.5
	1	Physical Link	

Figure 9-7a. Comparing HP OfficeShare and Novell NetWare with the OSI Reference Model *(Courtesy Hewlett-Packard Company)*

Novell, on the other hand, has a variety of Physical and Data Link Layer platform options, including Ethernet, IEEE 802.3, IEEE 802.5, and ARCNET, among others (IEEE 802.5 is shown in Figure 9-7a as an example). As we discussed in Section 7.5, Novell's IPX and SPX, based upon the XNS, IDP, and SPP protocols, are used at the Network and Transport Layers. The Session Layer interface is a NetBIOS emulation, with the NetWare Core Protocols (NCP) and Application programs operating at the Presentation and Application Layers.

Clearly, HP and Novell have a different view of network architectures. Communication between these two dissimilar systems is possible with the HP-Novell gateway shown in Figure 9-7b. The OfficeShare-NetWare gateway software resides in a dedicated PC-compatible. Two network interfaces (one supporting Ethernet/ IEEE 802.3 for communicating to the HP3000, and the other supporting the Novell network hardware—e.g. 802.5) within the gateway are required. Each PC on the NetWare side must also run a terminal emulation program that is compatible at both the Novell workstation and the HP3000 ends of the internetwork. HP provides one such program (known as HP AdvanceLink), although other software supporting TELNET and FTP protocols could also be used.

Interoperability is achieved for several specific applications with the HP-Novell gateway: terminal emulation for HP2622 terminals; file transfer via FTP (both achieved with AdvanceLink); Program-to-Program communication with HP NetIPC; and other services—such as printing—defined by the HP3000 as the network server.

The data communication path inside the OfficeShare-NetWare gateway is also shown in Figure 9-7b. Note that the left-hand side of the figure shows NetWare-compatible protocols, while the right-hand side communicates with OfficeShare. Let's trace the path of the AdvanceLink message from the Novell workstation to the HP3000 server. The AdvanceLink message (such as a file transfer request) is initiated by the user, generating an IP datagram. The IP datagram is passed to the NetBIOS SPX and IPX protocols in turn, which add their Protocol Control Information (PCI), and encapsulate the Advance Link message. An IEEE 802.5 frame is generated at the workstation, which then waits for a free token. The frame is transmitted over the Token Ring network cable, through Multistation Access Units (MSAUs) and possible repeaters, until it reaches the gateway. Inside the gateway the IPX, SPX, and NetBIOS PCI are removed from the message, leaving the Advance Link packet. This packet is then transferred across the gateway's internal bus to the IEEE 802.3 NIC. The NIC builds an 802.3 frame, which listens to the coaxial cable transmitting during an idle period. No collisions or retransmissions occur (remember, this is theoretical and utopian!) and the 802.3 frame successfully reaches the HP3000. At the server, the IP, TCP, NetIPC, and VT headers are removed in turn, revealing the AdvanceLink message. The AdvanceLink software does not know (or care) that the Novell workstation and gateway protocol were involved; it only sees an AdvanceLink packet. The requested file can then be accessed, and the file transfer commenced. An opposite (but equivalent) process would then occur with the reply from server to workstation. Reference [9-7] is an excellent article which details these protocol interactions.

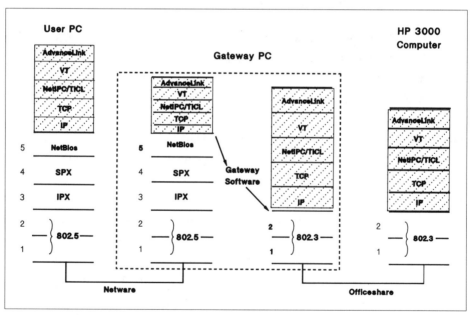

Figure 9-7b. HP-Novell Gateway Architecture
(Courtesy Hewlett-Packard Company)

This Hewlett-Packard gateway solves several problems—most obvious, the integration of the HP and Novell architectures. Two other, more subtle issues are also involved. First, an HP MPE-based host has been made interoperable with a Novell PC-based LAN. More importantly, the storage, backup, and redundancy capabilities are now available to the PC network as well. From an internetworking and interoperability point of view, this is an excellent merger of technologies.

9.8   ICC/LAN-Gateway and ICC/TCP/IP Access

Intercomputer Communications Corporation of Cincinnati, Ohio is a third-party vendor of peripherals and connectivity products that support the Unisys (formerly Burroughs and Sperry) mainframe environments. ICC has two product lines, each having similar characteristics. One line is used with Unisys A/V/B series mainframes ("Burroughs"). The other is for Unisys 1100/1200 mainframes ("Sperry"). We'll look at the Burroughs line in this section. Two examples from that line, ICC/LAN-Gateway and ICC/TCP/IP Access, provide internetworking to LAN environments.

ICC/LAN-Gateway is a combination hardware and software product that runs in a dedicated or non-dedicated communications server based in a PC-AT- or 80386-compatible workstation. (The choice of dedicated or non-dedicated depends upon network resources, needs, and the traffic loading from other applications.) The gateway can connect to a Unisys A Series (large), V Series, or B1000 Series (small) mainframe, by means of RS-232 or the Unisys TDI (Two-wire Direct Interface). The gateway software requires an intelligent communications adapter—either an ICC/UniCard+ or an ICC/UniCard IDC—that resides in the communications server (see Figure 9-8a). (The IDC—Intelligent DataComm Controller—is recommended for non-dedicated communication server applications. This allows the IDC to do the majority of the data communications processing, freeing the server's CPU for other tasks). Up to two of these cards can be installed in the same communications server. All other PCs attach to the communications server with normal LAN connections.

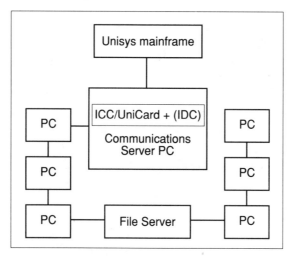

Figure 9-8a. ICC/LAN-Gateway Architecture
(Courtesy InterComputer Communications)

The ICC/LAN Gateway software contains three components (see Figure 9-8b): a background communications program, Datacomm, runs in the communications server and maintains communication between LAN workstations and the mainframe; a second module, MGATEWAY (for Master gateway), interprets the LAN workstation requests and passes them to the Datacomm module; and the third module, LGATEWAY (for local gateway), resides in each LAN workstation. The LGATEWAY module provides the interface between workstation applications and MGATEWAY. Typical interface applications would be ICC's terminal emulation package, ICC/InterCom, which emulates the Unisys ET 1100 and T 27 terminals, or ICC/FileXpress, for PC-to-mainframe file transfers. The software does not have a limit on the number of communication servers for the network. Most NetBIOS-compatible NOSs are compatible with LAN-Gateway, including 3Com 3+, Novell NetWare, DCA 10-NET, AT&T StarLAN, Banyan VINES, and IBM PC Network Programs and PC LAN Programs.

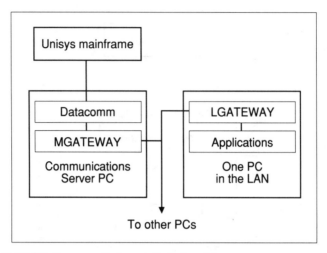

Figure 9-8b. ICC/LAN-Gateway Software Relationships
(Courtesy InterComputer Communications)

The second product, known as ICC/TCP/IP Access, provides connectivity between Unisys A Series mainframes and other workstations on an Ethernet LAN (see Figure 9-8c). Two different components are used for ICC/TCP/IP Access; the first is the A Series mainframe, and the second is the CP2000. The A Series mainframe uses Burroughs Network Architecture (BNA) Version 2.1.1 to communicate with other BNA hosts. TCP/IP is used to communicate with non-BNA hosts via the CP2000. Applications such as SMTP, TELNET, and FTP are supported. Communication with Ethernet workstations also requires those workstations to support the TCP/IP protocols. Products such as FTP Software's PC/TCP (see Section 6.7.3) or Novell's LAN WorkPlace for DOS (see Section 6.7.2) are examples of support hardware/software systems. An example of the Series A, CP2000, and NetWare workstation architecture is shown in Figure 9-8d. Note that the A Series and CP2000 communicate using the TCP/BNA protocol, while the CP2000 and NetWare workstation communicate with TCP/IP. Reference [9-8] discusses TCP/IP connections to Unisys A Series mainframes, and [9-9] looks at the Unisys 1100/2200 application.

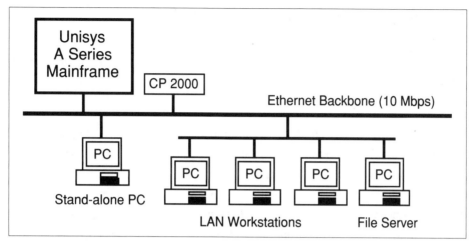

Figure 9-8c. Unisys to Ethernet Connectivity Via TCP/IP
(Courtesy InterComputer Communications)

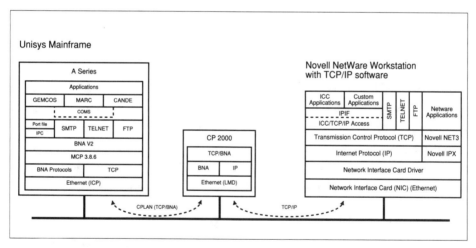

Figure 9-8d. Unisys to NetWare Connectivity Architecture
(Courtesy InterComputer Communications)

ICC provides these two gateway alternatives for Unisys to LAN internetworking, both of which are viable options for the non-IBM mainframe shops.

361

9.9   FEL LANLink-DECnet Gateway

FEL Computing, Inc. of Williamsville, Vermont specializes in connectivity solutions to DEC VAX minicomputers (see reference [9-10] for an excellent text on DECnet). One FEL product of interest to LAN designers is the LANLink-DECnet Gateway.

The gateway requires a PC/XT/AT-compatible hardware platform having two adapter cards: one to communicate to the DECnet (Phase IV) Ethernet, and the other to communicate with a LAN (see Figure 9-9). LANLink-DECnet is compatible with Novell, 3Com, Banyan, Ungermann-Bass, or any NetBIOS-compatible network software. Since it provides a software—not hardware interface—the LAN topology does not matter. If the NIC is supported by the LAN Operating System, it can be used in the gateway and workstation platforms. LANLink-DECnet connects client workstations on the LAN to any DEC host using the DECnet LAT (Local Area Transport) protocol. Compatible platforms include: VAX/VMS, VAX/Ultrix, DEC terminal servers, or any LAT-compatible terminal servers. Up to 100 simultaneous sessions can be supported. In addition to the gateway software, a 10 KB memory-resident module is required at every workstation.

LANLink-DECnet is installed on the gateway PC after it has been configured on a normal LAN workstation. The gateway is dedicated to this purpose, and should have no extraneous hardware or software installed. The workstation software is stored on the network server, and is licensed by a set number of simultaneous sessions. Client PCs can load all of LANLink-DECnet into high memory, and the memory used can then be released without rebooting the workstation.

The two primary applications of the LANLink-DECnet gateway are emulation of DEC VT320 terminals, and menu-driven file transfers using the Kermit protocol. LANLink-DECnet supplies the industry-standard INT-14 interface and DEC's PC interface, so that LAN-based PCs can run programs based upon these interfaces. This low-cost, but highly flexible product is an excellent alternative to individual PC-to-VAX attachments.

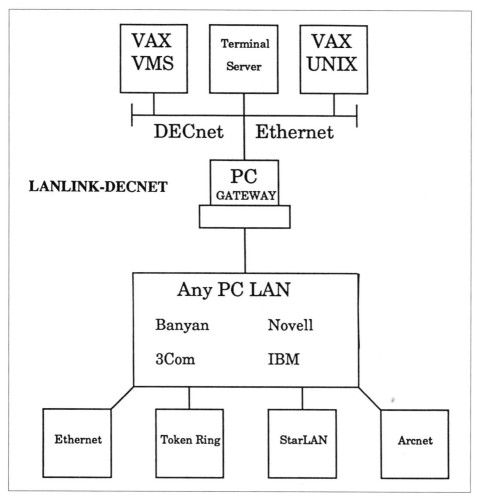

Figure 9-9. LANlink-DECnet Gateway
(Courtesy FEL Computing)

For applications that require advanced PC and VAX integration features, FEL Computing offers another product line for VAX/VMS connections called Mobius. Mobius provides PCs with a virtual file system, printer support, VT320 terminal emulation, and transparent file transfer. Mobius Plus adds virtual process, control of the PC from the VAX, task-to-task communication, and an advanced programmer's interface. Add-on modules include Mobius ACCESS, an automatic login utility, and

Task-Force, a high-level, task-description language for fast applications programming involving PC/network/VAX interactions. Mobius supports ASCII and Ethernet connections, and can be layered on top of LANLink-DECnet for networked PCs. Mobius requires software to be loaded on the VAX, as well as on the PC or network server.

In summary, the Mobius and LANLink-DECnet products allow a number of powerful PC network-to-DECnet applications.

9.10   InterConnections I* Software

Interconnections, Inc. of Bellevue, Washington markets a variety of software packages to connect PC LANs with DEC VAX/VMS systems. One of these packages—NetWare for VMS—was developed by InterConnections, and is marketed by Novell. NetWare for VMS allows VAX computers to be file servers on a NetWare LAN. A second product, DECnet/IPX Portal, is used to route NetWare IPX/SPX packets over a DECnet backbone. A third, Terminal Emulation Services (TES), permits NetWare workstations to login as interactive workstations on a VAX. Finally, Network Print Services (NPS) redirects VAX output to a NetWare LAN printer.

The I* software is InterConnections' implementation of Microsoft Networks (MS-Net) with Microsoft OS/2 LAN Manager interoperability for VAX/VMS minicomputers. Several versions of the I* package are available, supporting XNS and TCP/IP over Ethernet LANs, and NetBIOS over Token Ring LANs. We'll look at two of these products in depth.

I* for 3Com is a software-only solution that makes the resources of a VAX/VMS system available to MS-Net or LAN Manager clients. The VAX connects to the Ethernet via a DEC-provided Ethernet Controller card, and all other workstations connect via standard Ethernet/IEEE 802.3 NICs. Other devices (such as bridges) may attach to the Ethernet network as well, allowing connectivity to other networks (such as Token Ring). (See Figure 9-10a.)

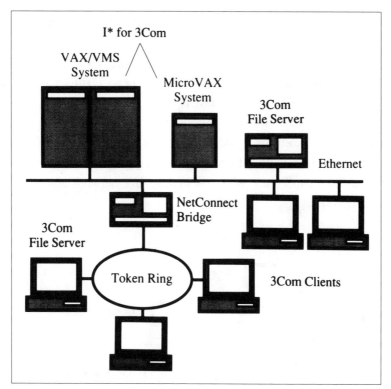

Figure 9-10a. I* for 3Com
(Courtesy InterConnections)

The I* architecture includes a Server Message Block implementation (known as ISMB), which provides PC-VAX file sharing. ISMB translates DOS and VMS differences in file attributes and naming conventions, allowing seamless file sharing. VAX files thus appear as DOS files to the PC users, but remain VMS RMS files to VAX users. LAN workstations can also submit their print or batch jobs to the VAX, accessing the VMS printing or batch queues.

The I* server supports XNS and TCP/IP protocols, and is compatible with both 3Com 3+, 3+Open, and IBM PC Network Programs. The server also supports Token Ring networks if they are running 3+ or 3+Open as a NOS and are physically connected to the Ethernet by means of a 3Com bridge.

A second I* implementation, I* for Token-Ring, allows a direct attachment of a Q-bus VAX to a Token Ring network running the IBM PC LAN Program (see Figure 9-10b). An additional hardware interface, the TRN5200 series adapter (manufactured by Simpact Associates, Inc. of San Diego, California), is required in the VAX. A NetBIOS implementation (in ROM) runs on this adapter, providing the logical connection to the I* software. As with the I* for 3Com software, transparent access to the VAX file and print services are available to the Token Ring workstations. Concurrent operation with the DECnet protocols is also permitted. A second server (noted as PC Server in Figure 9-10b) is optional for network administration and management services.

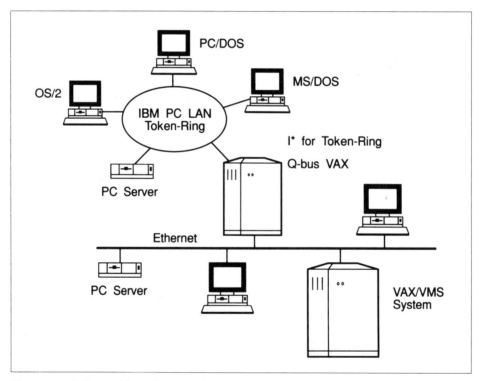

Figure 9-10b. I* for Token Ring
(Courtesy InterConnections)

The implementations of the Microsoft networks and its related interface (NetBIOS) and protocol (Server Message Block) continue to expand. InterConnections has provided a solid VAX/VMS implementation with the I* products.

9.11   Data Interface DI3270 Gateway

Data Interface Systems Corporation of Austin, Texas is a manufacturer of gateways between IBM mainframes and LANs. Before looking at the DI3270 product in detail, let's consider an evaluation checklist developed by DI for 3270 LAN gateways (reference [9-11]).

1. Verify compatibility of the 3270 terminal with the mainframe application.

2. Evaluate the various protocol, line speed, and attachment methods, and select the options that fit the user requirements.

3. Verify compatibility with the LAN operating system.

4. Determine the gateway capacities for attached devices (terminals and/or printers).

5. Understand the gateway pricing structure, which may be based upon a fixed rate for the gateway (with unlimited workstations), or a charge for the gateway and an additional charge for each workstation.

6. Consider if a requirement for multiple gateways (to multiple hosts) exists.

7. Study the hardware/software mix of the gateway. Hardware-intensive systems contain on-board processors and buffers, but are less flexible when upgrading.

8. Evaluate the gateway performance with a test system prior to making a purchase commitment.

9. Determine how the gateway handles disconnections from the mainframe or a cluster controller. The ease of recovery from failures should be a key factor for consideration.

10. Look at the printing capabilities, considering spooling functions and where, physically, the printers will be placed.

11. Evaluate DOS "hot-key" support, considering performance and processing concurrency.

12. Determine the flexibility for remapping the 3270 keyboard to the workstation.

13. What file transfer utility does the gateway support and is it compatible with the mainframe utility?

14. Define any Application Program Interfaces required, and determine if the gateway supports those APIs.

15. Look for user-related requirements, such as status line layout, configuration/ reconfiguration options, and management tools.

16. Consider any requirement for foreign-language support, such as with an emulated printer.

17. Ask previous users for their experience (good and bad) with the gateway. Consider installation, configuration, and vendor support.

18. Consider the vendors' support for future enhancements to SNA/SAA. Do they have a good track record of keeping up with recently announced products?

Given the above evaluation criterion, consider the various DI3270 gateway alternatives shown in Figure 9-11. Mainframe connections are possible using several different emulations: a remote 3174 or 3274 controller connected with a dial-up or leased line (Figure 9-11a); coaxial cable attachment to a 3174/3274 emulating a 3299 multiplexer (Figure 9-11b); or Token Ring attachment to 3174 or front-end processor (Figure 9-11c). Protocols available include SNA/SDLC, SNA/Coax DLC, SNA/802.2, remote BSC (Bisynchronous Communications), and coax non-SNA.

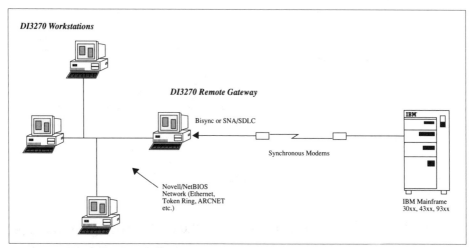

Figure 9-11a. 3270 Remote Connections
(Courtesy Data Interface Systems)

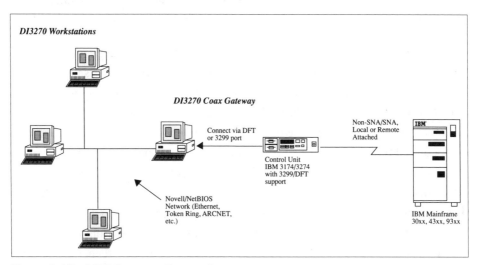

Figure 9-11b. 3270 Gateway Connections
(Courtesy Data Interface Systems)

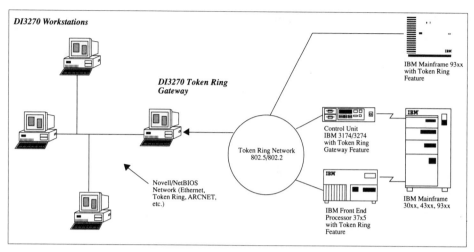

Figure 9-11c. 3270 Token Ring Connections
(Courtesy Data Interface Systems)

Up to 253 sessions are supported for SNA/SDLC or SNA/802.2 gateways; 32 per BSC gateway; 40 per 3299 SNA gateway; or 32 for the non-SNA version. Each workstation supports up to four concurrent host sessions, plus one DOS session. Hot-key switching is user-configurable. Workstation software is supported under DOS, Windows, and OS/2.

A number of physical connection alternatives are available depending upon the gateway attachment (e.g. controller, remote dial-up, or FEP) that is selected. In all cases, however, additional hardware is required within the gateway workstation. Data Interface supports a number of SNA/SDLC communications boards that work with their software. This choice of the accompanying hardware depends upon the protocol and transmission speed required. For LAN connections, two alternatives are available. If one TIC (Token-Ring Interface Coupler) is installed in the gateway, all workstations, the mainframe, and the gateway must share a common physical Token Ring network. For connections to other LANs (e.g. Ethernet), two adapters are required. One adapter will connect to the mainframe environment (e.g. via coaxial cable), and the other will connect to the LAN. In this scenario, the LAN connection could be any NetWare-compatible (IPX) topology, or any other NetBIOS-compatible network.

370

As reference [9-12] describes, well over a dozen vendors make 3270 gateways for LANs. What sets Data Interface Systems' products apart is the depth of understanding that they bring to the marketplace. A user gets a clear impression that DI understands the advantages (and pitfalls) of attaching a LAN to an IBM mainframe. (Several recent articles have reviewed and tested SNA gateway products. Reference [9-13] looks at 3174 TIC gateways; references [9-14] and [9-15] study IBM's approach; and reference [9-16] looks at a number of third-party products.)

9.12 BLUELYNX 5250 Gateways

Micro-Integration (manufacturer of BLUELYNX products) of Cumberland, Maryland specializes in both local and remote connections to IBM S/34, S/36, S/38, and AS/400 midrange systems. Four different connectivity options are available (see Figure 9-12).

BLUELYNX/5251-11 is used by PC or PS/2 compatibles to connect to IBM midrange systems or control units. The physical connection is via twinax cable (or baluns) running between a BLUELYNX communications card in the PC and the midrange system or control unit. Each PC can emulate up to seven 5250 display stations and printers. For remote PCs, BLUELYNX/5250-12 connects to the midrange via synchronous modems or null modem cables. An SDLC communications card and synchronous modem are required to complete the physical and logical connections.

For internetworking applications, BLUELYNX has developed two 5250 gateways. BLUELYNX/5251-11 Local Gateway allows a PC/XT/AT, PS/2, or compatible to function as a local gateway into a NetBIOS-compatible LAN. The gateway connects via twinax cable or baluns to an IBM 5251-12, 5294, or 5394 control unit, which in turn connects to the midrange system. (As an alternative, the gateway can connect directly to the midrange system.) With a single gateway adapter, the gateway PC routes information for up to seven node sessions distributed to other PCs on the network. Up to 32 gateways can operate on one network, making a total of 224

371

sessions on a single LAN. Each LAN workstation runs BLUELYNX-supplied 5250 emulation software. IBM devices that are supported include 5251 model 11, 5291, 5292 model 1, 3180 model 2, and 3196 displays; as well as 5219, 5224 model 1, 5225, 5256, and 3812 printers.

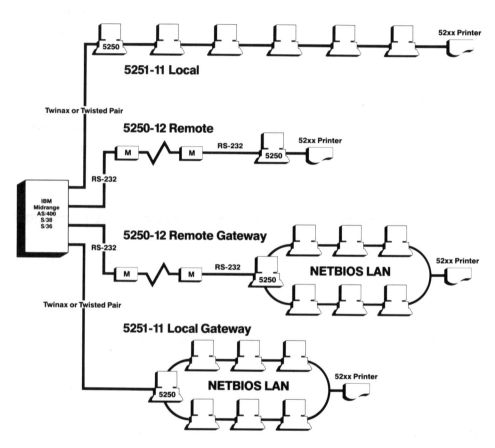

Figure 9-12. 5250 Gateway Connections
(Courtesy Micro-Integration)

Up to four of these gateways can be installed within a single PC, providing equipment savings. A second feature—IBM AS/400 PC Support on the nodes—allows all gateway users to access functions such as message, workstation, virtual printer, and transfer, as well as shared folders and PC Organizer.

Applications can interface through API Version 2.1, File Support Utility (FSU), PC Support/36, PC Support/38, PC Organizer, and DecisionLink A Enhanced, as well as other compatible file transfer programs. In addition, a hot-key permits DOS applications to run while 5250 applications are being executed as a background function.

BLUELYNX/5250-12 Remote Gateway provides remote connections via synchronous modems between NetBIOS-compatible LANs and IBM midrange processors. Both dial-up and leased line connections are available, at speeds of between 9.6 and 19.2 Kbps. Each gateway can support up to nine display stations and printers. Up to four gateway servers can operate on one network, making a total of 36 sessions on a single LAN. IBM AS/400 PC Support on the nodes is also provided for the remote gateway. With respect to the IBM midrange processor, the gateway emulates an IBM 5251 model 12, 5294, or 5394 controller. Diagnostics included with the gateway troubleshoot line errors on the communications lines, or provide an analog loopback between the gateway adapter and the synchronous modem.

To summarize, BLUELYNX permits a number of connectivity options between stand-alone PCs, LAN workstations, and IBM midrange computers. The products' abilities to easily integrate networking software with IBM applications make for a powerful internetworking solution.

In this chapter, we have studied gateways that provide Application Layer connectivity solutions. In most cases, third-party solutions provide the most creative and user-friendly solutions since they have been developed in direct response to marketplace needs. A listing of vendors supplying internetworking solutions is given in Appendix B. Another excellent source of gateway solutions is the Annual Buyer's Guides published by LAN Magazine or LAN Times (references [9-17] and [9-18], respectively).

9.13 References

[9-1] Communications Research Group. *Communications Concepts.* Manual no. 101.1, July 1989.

[9-2] Farris, Rick. "Connecting Xenix to NetWare," *LAN Times* (September 1990): 176 – 178.

[9-3] Beckman, Mel, et al. "Macintosh Twinaxial Emulators," *NEWS 3X/400* (August 1990): 54 – 109.

[9-4] Kosinr, Dave. "Corporate Connectivity Gets Macs Off SNA Sideline," *Data Communications* (August 1990): 101 – 106.

[9-5] Frenkel, Gerry. "Gateways Link Macs to IBM Mainframes," *PC Week* (October 8, 1990): 101 – 105.

[9-6] Zarley, Craig. "Missing TokenTalk Hook Sends Chevron on Mac-NetBIOS Hunt," *MacWEEK* (April 10, 1990): 40 – 42.

[9-7] Yori, Robert S. "Multivendor LANs," *LAN Computing* (October 1990): 33 – 37.

[9-8] Sayers , C. David and Trenton W. Simonson. "Linking PCs to Unisys A Series Systems Via TCP/IP," Intercomputer Communications Corporation, 1990.

[9-9] Tillman, Dave. "Using TCP/IP on 1100/2200 Systems," *Unisphere* (April 1990): 57 – 66.

[9-10] Malamud, Carl. *DEC Networks and Architectures.* New York: McGraw-Hill, 1989.

[9-11] Data Interface Systems Corp. *IBM Connectivity for PC LANs.* 2nd ed. September 1989.

[9-12] Chappell, Jim and John Siegal. "An Evaluation—Comparing LU Management Techniques in 3270 SNA Gateways," *LAN Magazine* (April 1990): 70 – 82.

[9-13] Gerber, Barry, et al. "TIC Gateways: Cost-Effective Way to Save Host Resources," *PC Week* (October 19, 1989): 69 – 73.

[9-14] Tolly, Kevin. "Playing to Win with IBM's LAN Gateways," *Data Communications* (February 1990): 74-84.

[9-15] Tolly, Kevin. "Opening the Gateways to SNA Connectivity," *Data Communications* (March 1990): 89 – 102.

[9-16] Tolly, Kevin. "SNA Gateways Are More Than Mere Child's Play," *Data Communications* (October 1990): 78 – 96.

[9-17] "LAN Products Buyers Guide," *LAN Magazine* (August 1990); 40 – 108.

[9-18] "1990-1991 Buyers Guide," *LAN Times,* September 3, 1990.

CHAPTER 10

Implementing the Internetwork

No reference on internetworking is complete without a discussion of network implementation and management. An attempt has been made to address general "internetwork" requirements (whatever that means), so not all steps may be applicable to your case. If some steps don't apply, skip them and forge ahead. In order to calm the sleepless nights of the implementors, here is a 40-step plan for guidance. Refer to the timeline (Figure 10-1) as you study.

10.1   The Internetwork Implementation Plan

1. Appoint a system manager, network contacts in each location, and an implementation committee, as required. Project-management theory teaches us that unless someone's feet are held to the fire and that person made responsible for a project's success, the likelihood of success is dramatically reduced. Beyond the technical qualifications, the system manager should have the personal interest and desire to see that the project succeeds. Don't forget that when responsibility is conveyed, the authority to make it happen must be authorized as well. Depending upon the size of the project, it may be advisable to appoint a management steering committee that can assist with resolving issues of project authority, budgets, etc.

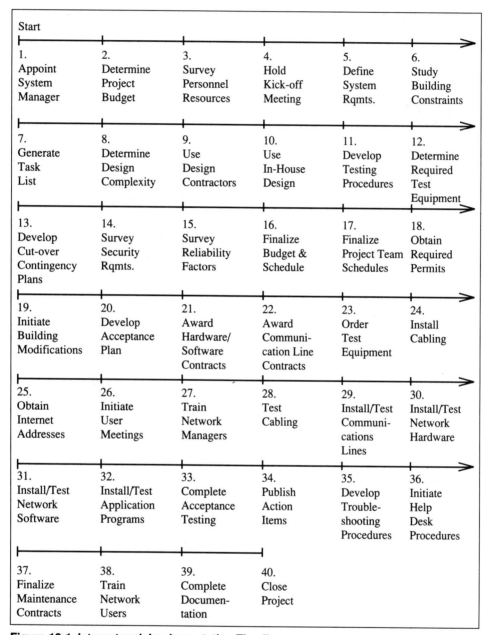

Figure 10-1. Internetwork Implementation Timeline

2.   Determine the available (or allowable) budget for the project, including such costs as personnel, equipment, cabling and contingencies. Don't initiate a project if sufficient funds are not available, and if a clear commitment from upper management is not evident.

3.   Survey the available personnel resources, and decide if you need to add outside contractors or consultants to your team. Several areas of expertise should be considered. Electrical codes and practices that might affect installation of the cable should be reviewed by an expert. Do not make a mistake (such as installing coaxial instead of fiber optic cable) that could affect the strategic direction of your company for years to come. Other areas to consider include telecommunications facility capacity planning and other growth projections for your industry type. The design may be more than you want to tackle technically; engineering assistance is available for traffic studies and protocol optimization.

4.   Hold a project kick-off meeting, assign responsibilities, and develop a project schedule. Some cleverness and innovation can go a long way here—remember that all team members need a "buy-in" since their contribution to this project may be only one of their responsibilities. Do what you can to get all members focused and pulling in the same direction. Initiate an action-item database that describes open issues, the responsible parties, due dates, etc. Circulate this database information on a periodic basis to all team members, the steering committee, and other relevant managers.

5.   Survey key personnel for their input about the system's requirements. It is impossible to define all aspects of the design without a written functional requirements document. The plan will also be used by vendors bidding on the project in order to define how their products fit into the complete internetwork. Circulate the functional-requirements document to upper management for approval, and to all project team members for review.

6. Consult the building owner, other tenants, and municipal authorities for any constraints that might affect the system's installation. Surprises such as fire walls that went unnoticed, or unknown conduit runs are not any fun to deal with. Take a walking tour of the building facility, and be on the lookout for anything that might need special attention.

7. Use the requirements document and building survey to generate a complete list of required tasks. (Project Managers refer to this as a work-breakdown structure.) If the project is large enough to so warrant, use a PC-based project management tool—such as Microsoft Corporation's Project—to generate a schedule and identify the critical path. Distribute the schedule to all team members.

8. Determine the complexity of the internetwork design, as influenced by factors such as the number of locations to connect, number of workstations and servers per location, protocols to be supported, etc. Proceed with Steps 9 or 10 as appropriate.

9. Solicit bids for the hardware, software, and communication facilities, and cabling system designs. In many cases, vendors will be willing (or eager) to provide a design without charge. Make sure that an impartial third party is available to lend a measure of objectivity to vendor-generated proposals.

10. Design the internetwork yourself, and draw a complete schematic of the system. Use the guidelines in Section 2.1 for the LAN to LAN portions, and the guidelines in Section 4.1 for the LAN to WAN portions. Beware of single-vendor or other sole-source solutions. Resist the urge to be a field trial or beta test site for a new product or system unless a fallback plan (i.e. "plan B") is clearly feasible.

11. Develop system testing procedures for all hardware and software components, as well as the transmission facilities. Identify all vendor-specific areas of responsibility—such as testing and maintenance—defined in the contracts and warranties, and develop a list of all vendor support contacts. Make sure that components are physically located so that test equipment can be used in close proximity. Also assure that adequate power and a telephone line is available close to critical components such as servers and routers. Access to a FAX machine can also speed up communication with vendor-support organizations.

12. Compile a list of required troubleshooting tools. Consider hand tools, meters, interface testers, cable testers and protocol analyzers. See reference [10-1], Chapter 3, for guidance in making your choices.

13. Develop a contingency plan if the new system is replacing an existing system. Determine if a flash cutover or phased cutover is more appropriate, based upon the "mission critical" nature of the project. Require that any installation vendors develop methods and procedures that support the sequencing required for a successful cutover.

14. Consider the security of the internetwork. Where remote (dial-in) access is involved, look at barrier codes, passwords, and other methods of authenticating network access. Putting yourself in the shoes of a potential hacker, determine the degree of difficulty involved in infiltrating the internetwork, and build appropriate safeguards into the design.

15. Make a review of the network reliability factors (reference [10-2]). Also consider the effects and costs that downtime would have on the network (reference[10-3]). For critical components and circuits, consider stocking spare parts on-site yourself, or adding additional hot-standby or dial-backup lines.

16. Finalize the project budget and schedule, allowing for contingencies. Obtain management approval before proceeding.

17. Now that the project is a go, develop a schedule for periodic project team meetings, and begin publishing and distributing schedules and meeting minutes to all affected organizations.

18. Obtain building permits, as required, for all installation locations.

19. Initiate major building additions, such as computer room modifications, required to accommodate the new system. Make a survey of all equipment and wiring closets to ensure that adequate power is readily available.

20. Develop a system-acceptance plan that will thoroughly test all cabling, communication facilities, hardware and software modules. This plan may take some time to develop, and will require a thorough understanding of the internetwork hardware and software operation and configuration. (In other words, if you don't understand how a router should operate, it's difficult to verify that it is performing correctly.) Good source information is often found in the installation guides for the components that are part of the entire system. Another valuable technique is to review the functional requirements document, and to outline the steps required to verify the individual requirements. For example: "connect to a remote IBM host via a Proteon TCP/IP router. Establish a TELNET session emulating a DEC VT220 terminal." Ask for vendor and user input to this testing plan to assure that all internetwork functions are covered.

21. Award contracts for hardware and software components. Obtain delivery dates from vendors to include in the project schedule. Obtain commitments from vendors for training personnel on the operation of the various components.

22. Award contracts for communication facilities from LEC, IXC, or PDN vendors. Coordinate cutover dates for facilities to correspond with hardware installation for end-to-end testing.

23. Order test equipment from the list developed in item 12.

24. Begin installation of new wiring or cabling systems needed to support the internetwork. Allow for plenty of growth—a factor of 2 to 3 times the initial requirement is often used for sizing twisted pair cables to avoid premature obsolescence.

25. Obtain internet addresses from a central authority (see reference [6-9]) if required. Distribute these addresses to all hardware and software vendors, as well as the project team.

26. Consider brown-bag lunch meetings to keep personnel that may be affected (but not directly involved in the project) informed of the progress. Since installation invariably creates workplace disruption, help those who will be affected to understand how the internetwork will improve their data and/or voice communication.

27. Schedule training classes on the installation and maintenance of all new hardware and software systems. For most projects, there is an interval between the time the equipment is ordered, and the time when it is to be installed. Take advantage of this interim period, educating yourself on the intricacies of the challenges ahead.

28. Thoroughly test the newly-installed cable plant prior to installing any other components.

29. Install and test all communication lines. Do not take noise or error rate measurements during evenings or weekends, as potential problem sources may not be operating during those hours.

30. Install hardware systems, and test them as stand-alone devices. Also install redundant systems such as powerful-transfer or uninterruptible power supplies (UPSs) that are supporting the internetwork.

31. Install network software modules, such as operating systems, TCP/IP drivers, bridge software, etc., paying very close attention to options such as internet addresses or other parameters. Where possible, install and test the various modules one at a time, to minimize any interaction between subsystems.

32. Install all application programs such as SMTP or FTP modules, and test them as a stand-alone device on that hardware platform.

33. Bring out the systems-acceptance plan, and start the testing process. Be sure to allow plenty of time for this step, as the integration of components from multiple vendors into a single internetwork may identify problems that were not anticipated. Should problems arise, schedule a round-table session with all vendors, and avoid placing blame or finger-pointing. Most vendors are eager to help resolve difficult problems when a cooperative—not confrontational—atmosphere is presented.

34. Develop a list of unresolved issues, define the responsible parties and due dates, and publish the list as high-priority action items in the project team meeting minutes. This list should also be added to the database discussed in item 4.

35. Develop troubleshooting procedures for all components of the internetwork. A model for fault-isolation flowcharts is given in Chapter 9 of reference [10-1], and many vendors' technical documents also provide valuable information. The time to learn how to use your new test equipment is now, when life is (relatively) calm. Don't wait until a failure forces you into troubleshooting mode. Prepare now.

36. Establish a problem-reporting procedure for the internetwork. This may consist of a centralized help desk, or contacts at each geographic location. Make sure that the help desk personnel know who they can call for additional assistance. Consider establishing a user's group for resolution of procedural or administrative complaints.

37. Finalize all maintenance contracts, if used, and develop clear procedures for interaction between the help desk and maintenance providers.

38. Train all users of the internetwork, based upon their need for information. Consider separate tutorials for clerical, professional, and executive staffs. Provide notes or quick reference guides to minimize calls to the help desk.

39. Complete all internetwork documentation, including system schematic, cable plant, equipment locations, internet addresses and any user-specific issues such as account codes or passwords. Chapter 2 of reference [10-1] provides some guidance.

40. Formally close the project by reviewing the budget, and allocating any excess funds for a project team party. Many people have contributed to the success of this project—make sure that they all are properly recognized.

10.2   A Final Word

As you would undoubtedly agree, a number of issues concerning internetwork design and implementation are never learned from a text. Painful as it sometimes is, experience is often the best teacher. While experiencing the pain, however, a good sense of humor is essential. In closing, I present RFC 968 (reference [10-4]), written by Vint Cerf, one of the most experienced "internetworkers." May his words be remembered during those frustrating moments.

"'Twas the Night Before Start-up"

'Twas the night before start-up and all through the net,
not a packet was moving; no bit nor octet.
The engineers rattled their cards in despair,
hoping a bad chip would blow with a flare.
The salesmen were nestled all snug in their beds,
while visions of data nets danced in their heads.

And I with my datascope tracings and dumps
　　　　prepared for some pretty bad bruises and lumps.
When out in the hall there arose such a clatter,
　　　　I sprang from my desk to see what was the matter.
There stood at the threshold with PC in tow,
　　　　An ARPANET hacker, all ready to go.
I could see from the creases that covered his brow,
　　　　he'd conquer the crisis confronting him now.
More rapid than eagles, he checked each alarm
　　　　and scrutinized each for its potential harm.

On LAPB, on OSI, X.25! TCP, SNA, V.35!

His eyes were afire with the strength of his gaze;
　　　　no bug could hide long; not for hours or days.
A wink of his eye and twitch of his head,
　　　　soon gave me to know I had little to dread.
He spoke not a word, but went straight to his work,
　　　　fixing a net that had gone plumb berserk;
And laying a finger on one suspect line,
　　　　he entered a patch and the net came up fine!
The packet flowed neatly and protocols matched;
　　　　he hosts interfaced and shift-registers latched.
He tested the system from Gateway to PAD;
　　　　not one bit was dropped; no checksum was bad.
At last he was finished and wearily sighed
　　　　and turned to explain why the system had died.
I twisted my fingers and counted to ten;
　　　　an off-by-one index had done it again...

10.3 References

[10-1] Miller, Mark A. *LAN Troubleshooting Handbook*. Redwood City, CA: M&T Books, 1989.

[10-2] Haverlock, Peter M. "The Formula for Network Immortality." *Data Communications* (August 1988): 112 – 116.

[10-3] Infonetics, Inc. *The Cost of LAN Downtime, An Executive Summary*. September 1989.

[10-4] DDN Network Information Center. *'Twas the Night Before Startup*. RFC 968, December 1985.

Addresses of Standard Organizations

AT&T Publications

AT&T Technologies
Commercial Sales
P.O. Box 19901
Indianapolis, IN 46219
Telephone (317) 352-8557 or
    (800) 432-6600

CCITT Recommendations and Federal Information Processing Standards (FIPS)

U. S. Department of Commerce
National Technical Information
    Service
5285 Port Royal Road
Springfield, VA 22161
Telephone (703) 487-4650

CSA Standards

Canadian Standards Association
178 Rexdale Boulevard
Rexdale, ONT M9W 1R9
Canada
Telephone (416) 747-4363

ECMA Standards

European Computer Manufacturers
    Association
114, Rue de rhone CH-1204
Geneva, Switzerland
Telephone 41 22 35-36-34

ECSA Standards

Exchange Carriers Standards
    Association
5430 Grosvenor Lane
Bethesda, MD 20814-2122
Telephone (301) 564-4505

EIA Standards

Electronic Industries Association
    Standards Sales
2001 Eye Street, NW
Washington, DC 20006
Telephone (202) 457-4966

Federal Standards Sales:

General Service Administration
GSA Specification Unit (WFSIS),
Room 6039
7th & D Streets SW
Washington, DC 20407
Telephone (202) 472-2205

FIPS Publication Sales:

National Technical Information
Service
5285 Port Royal Road
Springfield, VA 22161
Telephone (703) 487-4600

IEEE Standards

Institute of Electrical and Electronics
Engineers
445 Hoes Lane
Piscataway, NJ 08855
Telephone (908) 981-1393 or
(800) 678-IEEE

ISO and ANSI Standards

American National Standards Institute
1430 Broadway
New York, NY 10018
Telephone (212) 354-3300
Sales Department (212) 642-4900

ISO Standards

International Organization for
Standardization
1, Rue de Varembe Case Postale 56
CH-1211
Geneva 20, Switzerland
Telephone 41 22 34 12 40

Military Standards Sales:

Naval Publications and Forms Center
Commanding Officer
NPFC 43
5801 Tabor Avenue
Philadelphia, PA 19120
Telephone (215) 697-3321

National Communications System

Federal Telecommunications
Standards NCS-TS
8th Street & South Courthouse Road
Arlington, VA 22204

National Institute of Standards and Technology

Technology Building 225
Gaithersburg, MD 20899

APPENDIX B

Selected Manufacturers of Internetworking Products

Advanced Computer Communications
720 Santa Barbara Street
Santa Barbara, CA 93101
(805) 963-9431 or (800) 444-7854

Alisa Systems, Inc.
221 E. Walnut, Suite 175
Pasadena, CA 91101
(818) 792-9474 or (800) 992-5472

Alloy Computer Products, Inc.
165 Forrest Street
Marlboro, MA 01725
(508) 481-8500 or (800) 544-7551

Andrew KMW Systems
6034 W. Courtyard Drive
Austin, TX 78730
(512) 338-3000

Apple Computer, Inc.
20525 Mariani Avenue
Cupertino, CA 95014
(408) 996-1010

AST Research, Inc.
16215 Alton Parkway
Irvine, CA 92713-9658
(714) 727-4141

Atlantix
5401 NW Broken Sound Blvd.
Suite 100
Boca Raton, FL 33487
(407) 241-8108 or (800) 262-6526

AT&T Computer Systems
One Speedwell Avenue
Morristown, NJ 07960
(201) 898-6000 or (800) 247-1212

Attachmate Corp.
13231 S.E. 36th St.
Bellevue, WA 98006
(206) 644-4010 or (800) 426-6283

Banyan Systems, Inc.
20 Flanders Road
Westboro, MA 01581
(508) 898-1000 or (800) 828-2404

Bluelynx (Micro Integration)
215 Paca Street
Cumberland, MD 21502
(301) 777-3307 or (800) 832-4526

Brightwork Development, Inc.
766 Shrewsbury Avenue
Jerral Center
West Tinton Falls, NJ 07724
(201) 530-0440 or (800) 552-9876

Cabletron Systems, Inc.
35 Industrial Way
Rochester, NH 03867
(603) 332-9400

CBIS, Inc.
5875 Peachtree Industrial Blvd.
Bldg 100/170
Norcross, GA 30092
(404) 446-1332

Cheyenne Software, Inc.
55 Bryant Avenue
Roslyn, NY 11576
(516) 484-5110

cisco Systems Company
1525 O'Brien Drive
Menlo Park, CA 94025
(415) 326-1941 or (800) 553-6383

Codex Corporation
20 Cabot Blvd.
Mansfield, MA 02048
(508) 261-4000

Communication Machinery Corp.
125 Cremona Drive
Santa Barbara, CA 93117
(805) 968-4262

Communications Research Group
5615 Corporate Boulevard
Baton Rouge, LA 70808
(504) 923-0888 or (800) 24-BLAST

COMPAQ Computer Corporation
P.O. Box 69200
Houston, TX 77269
(713) 370-0670

CrossComm Corporation
133 East Main St.
P.O. Box 699
Marlboro, MA 01752
(508) 481-4060 or (800) 388-1200

Cross Information Company
1881 Ninth St., Suite 212
Boulder, CO 80302
(303) 444-7799

Crystal Point, Inc.
22122 20th Ave. SE
Bothell, WA 98021
(206) 487-3656

Data General Corporation
4400 Computer Drive
Westboro, MA 01500
(800) DATAGEN

Data Interface Systems, Corp.
8701 N. MoPac Expressway
Suite 415
Austin, TX 78759
(512) 346-5641 or (800) 351-4244

Datapoint Corporation
9725 Datapoint Drive
San Antonio, TX 78284
(512) 699-7000 or (800) 334-9968

Datastorm Technologies, Inc.
3212 Lemone Blvd.
P.O. Box 1471
Columbia, MO 65205
(314) 443-3282

David Systems
701 East Evelyn Avenue
Sunnyvale, CA 94087
(408) 720-8000

Daystar Digital, Inc.
5556 Atlanta Hwy.
Flowery Branch, GA 30542
(404) 967-2077 or (800) 962-2077

DCA
1000 Alderman Drive
Alpharetta, GA 30201
(404) 442-4553

DCA 10Net Communications
7887 Washington Village Drive
Suite 200
Dayton, OH 45459
(513) 433-2238

Digital Equipment Corporation
200 Baker Avenue
Concord, MA 01742
(508) 493-5111

Digi International, Inc.
6751 Oxford
Minneapolis, MN 55426
(612) 922-8055

Digital Link
252 Humboldt Ct.
Sunnyvale, CA 94089
(408) 745-6200 or (800) 441-1142

Earth Computer Technologies
10525 Lawson River Avenue
Fountain Valley, CA 92708
(714) 964-5784

Eicon Technology Corporation
2196 32nd Avenue
Lachine, Quebec H8T 3H7
Canada
(514) 631-2592

Emerald Systems
12230 World Trade Drive
San Diego, CA 92128
(619) 673-2161 or (800) 767-7267

FEL Industries, Inc.
10 Main Street
Williamsville, VT 05362
(802) 348-7171 or (800) 728-6829

FTP Software, Inc.
26 Princess Street
Wakefield, MA 01880
(617) 246-0900

Gateway Communications, Inc.
2951 Alton Avenue
Irvine, CA 92714
(714) 553-1555 or (800) 367-6555

General DataCom, Inc.
1579 Straits Turnpike
Middlebury, CT 06762
(203) 574-1118

Halley Systems, Inc.
2730 Orchard Pkwy.
San Jose, CA 95134
(408) 432-2600 or (800) 432-2600

Hayes Microcomputer Products, Inc.
P.O. Box 105203
Atlanta, GA 30348
(404) 441-1617

Hewlett-Packard Company
3301 Royal Lane
Irving, TX 75015
(214) 869-3377

Hughes LAN Systems
1225 Charleston Road
Mountain View, CA 94043
(415) 966-7300

IDEAssociates Inc.
29 Dunham Road
Billerica, MA 01821
(508) 663-6878

Infotron Systems Corp.
9 North Olney Avenue
Cherry Hill Industrial Center
Cherry Hill, NJ 08003
(609) 424-9400 or (800) 937-1010

InterComputer Communication Corp.
8230 Montgomery Rd.
Cincinnati, OH 45236
(513) 745-0500

InterConnections Incorporated
14711 N.E. 29th Place
Bellevue, Washington 98007
(206) 881-5773

Interlink Computer Sciences, Inc.
47370 Fremont Blvd.
Fremont, CA 94538
(415) 657-9800 or (800) 422-3711

International Business Machines (IBM)
1133 Westchester Avenue
White Plains, NY 10604
(800) IBM-2468

Internetix, Inc.
8903 Presidential Parkway
Suite 210
Upper Marlboro, MD 20772
(301) 420-7900

IQ Technologies, Inc.
22032 23rd Avenue SE
Bothell, WA 98021
(206) 483-3555 or (800) 752-6526

J & L Information Systems
9238 Deering Avenue
Chatsworth, CA 91311
(818) 709-1778

Larse Corporation
4600 Patrick Henry Drive
Santa Clara, CA 95052
(408) 988-6600

Madge Networks, Inc.
1580 Oakland Road, Suite C206
San Jose, CA 95131
(408) 441-1300

Miramar Systems, Inc.
201 N. Salsipuedes, Suite 204
Santa Barbara, CA 93103
(805) 966-2432

McData Corporation
310 Interlocken Pkwy
Broomfield, CO 80021
(303) 460-9200 or (800) 545-5773

Micom Systems, Inc.
4100 Los Angeles Ave.
Simi Valley, CA 93062
(805) 583-8600 or (800) MICOM-VS

Microcom, Inc.
500 River Ridge Drive
Norwood, MA 02062
(617) 551-1000 or (800) 822-8224

Microsoft Corporation
One Microsoft Way
Redmond, WA 98052-6399
(206) 882-8080 or (800) 426-9400

Microtest, Inc.
3519 E. Shea Boulevard, Suite 134
Phoenix, AZ 85028
(602) 971-6464 or (800) 526-9675

NCR Corporation
2700 Snelling Avenue North
St. Paul, MN 55113-1784
(612) 638-8400

Network General Corp.
4200 Bohannon Park
Menlo Park, CA 94043
(415) 688-2700

Networth, Inc.
8101 Ridgepoint Drive, Suite 107
Irving, TX 75063
(214) 869-1331

Newport Systems Solutions, Inc.
4020 Birch Street, Suite 107
Newport Beach, CA 92660
(714) 752-1511 or (800) 662-4677

Novell, Inc.
122 East 1700 South
Provo, UT 84601
(801) 379-5900 or (800) 526-5463

Novell, Inc.
2180 Fortune Drive
San Jose, CA 95131
(408) 434-2300 or (800) 243-8526

Nuvotech
2015 Bridgeway, Suite 204
Sausalito, CA 94965
(415) 331-7815

Phaser Systems, Inc.
651 Gateway Boulevard
San Francisco, CA 94080
(415) 952-6300

Prime Computer, Inc.
Prime Park
Natick, MA 01701
(508) 655-8000

Proteon, Inc.
2 Technology Drive
Westborough, MA 01581
(508) 898-2800

Pure Data

1740 South I-35
Carrollton, TX 75006
(214) 242-2040

Quintessential Solutions, Inc.

3570 Camino Del Rio North
Suite 201
San Diego, CA 92108
(619) 280-7535

Rabbit Software Corp.

Great Valley Corporate Center
7 Great Valley Parkway
East Malvern, PA 19355
(215) 647-0440 or (800) RABBITC

RAD Data Communications

151 West Passaic Street
Rochelle Park, NJ 07662
(201) 587-8822 or (800) 969-4RAD

Racal-Interlan, Inc.

155 Swanson Road
Boxborough, MA 01719
(508) 263-9929 or (800) LAN-TALK

Raycom Systems

6395 Gunpark Drive
Boulder, CO 80301
(303) 530-1620 or (800) 288-1620

Retix

2644 30th Street
Santa Monica, CA 90405
(213) 399-2200

Shiva Corporation

One Cambridge Center
Cambridge, MA 02142
(617) 252-6300 or (800) 458-3550

Simpact Associates, Inc.

9210 Sky Park Court
San Diego, CA 92123
(619) 565-1865 or (800) 488-4188

Sitka Corporation (TOPS)

950 Marina Village Parkway
Alameda, CA 94501
(415) 769-2496

Softronics

5085 List Drive
Colorado Springs, CO 80919
(719) 593-9540 or (800) 225-8590

Spider Systems

12 New England Executive Park
Burlington, MA 01803
(617) 270-3510 or (800) 447-7807

SMC

35 Marcos Blvd.
Hauppauge, NY 11788
(516) 273-3100 or (800) 992-4762

Stargate Technologies, Inc.

29300 Aurora Road
Bently Park South
Solon, OH 44139
(216) 349-1860 or (800) 782-7428

Sun Microsystems, Inc.

2550 Garcia Avenue
Mountain View, CA 94043
(415) 960-1300

SynOptics Communications, Inc.

P.O. Box 58185
4401 Great America Parkway
Santa Clara, CA 95052-8185
(408) 988-2400 or (800) 872-8023

Symicron, Inc.

23545 Crenshaw Boulevard
Suite 104
Torrance, CA 90505
(213) 530-2610

Tektronix, Inc.

P.O. Box 500
Beaverton, OR 97077
(503) 627-7111

3Com Corporation

5400 Bayfront Plaza
P.O. Box 58145
Santa Clara, CA 95052-8145
(408) 764-5000 or (800) 638-3266

The Santa Cruz Operation

400 Encinal Street
Santa Cruz, CA 95061
(408) 425-7222

TIL Systems, Ltd.

700 King Street West
10th Floor
Toronto, ONT M5V 2Y6
Canada
(416) 869-1157

Trellis Software, Inc.

85 Main Street
Hopkinton, MA 01748
(508) 435-3066

Ungermann-Bass, Inc.

3900 Freedom Circle
Santa Clara, CA 95052-8030
(408) 496-0111 or (800) 873-6381

Universal Data Systems

Motorola, Inc.
5000 Bradford Drive
Huntsville, AL 35805
(205) 721-8000

Verilink Corp.

145 Baytech Drive

San Jose, CA 95134

(408) 945-1199

Vitalink Communications Corp.

6607 Kaiser Drive

Fremont, CA 94555

(415) 794-1100 or (800) 443-5740

Wall Data, Inc.

17769 NE 78th Place

Redmond, WA 98052-4992

(206) 883-4777

WellFleet Communications Corp.

15 Crosby Drive

Bedford, MA 01730

(617) 275-2400

Western Digital Corporation

2445 McCabe Way

Irvine, CA 92714

(714) 863-0102 or (800) 847-6181

The Wollongong Group, Inc.

1129 San Antonio Road

Palo Alto, CA 94303

(415) 962-7243 or (800) 872-8649

Xerox Corporation

475 Oakmead Parkway

Sunnyvale, CA 94086

(408) 737-4400

Zenith Electronics Corporation

Communication Products Division

1000 Milwaukee Avenue

Glenview, IL 60025

(708) 391-8000

North American Private Line Carriers

American Private Line Services Inc.
140 Gould Street
Needham, MA 02194
(617) 455-9000

Ameritech
30 S. Wacker Drive
Chicago, IL 60606
(312) 750-5000

ATC
1515 S. Federal Highway, Suite 400
Boca Raton, FL 33432
(407) 392-2244

AT&T
295 N. Maple Avenue
Basking Ridge, NJ 07920
(201) 221-2000

Bell Atlantic Corporation
1600 Market Street
Philadelphia, PA 19103
(215) 963-6000

BellSouth Corporation
1155 Peachtree Street NE
Atlanta, GA 30367-6000
(404) 249-2000

Cable & Wireless Communications, Inc.
1919 Gallows Road
Vienna, VA 22182
(703) 790-5300

Consolidated Network Inc.
11701 Borman
St. Louis, MO 63146
(314) 993-9009

CNCP Telecommunications
3300 Bloor Street
W. Toronto, ONT M8X 2W9
Canada
(416) 232-6760

Digital Signal Inc.
26899 Northwestern Hwy.
Southfield, MI 48034
(313) 356-2090

LDL
4561 E. McDowell Road, Suite 211
Phoenix, AZ 85008
(602) 244-0707

LiTel Telecommunications Corporation
200 Old Wilson Bridge Road
Worthington, OH 43085
(614) 433-9200

MCI Communications Corporation
1133 19th Street NW
Washington, DC 20036
(202) 872-1600

Metromedia-ITT Long Distance
100 Plaza Drive
Secaucus, NJ 07096
(201) 330-5000

National Telecommunications Network
804 West Diamond Avenue
Gaithersburg, MD 20878
(301) 948-5000

Norlight
579 D'Onofrio Drive
Madison, WI 53719
(608) 833-8332

NYNEX Corporation
335 Madison Avenue
New York, NY 10017
(212) 370-7400

Pacific Telesis Group
140 New Montgomery Street
San Francisco, CA 94105
(415) 394-3000

RCI Long Distance
180 South Clinton Avenue
Rochester, NY 14646
(716) 777-8000

Southwest Network Services
4807 Spicewood Springs Road
Austin, TX 78759
(512) 338-1565

Southwestern Bell Corporation
1 Bell Center
St. Louis, MO 63101
(314) 235-9800

Telecom Canada
410 Laurier Avenue W.
Box 2410, Station D
Ottawa, ONT K1P 6H5
(613) 560-3000

Telecom* USA
780 Douglas Road, Suite 800
Atlanta, GA 30342
(404) 250-5500

US Sprint Communications Co.
8140 Ward Parkway
Kansas City, MO 64114
(816) 276-6000

US West, Inc.
7800 E. Orchard Road
Englewood, CO 80111
(303) 793-6500

**Williams Telecommunications
Group, Inc.**
P.O. Box 21348 Tulsa, OK 74121
(918) 588-3210

APPENDIX D

North American Public Data Networks

AT&T
295 N. Maple Avenue
Basking Ridge, NJ 07920
(201) 221-2000

BT Tymnet
2560 N. First Street
San Jose, CA 95131
(408) 922-0250

CompuServe
5000 Arlington Centre Boulevard
Columbus, OH 43220
(614) 457-8600

CNCP Telecommunications
3300 Bloor Street W.
Toronto, ONT M8X 2W9
Canada
(416) 232-6365

Fedex Network
2600 Thousand Oaks Blvd.
Memphis, TN 38118
(901) 360-2754

GE Information Services
401 N. Washington Street
Rockville, MD 20850
(301) 340-4000

IBM Information Network
3405 W. Buffalo Avenue
Tampa, FL 33607
(813) 878-3000

Infonet Services Corporation
2100 E. Grand Avenue
El Segundo, CA 90245
(213) 335-2600

Sprint International
12490 Sunrise Valley Drive
Reston, VA 22096
(703) 689-6000

Telecom Canada
410 Laurier Avenue W.
Ottawa, ONT K1P 6H5
(613) 560-3009

Wang Network Services
One Industrial Avenue
Lowell, MA 01851
(800) 926-4722

Western Union Corporation
Upper Saddle River, NJ
(201) 818-5000

Acronyms

ABP	Alternate Bipolar
ACK	Acknowledgement
ACDI	Asynchronous Communication Device Interface
ACS	Asynchronous Communication Server
ADSP	AppleTalk Data Stream Protocol
AEP	AppleTalk Echo Protocol
AFP	AppleTalk Filing Protocol
AGS	Asynchronous Gateway Server
AMI	Alternate Mark Inversion
ANSI	American National Standards Institute
API	Applications Programming Interface
ARP	Address Resolution Program
ARPANET	Advanced Research Projects Agency Network
ASP	AppleTalk Session Protocol
ATP	AppleTalk Transaction Protocol
B8ZS	Bipolar with 8 ZERO Substitution
BC	Block Check
BIOS	Basic Input/Output System
BPDU	Bridge Protocol Data Unit
bps	Bits Per Second
BRI	Basic Rate Interface
CCITT	International Telegraph and Telephone Consultative Committee
CLNS	Connectionless Network Services
CMIP	Common Management Information Protocol
CMOT	Common Management Information Protocol Over TCP/IP

CPE	Customer Premises Equipment
CSMA/CD	Carrier Sense, Multiple Access with Collision Detection
DARPA	Defense Advanced Research Projects Agency
DCE	Data Circuit-Terminating Equipment
DDP	Datagram Delivery Protocol
DL	Data Link
DOD	Department of Defense
DPA	Demand Protocol Architecture
DSAP	Destination Service Access Point
DSU/CSU	Data Service Unit/Channel Service Unit
DTE	Data Terminal Equipment
DTR	Data Terminal Ready
DTSX	Data Transport Station For X.25
EBIOS	Extended BIOS
EIA	Electronic Industries Association
ESF	Extended Superframe Format
FCS	Frame Check Sequence
FDDI	Fiber Data Distributed Interface
FDM	Frequency Division Multiplexing
FT-1	Fractional T-1
FTP	File Transfer Protocol
FSU	File Support Utility
HDLC	High Level Data Link Control
Hz	Hertz
ICMP	Internet Control Message Protocol
ICP	Internet Control Protocol
IDP	Internetwork Datagram Protocol
IEEE	Institute of Electrical and Electronics Engineers
I/G	Individual/Group
IOC	Inter-Office Channel
IP	Internet Protocol
IPC	Interprocess Communications Protocol

IPX	Internetwork Packet Exchange
ISDN	Integrated Services Digital Network
ISO	International Organization for Standardization
IXC	Inter-Exchange Carrier
Kbps	Kilo Bits per Second
KHz	Kilohertz
LAN	Local Area Network
LAP	Link Access Procedure
LAPB	Link Access Procedure Balanced
LAT	Local Area Transport
LATA	Local Access and Transport Area
LEC	Local Exchange Carrier
LLC	Logical Link Control
MAC	Medium Access Control
MAN	Metropolitan Area Network
Mbps	Mega Bits per Second
MHz	Megahertz
MLID	Multiple Link Interface Driver
MMAC	Multi Media Access Center
MNP	Microcom Networking Protocol
MSAU	Multistation Access Unit
MTTR	Mean Time To Repair
NAK	Negative Acknowledgement
NBP	Name Binding Protocol
NCSI	Network Communications Services Interface
NASI	Network Asynchronous Services Interface
NDIS	Network Driver Interface Standard
NetBEUI	NetBIOS Extended User Interface
NOS	Network Operating System
ODI	Open Data Link Interface
OSI	Open Systems Interconnection
OSPF	Open Shortest Path First

PAD	Packet Assembler and Disassembler
PAP	Printer Access Protocol
PBX	Private Branch Exchange
PDN	Public Data Network
PDU	Protocol Data Unit
PEP	Packet Exchange Protocol
POP	Point of Presence
PSTN	Public Switched Telephone Network
PVC	Permanent Virtual Circuit
QLLC	Qualified Logical Link Control
RBOC	Regional Bell Operating Company
RFC	Request For Comments
RI	Routing Information
RII	Routing Information Indicator
RIP	Routing Information Protocol
RPC	Remote Procedure Call
RTMP	Routing Table Maintenance Protocol
RTP	Routing Update Protocol
RTS	Request To Send
SAP	Service Access Points
SDLC	Synchronous Data Link Control
SEF	Source Explicit Forwarding
SLIP	Serial Line Internet Protocol
SMB	Server Message Block
SMTP	Simple Mail Transfer Protocol
SNA	System Network Architecture
SNAP	Sub-Network Access Protocol
SNMP	Simple Network Management Protocol
SONET	Synchronous Optical Network
SPP	Sequenced Packet Protocol
SPX	Sequenced Packet Exchange
SR	Source Routing

SRI	Stanford Research Institute
SRT	Source Routing Transparent
SSAP	Source Service Access Point
STP	Shielded Twisted Pair
SVC	Switched Virtual Circuit
TB	Transparent Bridging
TCP	Transmission Control Protocol
TCP/IP	Transmission Control Protocol/Internet Protocol
TDM	Time Division Multiplexing
TIC	Token Ring Interface Coupler
TIMS	Transmission Impairment Measurement Set
TLI	Transport Layer Interface
UART	Universal Asynchronous Receiver/Transmitter
UDP	User Datagram Protocol
U/L	Universal/Local
UTP	Unshielded Twisted Pair
VAN	Value Added Network
WAN	Wide Area Network
XNS	Xerox Network System
ZIP	Zone Information Protocol

Trademarks

3Com is a trademark of 3Com Corporation.

3+Open is a trademark of 3Com Corporation.

ACCUNET is a registered trademark of AT&T.

Access/One is a registered trademark of Ungermann-Bass, Inc.

Adobe Type Manager is a registered trademark of Adobe Systems, Inc.

AIX is a trademark of IBM Corporation.

AppleTalk is a trademark of Apple Computer Inc.

Apollo is a registered trademark of Apollo Computers, Inc.

ARCNET is a trademark of Datapoint Corporation.

Arpanet is a trademark of Bolt, Beranek and Newman, Inc.

ATM is a registered trademark of Adobe Systems, Inc.

BLAST PC Plus LAN is a trademark of Communications Research Group.

Bluelynx is a registered trademark of Micro-Integration Corporation.

BPS is a trademark of Unisys Corporation.

Burroughs is a trademark of Unisys Corporation.

CocoNet is a trademark of CocoNet, Inc.

ConnectLAN is a trademark of Halley Systems, Inc.

DCA is a registered trademark of Digital Communications Associates.

DEC is a trademark of Digital Equipment Corporation.

DECnet is a registered trademark of Digital Equipment Corporation.

Etherand is a trademark of International Business Machines Corporation.

EtherGate is a trademark of Shiva Corporation.

Ethernet is a registered trademark of Xerox, Inc.

EtherTalk is a trademark of Apple Computer, Inc.

Excelan is a trademark of Excelan.

EXOS is a trademark of Excelan.

ezBRIDGE is a trademark of Systems Strategies, Inc.

FIXED-X25 is a service mark of CompuServe.

Forest is a trademark of Forest Computer Incorporated.

Hayes and Smartmodem are trademarks of Hayes Microcomputer Products, Inc.

HostAccess is a trademark of Excelan.

HostShare is a trademark of Excelan.

HYPERchannel is a registered trademark of Network Systems Corporation.

IBM is a registered trademark of International Business Machines Corporation.

ICA is a trademark of Banyan.

ICC/FileXpress is a registered trademark of Intercomputer Communications Corporation.

ICC/Intercom is a trademark of Intercomputer Communications Corporation.

ILAN is a trademark of CrossComm Corporation.

InBox is a trademark of Sitka Corporation.

Internetwork Packet Exchange (IPX) is a trademark of Novell, Inc.

InterBridge is a trademark of Hayes Microcomputer Products, Inc.

LAN WorkPlace is a trademark of Excelan, Inc.

LANlink is a trademark of FEL Industries, Inc.

LAN Manager is a trademark of International Business Machines Corporation.

LocalTalk is a trademark of Apple Computer, Inc.

MacAPPC is a trademark of Apple Computer, Inc.

MacDFT is a registered trademark of Apple Computer, Inc.

MacGateway AT is a trademark of The Wollongong Group.

MacPathWay is a trademark of The Wollongong Group.

Microcom LAN Bridge is a trademark of Microcom Systems, Inc.

Microcom Management Station is a trademark of Microcom Systems, Inc.

Microcom Networking Protocol is a trademark of Microcom Systems, Inc.

MicroChannel is a trademark of IBM Corporation.

MicroSoft is a registered trademark of Microsoft Corporation.

MITEK is a trademark of Mitek System Corporation.

MLB, MMS and MNP are trademarks of Microcom Systems, Inc.

Mobius is a registered trademark of FEL Industries, Inc.

Mobius ACCESS is a trademark of FEL Industries, Inc.

NetAxcess is a trademark of KMW Systems, Corporation.

NetBIOS is a trademark of IBM Corporation.

Network Bundle is a trademark of Sitka Corporation.

NetWare and Novell are registered trademarks of Novell, Inc.

NFS is a trademark of SUN Microsystems, Inc.

OfficeVision is a trademark of IBM Corporation.

OS/2 is a trademark of IBM Corporation.

OX/400 is a trademark of IBM Corporation.

Personal Computer AT and AT are registered trademarks of IBM Corporation.

Personal Computer XT and XT are registered trademarks of IBM Corporation.

Personal System/2 and PS/2 are registered trademarks of IBM Corporation.

Postscript is a registered trademark of Adobe Systems, Inc.

RT and RISC SYSTEM/6000 are trademarks of IBM Corporation.

Sequenced Packet Exchange (SPX) is a trademark of Novell, Inc.

Sitka is a trademark of Sitka Corporation.

SNS/SNA Gateway is a trademark of Interlink Computer Sciences, Inc.

ST is a registered trademark of AT&T.

StarGROUP is a trademark of AT&T.

Sun is a registered trademark of Sun Microsystems, Inc.

System Application Architecture and SAA are trademarks of IBM Corporation.

Tandem is a trademark of Tandem Corporation.

Task-Force is a trademark of FEL Industries, Inc.

TeleBridge is a trademark of Shiva Corporation.

TOPS is a registered trademark of Sun Microsystems, Inc.

TransLAN is a trademark of Vitalink Communications Corporation.

TransRING is a trademark of Vitalink Communications Corporation.

Trellis is a trademark of Trellis Group, Inc.

TSSnet is a trademark of Thursby Software Systems, Inc.

Unisys is a trademark of Unisys Corporation.

Ungermann-Bass is a trademark of Ungermann-Bass, Inc.

UNIX is a registered trademark of AT&T.

VAX is a registered trademark of Digital Equipment Corporation.

VT100 is a trademark of Digital Equipment Corporation.

VT220 is a trademark of Digital Equipment Corporation.

VINES is a registered trademark of Banyan Systems, Inc.

Windows 3.0 is a trademark of MicroSoft Corporation.

XPERT is a trademark of TIL Systems, Ltd.

X-Window System is a trademark of Massachusetts Institute of Technology.

Index

423

A Library of Technical References from M&T Books

Internetworking
A Guide to Network Communications
LAN to LAN; LAN to WAN
by Mark A. Miller, P.E.

This book addresses all aspects of LAN and WAN (wide-area network) integrations, detailing the hardware, software, and communication products available. In-depth discussions describe the functions, design, and performance of repeaters, bridges, routers, and gateways. Communication facilities such as leased lines, T-1 circuits and access to packed switched public data networks (PSPDNs) are compared, helping LAN managers decide which is most viable for their internetwork. Also examined are the X.25, TCP/IP, and XNS protocols, as well as the internetworking capabilities and interoperability constraints of the most popular networks, including NetWare, LAN Server, 3+Open™, VINES®, and AppleTalk. 425 pp.

Book only   **Item #143-1**   **$34.95**

LAN Primer
An Introduction to Local Area Networks
by Greg Nunemacher

A complete introduction to local area networks (LANs), this book is a must for anyone who needs to know basic LAN principles. It includes a complete overview of LANs, clearly defining what a LAN is, the functions of a LAN, and how LANs fit into the field of telecommunications. The author discusses the specifics of building a LAN, including the required hardware and software, an overview of the types of products available, deciding what products to purchase, and assembling the pieces into a working LAN system. *LAN Primer* also includes case studies that illustrate how LAN principles work. Particular focus is given to Ethernet and Token-Ring. 221 pp.

Book only   **Item #127-X**   **$24.95**

Available at bookstores everywhere or call
1-800-533-4372 (in CA 1-800-356-2002)

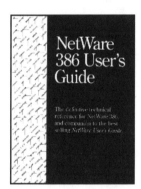

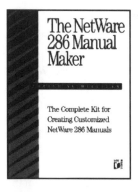
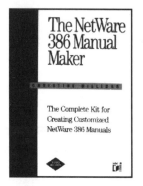
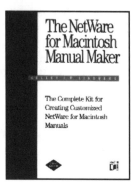

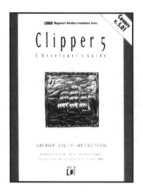

ORDER FORM

To Order: Return this form with your payment to M&T Books, 411 Borel Ave., Suite 100, San Mateo, CA 94402-3522 or **call toll-free 1-800-533-4372 (in California, call 1-800-356-2002).**

ITEM #	DESCRIPTION	DISK	PRICE

Subtotal

CA residents add sales tax ___ %

Add $4.50 per item for shipping and handling

TOTAL

Charge my:
- ❏ **Visa**
- ❏ **MasterCard**
- ❏ **AmExpress**

- ❏ **Check enclosed, payable to M&T Books.**

CARD NO.

SIGNATURE   EXP. DATE

NAME

ADDRESS

CITY

STATE   ZIP

M&T GUARANTEE: If your are not satisfied with your order for any reason, return it to us within 25 days of receipt for a full refund. Note: Refunds on disks apply only when returned with book within guarantee period. Disks damaged in transit or defective will be promptly replaced, but cannot be exchanged for a disk from a different title.

8015

Available at bookstores everywhere or call
1-800-533-4372 (in CA 1-800-356-2002)